D1244085

The JUNIOR CLASSICS

VOLUME SEVEN · THE ANIMAL BOOK

Frank Shields

Kari threw his trunk about Sudu and flung him into the water.

[See page 284]

The JUNIOR CLASSICS

Edited by MABEL WILLIAMS *and* MARCIA DALPHIN.

With Introduction by WILLIAM ALLAN NEILSON, *Former*

President of Smith College; Introduction to First Edition by

CHARLES W. ELIOT, *Former President of Harvard University*

TAYLORVILLE C.U. No. 3
WEST SCHOOL

808.8
Jun

910107W

Popular Edition

ILLUSTRATED

VOLUME
SEVEN

THE ANIMAL
BOOK

P. F. COLLIER & SON CORPORATION

COPYRIGHT, 1938, 1948, 1949, BY

P. F. COLLIER & SON CORPORATION

FIFTY-FOURTH PRINTING, 1956

"Buster," "Zinnia and Her Babies," "Jim Crow," from "More About Animals," copyright, 1934, by The Macmillan Company. "Jimmie, the Black Bear Cub," from "Jimmie, the Story of a Black Bear Cub," copyright, 1923, by Ernest Harold Baynes. "The Wild Bull," from "Herdboy of Hungary," copyright, 1932, by Alexander Finta. "A Cowboy and His Pony," from "Lone Cowboy," copyright, 1930, by Charles Scribner's Sons. "Buddy, Seeing Eye Pioneer," from "Dogs Against Darkness," copyright, 1942, by Dickson Hartwell. "Shipping Wild Animals," from "Trapping Wild Animals in Malay Jungles," copyright, 1920, by Asia Publishing Company; copyright, 1921, by Duffield and Company. "King Cobra Takes the Stage," from "Thrills of a Naturalist's Quest," copyright, 1932, by The Macmillan Company. "Leopards and Rhinos," from "In Brightest Africa," copyright, 1920, 1921, 1922, 1923, by Doubleday, Page & Company, "My Fight with a Catamount," copyright, 1898, by Perry Mason Company. "Stickeen," copyright, 1909, by John Muir. "The Cat and the Captain," copyright, 1927, by The Macmillan Company. "The Monkey That Would Not Kill," copyright, 1897, 1925, by Dodd, Mead & Company, Inc. "One Minute Longer," from "Buff, a Collie, and Other Dog Stories," copyright, 1921, by the George H. Doran Company. "Bringing Up Kari," from "Kari, the Elephant," copyright, 1922, by E. P. Dutton & Company, Inc. "Coaly-Bay, the Outlaw Horse," from "Wild Animal Ways," copyright, 1916, by Ernest Thompson Seton. "Gulliver the Great," from "Gulliver the Great, and Other Dog Stories," copyright, 1916, by The Century Company. "Brown Wolf," from "Brown Wolf, and Other Jack London Stories for Boys," copyright, 1904, 1906, 1910, 1911, 1912, 1920, by The Macmillan Company. "The Assault of Wings," from "Hoof and Claw," copyright, 1914, by The Macmillan Company. "Sea Otter," from "Wild Folk," copyright, 1922, by Samuel Scoville, Jr. "Lassie Come Home," copyright, 1938, by the Curtis Publishing Company, reprinted by permission of the author's estate. "Jody Finds the Fawn," from "The Yearling," copyright, 1938, by Marjorie Kinnan Rawlings; copyright, 1939, by Charles Scribner's Sons.

All rights are reserved to the original publishers for
illustrations in this volume protected by copyright.

Acknowledgments of permissions given by authors and publishers for the use
of copyright material appear in Volume X.

CFED

MANUFACTURED IN THE UNITED STATES OF AMERICA

TAYLORVILLE C.U. No. 3
WEST SCHOOL

CONTENTS

TRUE ADVENTURES

v

CONTENTS

STORIES ABOUT ANIMALS

(The sources of the stories in this volume will be found listed on page 376.)

True Adventures

BUSTER

By MARGERY BIANCO

SOMETIMES people adopt dogs, and sometimes dogs adopt people. One of the most determined cases of adoption by a dog that I ever knew was that of Buster.

I didn't blame Buster at all; in fact I had every sympathy with him. His own family were very nice people and quite kind to him, but they were dull. They were the sort of people who thought that if you fed a dog regularly and gave him a roof over his head that was all that he could possibly need.

We were living in an old roomy house on the outskirts of a village, and Buster's people lived in one of a little group of new bungalows that had sprung up just across the way. The family consisted of two grown sons who were away all day at business, and a stout middle-aged mother who divided her time between housework and listening to the radio, preferably nice cheerful jazz. Buster himself (we knew his name from hearing it called so often) was a lanky, half-grown, brown and white hound puppy, with floppy ears and enormous paws, built for romping. I think that the continual atmosphere of scrubbing and polishing around the bungalow preyed on his mind, and I suspect that he did not at all care for radio. A good many hounds dislike music, especially jazz. He was a sociable dog, and what he wanted was someone to pass the time of day with. At any rate he decided that our family suited him a great deal better than his own.

He began by appearing casually at odd moments in the dooryard, just loitering about, in an expectant sort of way. It was useless to ignore him because sooner or later you were bound to catch his eye, and once you caught his eye the mischief was done. He would then begin to wag his tail and wiggle all over, and act exactly as if you had called him in on purpose and were just as delighted about it as he was. Nothing discouraged him, and it was impossible to offend him.

3

For one thing, his own family never went for walks, and we did. Buster loved walks. He liked long half-day tramps through the pine woods, and he never missed a chance to go along. If by any accident he did not see us set out, he was sure to follow our trail and catch up, panting and triumphant, before we had gone a mile from home. If no one was going out walking, or down to the river, or doing any of those things he particularly enjoyed, then he would just hang wistfully about the yard. And every evening, last thing, when I went to close the front door, I would hear a gentle tail-thumping from the darkest corner of the porch. It was Buster, settled down to guard our house for the night.

One always has rather a guilty feeling at the idea of having lured somebody else's dog away from them, though to be sure Buster never needed any luring—quite the contrary. So to salve our consciences we sent him home whenever we could, never an easy job, for he was singularly dense about commands of any sort; and we made it a strict rule never to feed him, in order that he should associate meal-times at least with his own household. But he was so engaging, and so pathetically anxious for our company, that we were apt to be rather weak-minded about the whole business.

All of us, that is, except Grannie. Grannie was the only one who succeeded in being at all stern with Buster. She was very fond of dogs, but she liked them in their proper place, and she felt that a dog's proper place was guarding his own home. She believed, moreover, that if one really made it sufficiently plain to Buster that he belonged to the bungalow lady and not to us, he would end by understanding.

She would point a finger at him and say: "Now, Buster, you *go home!*" And Buster, who was always anxious to please everyone, would sometimes actually go, though only to reappear again the moment her back was turned. It was after one of these lectures, so often repeated, that Grannie said: "I really do think I've taught that dog at last where his proper home is, and now I hope he'll stay there!"

The rest of us said nothing. We knew Buster.

Early next morning my daughter called me to the door. She was laughing. "Look, there's Buster back again! And what's more, he's bringing his bed with him!"

There was Buster coming up the front path, looking more than usually pleased with himself and dragging with him, to our consternation, one of the bungalow lady's best parlor rugs! It was a beautiful rug with fringed ends and big pink and yellow roses on it, though not at all improved by being dragged across a sandy road and over the wet grass edges. He brought it on the porch, laid it down and sat on it, wagging his tail and looking at us very proudly, as if to say: "There! Now aren't you pleased? Just feast your eyes on *that!*"

Whether he really meant it as a hint that he was moving over, bag and baggage, so that this tiresome question of residence should be settled once for all, or whether he had caught the rug up in a sudden burst of generosity, wishing to make us a present of it, I don't know. Personally I think he intended it as a peace offering to Grannie, being in his opinion just the sort of gift calculated to soften and delight an old lady's heart. We glanced guiltily over the way. Fortunately Buster's lady was invisible. Hurriedly we rolled the rug up, tiptoed across the road and dropped it in her front garden.

Buster looked puzzled and disappointed. He had brought us a beautiful present, why should we refuse it? Human beings, he sighed, were very strange. You did your best to please them, and there—they would have none of it!

For several days we went in terror lest Buster should bring us more gifts; a set of fish knives perhaps, or a bedspread. But evidently he had taken the rug incident very much to heart. He made no further advances of the kind.

Fall turned to winter, but not even the snow could keep Buster from our threshold. He still came for walks, accompanied the young people skating and sledding. And every evening, just as we settled down round the fire after supper, there would be a gentle scratching at the door. Buster had come for his usual visit. We let him stay until bedtime and then firmly put him out, the theory being that he then went home to sleep in his kennel, or whatever other accommodation his owners provided for him.

It was only on condition of his being sent home strictly at ten that Grannie would at all consent to his being allowed indoors. And he was so strangely good about going that Grannie remarked more than once: "You see, that dog can be obedient if you are firm with him. He is trained now so that he will go home by himself with no trouble!"

It was just well that she never noticed the wink Buster gave me as he went out of the front door and heard the key turned on him.

For Buster and I had our own conspiracy, due to the coldness of those winter nights. He would patter noisily off the porch, stretch himself, listen a moment, and then creep silently back to the shelter of the big wistaria vine. There he would wait until he heard the house bolted for the night and saw, a little later, the light turned out in my room. I slept on the ground floor, and the windows were a few feet from the ground, just high enough for Buster to reach the sill with his front paws. When I pushed up the window, very quietly (Grannie slept in the room just above), there he was waiting. I would reach out and get a firm hold of his collar, there was a yank and a heave, and an armful of cold and snowy dog would come hurtling through the window. And if I wasn't very quick to get the window closed down again and make a dash for the bed, Buster would be there before me, diving in, snowy paws and all, to bury himself as deep down under the blankets as he could get.

Of course it was all very wrong, but thin-coated dogs can't sleep out on a porch in winter, and nothing—nothing would induce Buster to sleep at his own house!

One thing puzzled me: that he was always so ready to go home first thing in the morning, almost ungratefully so, considering. If I was a few moments late in letting him out, he seemed in a desperate hurry, and he always dashed straight across the road, looking neither to right nor left.

It seemed a good idea to call on Buster's lady, and find out tact-fully where the dog really was supposed to sleep, so one morning I went over. I told her how much we all liked Buster and what a nice dog he was, and she said what a nice quiet dog he was, too, no trouble at all. And then we chatted a little, and by-and-by I asked her, casually, where Buster slept at night. It seemed rather cold, I suggested, for a dog like that to stay outdoors. Maybe he had a kennel?

Indeed he had, Buster's lady assured me, and a nice kennel, too, only he didn't seem to use it much. I could have told her that myself.

"But ever since the real cold weather set in," she continued, "he's taken to sleeping under the house here. We put some old sacks there for him to lie on and he seems perfectly comfortable. There's not a sound from him all night. Every morning, when I open the kitchen door to call him in for breakfast, he comes out from under the back porch, stretching and yawning like he'd had a real good night, and he's always just as warm and dry as can be!"

Not for worlds would I have given Buster's secret away. But I had found out his trick. The bungalow had no cellar, but was built on a brick foundation, open in places where a dog could creep through, and it was under here that Buster was supposed to sleep. Next morning, when I let him out before the rest of the household was astir, I watched carefully. Smoke was rising from the bungalow chimney; undoubtedly there were bacon and griddle cakes that moment on the stove. Buster made a straight leap across the road and I saw him squeeze himself under the front porch, only to crawl out next moment, I felt sure, at the back, yawning and stretching as the bungalow lady had described, all ready for the breakfast that was awaiting him.

There was no need to worry about Buster! A dog as clever as that could take care of himself anywhere.

ZINNIA AND HER BABIES

By *MARGERY BIANCO*

Illustration by Helen Torrey

SOME time ago, in writing about cats, I spoke of Zinnia, the little black cat who has such a liking for dogs. I told how she will sit staring pensively at some dog which may happen to be in the room, and then all at once jump up, walk over to him, and begin washing his face and smoothing his hair, just like a nursemaid, holding his head between her two paws if he tries to move. And what a terrible time she had trying to straighten out the big long-haired collie! Much as she likes dogs, their occasional untidiness gets very much upon Zinnia's mind, and sooner or later she decides that something must be done about it.

I think Zinnia made up her mind long ago that all this so-called "cat and dog" business was just nonsense. Dogs are just like cats, if you treat them the right way, and a little good sound cat training would do them all the good in the world. Zinnia's owners are always afraid that she will one day, in her fearlessness, happen upon the wrong dog, and then she may get unpleasantly surprised. But so far all the dogs she has met have either returned her friendliness, or been far too surprised by it to think of attacking her.

The only other creatures that Zinnia seems to like better than dogs are—not human beings, for she is quite indifferent to petting or attention; and not even other cats, whom she just tolerates, but kittens. Anybody's kittens, though naturally she prefers her own. She is a born mother, and the voice of a kitten mewing will always bring her on a trot to see what the trouble is. Quite likely she may decide that the kittens are fretful because they are not in what she considers a good and comfortable place for them. In that case she will probably pick them up one by one and carry them off somewhere else, without bothering to consult their own mother at all.

One summer I remember Zinnia was bringing up a family of her own, four babies of a few weeks old, and she had them in the barn. There was a good deal of painting and other work going on about

8

TAYLORVILLE C.U. No. 3
WEST SCHOOL

the house at that time, and Zinnia's mistress thought that the barn
was the safest place for the kittens to stay in, at least until they were
a little older, when there would be less danger of their tumbling
into paint pots, or getting stepped upon by accident. So the barn
door was kept closed, and Zinnia's own food and saucers of milk
were carried out to her there twice a day.

Zinnia, however, had her own ideas. The barn was big and airy;
the kittens had their own box lined with hay, and plenty of space
to crawl safely about in. But that didn't satisfy her. It was sunny
June weather; kittens should be out in the garden, enjoying the
fresh air.

And every morning there they were, all four of them, packed into
an old wheelbarrow by the woodshed, where they whimpered and
blinked at the sunlight, looking, poor mites, anything but comfortable on the bare earthy boards. And there Zinnia would leave them,
while she went off on some hunting excursion of her own.

For a long while no one could discover how Zinnia managed to
bring those kittens out. Every evening, and often during the day as
well, they were carried back to their own bed, and the barn door
closed and bolted, with Zinnia and her babies inside. But it made no
difference. Every morning, there they were back again in the
wheelbarrow.

But at last we found out Zinnia's secret.

High up in the barn wall, near the rafters, was a window with
one small pane missing. Because of the slope of the ground, the barn
was so built as to be two stories high at the back instead of one, so
that from the outside this window was even higher from the ground,
some fourteen feet or more. One morning Zinnia's mistress, passing
near the barn, heard a queer scraping sound, like the noise a squirrel
makes scrambling down a tree trunk, and looked up to see Zinnia,
who had just squeezed through the broken window with a kitten
in her mouth and was letting herself down cautiously, backward,
inch by inch, clinging with her claws to the smooth side of the barn.

The kitten safely landed on the ground, and dragged over to the
wheelbarrow, Zinnia turned right around and went back for the
next, by the same route.

Seeing that she was so determined about it, it seemed useless to shut the kittens up any longer, so after that the barn door was left ajar and Zinnia was free to carry her babies in and out in a less dangerous way. It was just like obstinate little Zinnia, however, that having once got her own way in the matter she didn't seem to care any longer whether the kittens were indoors or out, but left them most of the time to crawl about by themselves on the barn floor, where they certainly seemed happier than when they were being dragged to and fro so ruthlessly every day.

All but one, the smallest of the four. Nearly always, if there happens to be one kitten in a litter smaller and weaker than the rest, the mother cat will choose it as her special favorite, and so it was with Zinnia. This particular kitten, a tiny maltese with a white chin, Zinnia took extra pains with. It was slower in learning to crawl and eat, due, everyone thought, to having been carried about so persistently by its mother, and perhaps getting a few bumps here and there sliding down the barn wall. Every day, long after she had left the other kittens to their own devices, Zinnia would still drag this weakly one out into the sunshine, whether or no, and leave it there for several hours in the wheelbarrow, and either her devotion, or the warm sunshine, had its good effect, for the little malty grew up in time just as strong as her brothers and sisters, though always a bit smaller.

But the queerest thing that Zinnia ever did was in regard to another sort of kitten altogether.

It happened one year that there was a new baby in the house—a real two-legged baby this time. Zinnia, of course, knew about the baby; cats know all about everything. But she had never shown any great curiosity about it, possibly because she was busy herself, just then, bringing up a family of her own tucked away in a basket on the porch.

It was pleasant spring weather and the baby, who was just a few weeks old, was put out every morning to take her nap in a wicker cradle on the lawn. Usually she slept soundly, but one morning she happened to be a little restless and fretful. Now the crying of a young baby does sometimes sound rather like the mewing of a kitten, especially if the baby is sleepy, and just complaining to itself as this one was.

Zinnia was seated on the doorstep, washing her face, and when she heard this peculiar sort of noise she pricked her ears up and strolled over to see what it was all about. Standing up with her front

Illustration by Helen Torrey

paws on the edge of the cradle she peered in, and it evidently didn't take her long to make up her mind just why the baby was crying. "What that child needs," thought Zinnia, "is a mouse!"

So off she trotted down the garden, and round to the barn, to reappear a moment or so later with a nice fat mouse dangling from her mouth. Straight over to the cradle she went, and dropped the mouse in, with a little crooning mew, just to draw the baby's attention to it.

Now the baby's mother had watched all this, and she thought at first that Zinnia had just made a very funny mistake, and had dropped the mouse there by accident. So she picked it up by its tail and took it over to Zinnia's own babies in their basket. But Zinnia would have none of this. She fished that dead mouse right out again and carried it over to the baby's cradle a second time, dropping it in with a little thump, as though to say: "You may think you know a lot about babies, but I've had more experience than you and, believe me or not, what that child needs is a *mouse!*"

Zinnia is a grandmother now, many times over. Most of her various babies are grown up and have families of their own, though each summer there are new ones to take their place.

Zinnia herself is growing middle-aged. Her little pointed face, with its pale-green slanting eyes, is a shade more pointed than it used to be; her black fur, always a little reddish in the light, is taking on more and more of a rusty tone, the color of an old iron kettle that has been lying out in the sun. But she is as keen a mouser as ever, and her sense of responsibility is, if anything, more marked as time goes by. When I visited her last, only a short time ago, we had a very characteristic example of it.

A grown-up daughter of Zinnia's, Topsy, had died quite suddenly after only a couple of days' illness, leaving two pretty little kittens, about ten days older than Zinnia's own kittens. Luckily they were nearly big enough to lap for themselves, and meantime could be fed warm milk with a medicine dropper, but they missed their mother sadly, and the warmth and comfort of her body curled up beside them in the basket. Everyone was worried about poor Topsy's kittens and how they would get along without her, but before twenty-four hours had passed, Zinnia, as usual, had come to the rescue. She heard the little orphans mewing, took one look at them, and without more ado seized first one and then the other and dragged them up two flights of stairs to the attic, where she settled them comfortably in the box with her own three babies.

There will be no neglected kittens in any house where Zinnia lives, as long as she is there to look after them.

JIM CROW

By MARGARET BIANCO

SOME relatives who lived in the country once had a tame crow, who, like most country crows, was called Jim. They had brought him up from a nestling; he had never been caged, nor had his wings been clipped, so that he had the freedom of the whole place, just like the dogs and the cats. He preferred, however, to spend most of his time about the dooryard and the house, where there was usually something going on to interest him.

Jim liked to help in everything, planting the garden, weeding, mowing the lawn, and often he was far more hindrance than help. He loved shelling peas or beans, and would always take the empty pods, carry them off one at a time and lay them in a pile. He learned to shell peas himself, holding the pod down with one foot and splitting it open with his bill.

There was a broken floor board on the back porch, and here Jim used to hide all his treasures, poking them down through the hole. If one of the dogs or cats went near this cubbyhole he would be driven off promptly, with indignant squawks, but if a member of the household strolled toward that end of the porch, then poor Jim would get dreadfully worried and uneasy, and do everything possible to divert his attention. Usually they would only pretend to look into this hole, just to tease him, but once in a while, when there seemed to be an unusual disappearance of small objects from about the house, or if some particular thing was being searched for, then the broken board would have to be pried up, and poor Jim's little treasure hoard laid bare, making him very unhappy and embarrassed.

Besides bean pods, bits of string, and pencil stubs, there would be all sorts of things the existence of which perhaps had been almost forgotten, but which at some time or other had caught Jim's envious eye: a thimble, a little glass knob belonging to some bit of furniture, a fancy cigarette holder, oddments of nails and screws, ends of colored wool, and usually some small change as well. Then that particular object for which the hunt had been organized would be pounced on triumphantly, the board replaced, and the hoard left undisturbed till next time, while Jim, perched on the porch rail, flapped his wings and cawed dismally.

Jim was never spiteful, but he was a great tease, and would make the cats' and dogs' lives a misery to them by tweaking their tails, shouting in their ears, and pretending to steal their food.

There was an Airedale in the family named Mike, who had been blind for many years, ever since he had distemper. The farm was high on a hillside, there was no passing traffic, so Mike was perfectly safe, and although blind he had learned his way about so well that he could wander anywhere about the house and garden and knew the position of each rock and tree. He had been taught that dogs must not walk on garden beds, so whenever he felt soft, fresh-raked earth under his feet he would paw it a moment, to make quite sure, and then turn carefully and back away. He could pick his way quite easily, turning out to avoid an obstacle just before he came to it, and as everyone was careful, on his account, not to leave any large object like a wheelbarrow or a bench in any unaccustomed place, he very seldom bumped into anything. In fact, a stranger seeing Mike walking about the grounds would never have known that he was blind at all, unless perhaps for the way he would stand and listen, very carefully, with his head on one side, if one spoke or called to him.

Mike could fetch and carry, and he loved having stones thrown for him; a ball or stick was no use, because it made no noise in falling. He would prick his ears, listening for the exact sound of the stone as it fell, and with only that slight thud to guide him would rush straight off and pick it up. If he did not get it the first time, he would nose about in the grass and find it by his sense of smell. Sometimes he brought the wrong stone by mistake, but very seldom.

Being blind, and also very good natured and trustful, poor Mike fell an easy victim to Jim's tricks. Jim liked particularly to hop up very quietly and give a sudden tweak to Mike's toes as he lay asleep, and then caw with delight when Mike started up and barked. Sometimes he would keep this game up for so long that Mike really would get cross, in which case he laid his head down on his paws and sulked, a sign to Jim that the game had gone far enough. They were actually very good friends, for Mike was always gentle, and although Jim teased him so much he was really fonder of him than of any other animal on the farm. And on chilly mornings he would spend hours perched on Mike's back as he lay sleeping, warming his toes in the dog's long shaggy coat.

Jim never flew far alone, but he liked going for walks. When any of the family set out for a walk he would first watch till he saw in which direction they were going, and let them get some distance. Then he would sail along to overtake them, swooping down as he flew quite close to their heads with a loud caw, and alight on some tree or fence post a little farther on, where he would wait till they had passed and then catch up with them again, and this he would repeat for miles. And as the other pets liked going for walks too, the procession usually consisted of a dog first, leading the way, then someone of the family, and a cat or two tagging along in the rear, and as Jim flew past each he would swoop down and caw at them.

When Jim was about two years old the family moved to a town some distance away. Uncle Ted stayed behind for a couple of weeks alone, to see to the closing of the house, and various other things. One of his tasks was to build comfortable crates in which the cats—and Jim—could be shipped down to their new home. The dogs had already gone on ahead.

One trouble about a pet crow is that he cannot very well be left to shift for himself, however accustomed he is to complete freedom. The wild crows will seldom accept him again as one of themselves, and though he can pick up plenty of food he is likely to be lonely, and there is always the danger that some farmer may shoot him by mistake for a wild bird. So it was thought best to bring Jim too, although he would probably have to spend much of his time shut up.

It was clear fall weather, just turning a little frosty at night, and Uncle Ted did most of his carpentering out of doors, while Jim hopped about, watching him with the greatest interest. The cats had traveled before, and knew what all these preparations were about.

Jim had never seen a cage in his life, but he too seemed to know by instinct what it was. He watched the crates being built, with their barred sides, and he watched the cats trying them on, so to speak, being measured each in turn to make sure its particular crate would be roomy and comfortable. And he must have put two and two together.

He had always been so tame that he would fly down at a call, and anyone could pick him up or pet him as he hopped about the garden. But not now. With the driving of each nail he seemed to grow more and more wary, and more and more suspicious, until when it came to the building of the last crate, his own, it was impossible to lay a hand on him. He hopped about, very inquisitive but always just out of reach, and by the time the last nail was driven home he took to the trees, and refused to come down to the ground at all. There he perched, staring at the crate with his head on one side and cawing derisively at any attempt to coax him down.

He had guessed only too well whom that last crate was for, and he was not going to be caught napping.

So in the end there was nothing for it but to leave him there alone to keep house by himself, with a bag of corn in the barn where he could reach it easily through the open window.

When spring came again the corn was all gone, and so was Jim. Very likely he had been clever enough to use that wealth to make peace with his old friends and relatives in one grand feast, and had retired to end his days in honor and glory as a crow millionaire.

JIMMIE, THE BLACK BEAR CUB

By ERNEST HAROLD BAYNES

PECK'S bad boy was a super-cherub compared with Jimmie. The hunter who sent him to me from Parry Sound said that he was the "bad egg" of a family of three, and frankly admitted that that was why he had sent him, though what I had done to incur the enmity of a man at Parry Sound I have never learned to this day.

The mother of these cubs had been killed in her den by Indian hunters, and the white trapper who was with them had rescued the babies and taken them home to his own cabin for company.

Jimmie's baby brothers, it seems, were very good—that is for little bears—and one cuff on the ear was enough to make either of them lie down and be quiet. But Jimmie would stand up on his hind legs and put up a fight that would have been dangerous had the fighter's weight and reach been in proportion to his courage and determination.

So one day the trapper, with his thumb done up in a white rag, and the back of his right hand looking like a contour map of the Rocky Mountains done in red ink, picked up a small and screaming black bear cub, dropped it into a stout wooden box, carried it to the nearest railway station and addressed it to me.

JIMMIE ARRIVES IN NEW HAMPSHIRE

I never shall forget Jimmie's arrival. It was late afternoon on a peaceful summer day and we were not expecting him. We were living at the "Haven Cottage," seven miles north of Newport, New Hampshire, and we were all seated on the piazza, looking out over a sunlit daisy field and listening to the song of a hermit thrush. I happened to glance down the road, and far away I could see a cloud of dust. It heralded the coming of the stage which brought our mail and express packages. Even at that distance I could hear strange sounds which did not harmonize with the song of the hermit thrush.

Finally the stage drove up and the driver dumped a wooden box into the middle of the lawn. From the inside of that box was coming a perfectly awful noise. There was a continuous and frantic scratching at the woodwork and a vocal sound which seemed to grow louder every moment.

"Wow! Wow! WOW!" yelled an angry voice.

"No! No! NO-O-O!" it wailed.

I said to the stage driver, "What in the world have you got in that box?"

But the stage driver had been sitting alongside that noise for seven miles and was in no humor for talk. So he climbed to his seat, whipped up his lathering horses, and left me to find out for myself what was in the box. I took a hammer and a chisel and pried off a corner of it, and out of the hole I made there was thrust a little, black, furry face with a tawny muzzle, round, furry ears, a pair of beady black eyes, and the most impudent expression I have ever seen on the face of any animal. I recognized my guest at once as a black bear cub. He stepped out on to the lawn, and deliberately looked around as if in search of the man who was responsible for his discomfort. Then his anger gave away to sobs and wails of grief.

There was a sentimental lady calling on us at the time and at a glance she saw that the little stranger needed comforting. She ran down the steps, snapped the bear cub into her arms and murmured, "Oh, the poor little dear." Now "the poor little dear" had been in that box for several days, he was looking for something more substantial than love murmurings, and his naturally short temper was not quite as long as usual. With a savage little growl he bit the sentimental arm, and with a raking stroke of his sturdy hind legs he tore a long rent in the lady's dress. She promptly dropped him and rushed back to her place on the piazza. In the meantime our housekeeper, Lucy, had looked upon the scene. No kinder person lived than she, but her kindness to animals was based on knowledge and common sense. She knew that, no matter what the anatomists might tell you, the way to the heart of a hungry little bear was right down through his "tummy," and she lost no time in getting to his tummy. With the aid of a bowl of crackers and milk she found his heart, badly bent but not quite broken, and it was hers forevermore.

Haven Cottage, where Jimmie came to us, stands on the eastern border of the Blue Mountain Forest. This great game preserve comprises about forty square miles of beautiful wild country, surrounded by a high fence and stocked with buffalo, elk, white-tailed deer, and many other wild creatures both native and introduced. Down the middle of it, roughly north and south, like a mighty backbone, stretches the spruce-clad Croydon range—the "Blue Mountain" which gives the place its name. In the hilly country round about "the Park," as the country folk call it, lie old farms with white, green-shuttered, maple-shaded houses, gray barns, gnarled apple trees, and scrub-grown, rock-studded cattle pastures. Here and there may be found more prosperous homesteads, with well-kept lawns and flower beds, painted outbuildings, and herds of thoroughbred cattle. It was in this farming country and in the Blue Mountain Forest itself that the little bear passed his New Hampshire days.

His life with us was one long series of humorous adventures—humorous for Jimmie, for us, or our neighbors, according to the point of view. But it made no difference what he did, Lucy always defended him with her tongue at least, and with the fire irons if necessary. If the paint were scratched off the front door, if all the strawberry jam in the pantry were eaten, if the coverlet of a bed were decorated with paw-painted bear tracks done in muddy water colors, it was the tame deer that did these things. Or, if the deer could prove an alibi, it was the wolves, the foxes, the opossums, or even the skunks—any living thing on the face of the landscape except Jimmie Bear; he never did anything wrong. And whenever we succeeded in actually "pinning it on him," she would either remind us that "we're all human you know," or make us feel that somehow we were trying to take advantage of an infant who had no parents to stand up for him. Once when I caught him on the kitchen dresser, sitting among the fragments of some china he had pulled from a shelf above, I called the housekeeper and remarked sternly, "Well, I suppose you'll admit he did that?"

Now Lucy had been in our family for a long time, and had served my father and mother before us. Looking from me to the culprit bear and then at me again, her mind flashed back a score of years. Straightening to her full height and folding her arms she said reminiscently and half reproachfully: "Well, Master Harold, I don't think you should be so hard on him. Please remember you were a boy yourself once." And of course I remembered and did not press her for details.

Jimmie differed somewhat from the little girl who had a curl right in the middle of her forehead, for—

> "When he was fed he was never very good,
> But when he was hungry he was horrid."

When that comfortable feeling which followed a meal began to wear off, the cub would let us know it by mutterings and grumblings, low and unobtrusive at first, like the warnings of a miniature volcano about to become active. Unless the growing fires of his hunger were quenched with milk or something equally good, the rumblings grew deeper and louder, until at last there came an uncontrolled outpouring of ursuline profanity which told us that the volcano was in full eruption. At such a time it was quite useless to try and divert his attention. He was hungry and wanted his food and no one could persuade him that he didn't. If he were loose, he would probably make for the screen door of the kitchen and, opening it deftly with the aid of his sharp claws, march straight to the sink. Standing on his hind legs he would stretch until he reached the edge with his forefeet, and with a single hoist he would reach his goal. Here he was likely to find a pail of fresh drinking water, which might occupy his attention for a moment, though he would probably be grumbling all the time he was drinking. Then turning round he would let himself down backward until his hind feet touched the floor.

By this time Lucy would be preparing a basin of bread and milk. Jimmie would see her and at once start to hurry things by dancing on his hind legs in front of her, clasping her about the knees, biting and tugging at her skirts. She was not in the least afraid of him, and sometimes in order to try his patience, or rather his impatience, a little more, she would hold the coveted basin just above his reach.

Shrieking with rage, he would dance around her, wildly snatching at the food. Finally one swift paw would "make connections" and then the game began to go his way. His claws hung on to the rim of the basin like so many iron hooks, and if it were lifted any higher Jimmie went with it. Then Lucy would carry him out dinner and all, and set the basin on the lawn, whereupon we were treated to a moving picture showing the real meaning of the expression "as hungry as a bear." Lying flat on his tummy before the food, and with forearms wrapped around the basin right and left, he would thrust his muzzle, almost to the eyes, into the bread and milk, which rapidly disappeared to a combination of sounds showing greed, satisfaction, and distrust.

When he had licked the vessel so clean that it needed no further washing, he seemed to feel much better, and the time had come for play. He would roll about on the lawn, turn somersaults, and scramble up the piazza posts, seemingly as much to his own delight as to that of the neighbors' children who often gathered to see him. And here I might add that never before or since have we had so much attention from those children as we had when Jimmie was our guest. Before he arrived we had our milk delivered once a day. Now it came twice a day, and a contribution to our standing order for eggs was made, it seemed, every time a hen gave a declaratory cackle. Wide-eyed youngsters were always coming to inquire if we needed any maple sugar or fresh butter, whether we would like to sell our hay, or if we wanted some one to saw the wood. Of course the inquirer never left the premises until Jimmie had been seen, whether our needs were urgent or not at all. Jimmie evidently enjoyed his young visitors and seemed to make special efforts for their amusement.

Some of the grown-ups were not quite so much amused. Among these were men who drove daily past our house. Horses are affected differently by the odor of a bear, but many of them dislike it intensely, and a few at least are thrown into paroxysms of fear. Usually a spirited horse would begin to manifest uneasiness when he came within a few hundred yards of our place, and the uneasiness, accompanied by snorting, pricked ears, and sidelong glances, increased until he drew close to the house, when the tendency was to bolt. This tendency was greatly increased if the bear was actually in sight or giving vocal evidence of his presence.

One morning a farmer neighbor, driving a nettlesome young horse, was passing the house, and, seeing the bear, drew up to have a better look at him. But the horse, which had been exhibiting great nervousness, now went wild with fear, and leaping into the air, came down upon his side. With the nimbleness of a cat the man sprang clear and seized the horse by the head, and a moment later the animal was on his feet again, fortunately unhurt. The driver, a good sport, asked me to bring the cub close up, as he wished his horse to become used to the sight and smell of it. I turned round to look for Jimmie, but apparently he had not liked the behavior of the horse, for he had climbed to the top of a nearby tree, where he now sat calmly munching a cluster of green wild cherries. It was fifteen minutes before he saw fit to come down and be introduced, and then it was with an air of conferring an honor upon the horse.

Jimmie loved farms and never tired of exploring them. The odors of orchards and dairies seemed to tickle his nostrils pleasantly, and of course there was always a fair chance of finding something to tickle his palate as well. Then there was the fun of frightening things—hens, ducks, and sheep—and the greater fun of chasing them afterwards.

Sometimes even the owners of the farms were the victims of his pranks. One of our neighbors, who sleeps on the first floor, has a rare, almost extinct, passion for fresh air. One day the cub climbed through his open window, and when that night the man got into bed in the dark, he thought somebody had been setting a steel trap for him. It was only Jimmie who resented being disturbed at that late hour, and who bit one great toe so badly that it had to be carried in a sling.

Lucy seemed to think it was her duty to give him a personal introduction to all the other animals round her. Usually this was not at all necessary from his standpoint because Jimmie had no difficulty in becoming acquainted with anyone he cared to meet. He simply walked right up and introduced himself. Possibly she thought that there would be fewer misunderstandings if she were present, and in this no doubt she was right. But if he didn't want to be introduced not even her kindly offices could persuade him to extend the friendly paw. Once, I remember, she wished to introduce him to a fine, tri-colored collie dog named Bruce. She sat on the lawn beside the dog and tried to call Jimmie to her side. The cub refused to come. He walked around in circles regarding Bruce with a suspicious eye and finally went away leaving Lucy and the visitor to make the best of their own company. Lucy did not understand this behavior but I had seen a previous meeting. A few days before, a young Scotch farmer, the owner of Bruce, drove up in a buggy, with the dog at his side. Bruce jumped out and there was Jimmie standing on the lawn. The two eyed one another for a moment and then Jimmie advanced, rising to his hind legs and putting out his arms. The smell of bear was a new one to the collie and he retreated, growling, under the buggy. He seemed ashamed of his caution, but here was a queer new creature—a very dangerous one for all he knew—and Bruce was a canny dog. Had he known a little more about bear cubs he would not have been the least afraid; if Jimmie had known a little more about dogs he would have been more cautious. Just then Bruce's owner stepped out of the buggy. Now a dog by himself is one dog, but a dog backed by a real man whom he loves and trusts is three dogs, and three dogs are not to be daunted by one bear cub no matter how dangerous he may look. As the Scotchman's foot touched the ground, it seemed to release a spring which hurled Bruce from between the buggy wheels straight at the black and furry thing before him. Jimmie turned several somersaults backward and when he stopped rolling he was wrong side up with the collie astride of him.

"Bruceie!"

The Scotchman's voice was low but the tone of disapproval was perfectly understood, and, the dog, crestfallen, trotted back to his side.

"Na! Na! Ye mauna hoort the wee cub, Bruceie. He wadna hoort yew."

Bruce didn't seem at all sure of this. But his god had spoken, and the bear cub was safe even if it should try to chew the dog's tail off. But Jimmie didn't understand. He didn't know that dogs have gods and that it was to Bruce's god that he owed his life. All that Jimmie knew was that he had been scared almost to death and that the thing which scared him was to be avoided in future. Hence Lucy's failure to effect a formal introduction.

But Jimmie's disapproval of Bruce did not necessarily extend to other dogs, and he had some very intimate canine friends. One of these was a cur of low degree named Bingo, who lived at a farm half a mile away. Sometimes Jimmie went to call on him, but usually Bingo came to our house. Bingo was of no particular breed—or as some one put it he was of many unparticular breeds. Nevertheless, he was a very lovable dog. He was black and tan in color, and his eyes and tail seemed to vie with one another in appearing happy and friendly. All the small boys for miles around made a pal of Bingo. He was the dog they took with them when they went fishing or berrying or when they went to round up the cows. There was only one youngster whom Bingo liked better than these—that was Jimmie. The two seemed to have a complete understanding and I have seldom seen two animals have such glorious times together. They ran side by side through the fields, played tag around the barn, and when they were so winded that they didn't seem able to run another yard they would lie on the lawn about a foot apart and just gaze at one another until they recovered their breath. Then perhaps they would wrestle, each animal rising on his hind legs in an effort to down his opponent. Usually they would keep up the wrestling match until Jimmie was tired. Sometimes Bingo seemed to be tired first, but if Jimmie had a good hold on him, that didn't make any difference—they went straight on with the game. If, as occasionally happened, Bingo continued to be strenuous after Jimmie had had enough, the bear would try to escape by climbing a tree. In this he was seldom successful, for although the dog could not climb, he could jump beautifully. Just as the cub seemed to be safe, Bingo would leap after him, and, seizing his short tail or hind foot, bring him tumbling to the ground again.

Jimmie wanted but little here below; in fact he wanted nothing but his own way. And he usually had it because it made life easier for the rest of us—not much easier, just easier. One thing he was very particular about was the milk he drank for breakfast—it had to be "this morning's" milk. It was of no use to offer him "last night's" milk, no matter how cool it had been kept or how sweet it was. Jimmie was a connoisseur of milk. He would detect the "fraud" at once and set up a wail which we were glad to stop at almost any price. As soon as the new milk was set before him he almost wallowed in it and the wailing ceased automatically. After he had absorbed all the milk and crackers he wanted, he was ready to play. He would roll about, on the lawn, biting his own feet, and then for no apparent reason he would dash straight up a tree. His method of climbing was interesting and different from that used by most animals. He ascended a trunk by a series of leaps, digging his hind toes in below him, springing from them, throwing his sturdy forearms upward and around the tree to get a fresh and loftier hold after every jump. He mounted with an agility one hardly would have accredited him. Coming down was a much more serious business, at least in the early days. Later he became more skillful and could even slide, but at first he would come down very slowly, and with almost unbelievable caution, like an elderly gentleman descending a precipice. Tail first he would come, stopping frequently to look down as though seeking a new foothold, and sometimes grumbling a little as if to let us know that he realized the horrible danger he was in. But he always reached the ground in safety, and at once was ready for another adventure.

Next to feeding, his greatest pleasure was bathing; so, soon after breakfast we would bring out a large washtub, fill it with water, and into it he would get. Sometimes before getting in he would walk around it on his hind legs, dipping in his forepaws as though to see if the temperature was all right. Or, perhaps, he would dance around it like a young Indian, scooping up the water with his little "hands" and dashing it over everything and everybody within reach. Then he would get into the tub and sit down on his haunches, or if the water was not too deep, he would roll around on his back and wash his face with his wet paws. After he had splashed as much as he cared to, he would suddenly jump out of his bath, and with water squirting from his long coat at every leap, chase anyone who happened to be near. If it were a woman, so much the better, because she would probably scream and that always seemed to add to the fun. It was quite useless for the pursued to try to climb out of his reach; climbing was Jimmie's long suit. The only safety was behind a closed door—a door with a latch. A door which closed simply with a spring, he could open as well as I could. First he would pull it ajar with one of his forepaws, and then insert his muzzle. In the kitchen there was a screen door which closed with a spring in this way, and he knew how to open this door at once. Whether he had done the trick before or not, I don't know. At the front hall there was another screen door, and it so happened that while the kitchen door opened at the right, the front door opened at the left.

Here was a chance to test the little bear's knowledge of doors, so, when I saw that he was very anxious to enter the house, I latched the kitchen door, and let him go around to the front. At once it was evident that he had had no experience with doors which opened at the left, for he devoted all his energies to the right-hand side, and for many minutes worked hard at the crack close to the springs and hinges. After he had given it up as a bad job, I brought him back, and opened the door just an inch or two. In a moment he inserted his nose, and ever afterwards he was able to open that door as easily as the other one.

As soon as Jimmie was considered big enough to go for a walk with me, he went. I took one black paw in my right hand and for a short distance he walked along like a little man. But he soon got tired of the upright position and I let him go on all fours. The world was very new and full of interest for him, and apparently he wanted to see it all that very day. He chewed the grass and sniffed the wild flowers and made clumsy attempts to catch the butterflies which hovered over them. He entered all the deserted houses, climbed into the cupboards, looked carefully up the chimneys, and acted generally as if he were thinking of renting a place for the summer. Once he had a fearful adventure. In the yard of one of the houses was an old-fashioned well sweep and Jimmie, after eyeing the tall, slanting pole, decided to climb it. It was stiff from disuse and never moved until he reached the very top, when to his surprise and horror it tipped over and brought him to the ground with a bump. Luckily the well itself had been boarded up. But young bears are very strongly made and he was much more scared than hurt. A few minutes later he seemed to have forgotten all about it. At any rate he shinned to the top of the next signpost we came to, very much to the amusement of a passing rustic who remarked with a grin, "I guess that b'ar wants to see how fur he is from hum."

Along the country road we went, Jimmie galloping gaily, now in front, now behind, and making frequent excursions into the woods on either hand to satisfy his curiosity, or to pick wild raspberries, of which he was very fond. When he came to a raspberry bush, he would first eat those which hung near the ground, and then, standing on his hind legs, he would pull the tall branches down to him with his forepaws. The amount of energy he displayed was remarkable. He never seemed to know what it was to be tired even after the most violent exertion. After galloping perhaps a hundred yards to catch up, he would make a playful run at me, biting at my legs and giving me a vigorous hug and shake with his forepaws, breaking away only to dash up a tree to a point perhaps fifty feet from the ground, without so much as a twig to aid him in his ascent. Here he would probably chew the green leaves for a moment, and then he would come sliding down, tail first, and at once break into a gallop to make up for the ground he had lost. He would march boldly along the tops of stone walls, walk slowly and cautiously on wobbly rail fences, and rush up the trunks of trees when there was nothing more exciting on hand. Sometimes he would remain up a tree so long that I got far ahead of him on the road, or sometimes I would hide in the long grass and call him to see what he would do. Apparently he seldom followed my trail by scent, as a dog would have done, but relied on his ears and eyes, and chiefly on the latter. At the sound of my voice, he would stand straight up on his hind legs, and I would see him peering in my direction, over the tops of the grass blades. If I called again, or if he caught sight of me, down he would drop, and, taking the general direction, he would gallop toward me. Then, as soon as he was in doubt, up on his hind legs he would go to get his bearings again. When at last he found me, he seemed satisfied, but showed not the least sign of affection, such as a fox or even a wolf would have shown, but simply ran along as before.

Presently at the crossroads, he spied a large stone watering trough, and he seemed to decide at once just what it was for. He scrambled up the side, flopped into the water, swam back and forth a few times, slipped down into the road again, and—shook his dripping coat all over me. We crossed a wall and were walking through the fields when I saw a farmer driving down the road on a mowing machine. His horses, evidently thirsty from their work in the sun, swung expectantly toward the watering trough. Their muzzles had almost touched the water when up came their heads, and they stood there snorting and refusing to drink. Then I called to their owner and told him that Jimmie had spoiled the water for them by swimming through it. Only after he had emptied the trough, scrubbed it thoroughly from end to end with bunches of coarse grass, rinsed it well, and filled it again, would the horses slake their thirst.

By and by we came to a lake, and Jimmie plunged in and took a swim, after which he came out and shook himself like a dog. Then I sat down to see what he would do. He wandered away, paddling in the shallow water near the margin. On a flat stone, close to the bank, a muskrat was sitting, quietly rubbing his nose, and I expected to see him dive long before Jimmie came near him. But he didn't move, and Jimmie failed to see him until they were close together. Then the little bear stuck out his nose to investigate, and the muskrat turned to face him, whereupon Jimmie rose on his hind legs, and looked down on the muskrat, as though not quite sure what to do. Then he came down on all fours, and again advanced, sniffing for information. The muskrat, perhaps thinking it was time to resent this impudence, made a jump at the bear, snapped his teeth once, and quickly turned to run. But he was not quick enough for Jimmie, who struck out with one black paw and bowled the muskrat over on the bank. But the rat quickly recovered his balance, and dived into the water.

Jimmie's blood was up now, and into the lake he plunged. Just what took place then I cannot say, as there was such a splashing of water, but at any rate the muskrat turned and bit the little bear in the nose, and Jimmie, perhaps realizing that he was at a disadvantage in the water, turned and fled, howling and panic-stricken, to the bank, and did not stop until he was safe in the branches of a tree. I have seldom seen so funny a sight, and it was a pity that Jimmie could not enjoy it as much as I did. He stayed up in that tree and amused himself by chewing the leaves and bark until he was ready to go home.

When we got back I saw a man on our roof, shingling it, and after a few words with him I went into the house, leaving Jimmie outside. Presently I heard a frightful yell, and running into the garden I saw the man, perfectly white, leaning against a chimney and wiping the moisture from his forehead. It appeared that Jimmie, seeing some one on the roof, had gone up the ladder to find out who it was. The man bending over his work did not even know of the bear's existence, and the noise of his hammer prevented him from hearing the slight sound behind him. Imagine his terror, when, without a word of warning, two stout hairy arms were thrown tight round his throat, and jaws like a steel trap closed on the back of his neck. He said he thought that the Devil had got him, and judging by the yell he gave I can quite believe him.

After that Jimmie went walking with me almost every day. Indeed, it was by no means an easy matter to leave him at home even if I wanted to. If he were loose he would go with me whether he was invited or not, and if I shut him up—well, I had no one to blame but myself. I tried it once, and the hole he chewed in the door was almost as big as the noise he made. I didn't hear the noise, because I was away, but I heard other things when I returned, and the orders from headquarters were that in the future Jimmie was to accompany me everywhere except to church unless there was some awfully good reason why he shouldn't. So I had a great deal of his company that summer, and I enjoyed it immensely. There was nothing monotonous about him, he was always doing something different.

I shall never forget the first time he saw a cow. There were several grazing in a field next to the road and Jimmie stood up on his hind legs at a fence post to watch them. Presently the cows looked up and saw him standing there, and no doubt he was just as strange a sight to them as they were to him. So one of them, overcome by curiosity, I suppose, walked over to get a better look at him. When she got reasonably near she stopped, and Jimmie, as if willing to meet her halfway, ducked under the barbed wire and walked straight up to her. Then when they were face to face, he stood erect. He seemed to be especially attracted by her ears—the largest, the hairiest, the most interesting ears he had ever seen. He put out his paws and began to examine one of them. This was a liberty which the cow resented promptly. Charging like a battering ram, she knocked him spinning under the barbed wire fence and for twenty feet among the clover and buttercups on the other side. With a disgusted "Wow!" the cub picked himself up, and came running to me, muttering and grumbling as if he thought I was to blame for his discomfiture. Perhaps he came only for sympathy, in which case he got what he came for, because after all he was only a baby and the cow had been very rough!

A few days later we were going through a pasture where there was a cow with a small calf. As soon as she saw Jimmie, she seemed to remember an appointment she had with him. She threw her tail in the air and started for him at her very best pace, but Jimmie had had one painful experience with a cow quite recently and he wasn't going to have another one right away if he could help it. The fence around the pasture was a high one, and he ran for it just as hard as he could hump his little back. The cow followed in hot pursuit. Jimmie got there first and quickly scrambled up a fence post out of reach. Bossy, seeing him safe, stopped about ten feet away and looked up at him. The cub, from the top of the post looked down at the cow. Then, as if a bright idea had occurred to him, he scrambled down again and walked slowly out to meet the enemy. The cow seemed to realize that her chance was coming and she lowered her head, all ready to rush in and toss him over the fence the moment she was sure of him. But Jimmie had a surprise in store for her. Instead of walking right up as he did to the other cow, he stopped a little short of this one, and arose on his sturdy hind legs. Then, without preliminaries, he "squared off" like a flyweight prize fighter, swung for her jaw with a "right" and "left," and landed twice. Then, with something very like a sneer on his impudent little face, he scrambled back up the fence post before the cow could recover from her astonishment.

JIMMIE SAYS GOOD-BYE

Toward the following spring, after long deliberation, we decided that Jimmie was getting too large for private use. Good-natured as he was, he was growing very strong, and quite too strenuous and demonstrative for the liking of some of the people he made it his business to meet. If he saw a man coming up the road, that man was in for a wrestling match whether he was in training or not, and if his apparel happened to be quite unsuitable for work "on the mat" it made not the slightest difference to the black imp who challenged him. A very nice young man walked all the way from Lebanon one day to try to sell us a copy of "To Heaven through Nature." Jimmie happened to meet him a quarter of a mile down the road, and by the time I was able to respond to his very vigorous call for help, he looked as if he had been trying to hurry through a series of barbed wire entanglements. We simply had to ask him to lunch, and Lucy spent most of the afternoon mending his trousers. As he was leaving, her eyes twinkled and she called to him, "When you get out a new edition of your book, don't forget to have a chapter on bears."

Even Lucy was no longer sure that she could hold her own against Jimmie. One day he caught her away from the house and in his playful, bearish way tore her skirt and apron and at last, to her great mortification, she was obliged to call for help.

But the climax was reached one evening, when, as Mrs. Baynes was coming home from a walk, Jimmie seized her, and in spite of all she could do to prevent him, tripped her up and threw her on to the snow. Of course it was in fun from his point of view, but from hers it was becoming serious, and she called to me. I ran as fast as I could, but by the time I got there he had taken the knot of her hair in his mouth and pushed her head into a soft snowbank. He was getting too funny to laugh at, and I determined to find a new home for him.

That was not entirely easy. When he was very little everybody wanted him, but as he had grown larger and stronger the offers which were made for him grew fewer and fewer. One friend, when asked if he didn't want a nice young bear about Jimmie's size, answered, "No thanks—what have I done to you?"

But at last I learned that the New York Zoological Society wanted a Canadian black bear, and the Director kindly wrote to me offering to buy him. I could not accept the offer, as I have always made it a point never to sell an animal which has been a member of my household. But I promptly presented him, and I confess it was with mingled feelings. Next morning we went for our last walk together, and when I marked his height as he stood on his hind legs and felt the strength of his arms and the grip of his teeth when he closed with me for a wrestling bout, I knew that we had not made our decision too soon. But that afternoon when he walked out on to the piazza, stood up at one of the posts, and with a strangely sad expression on his face looked away across those blue hills and valleys which he was never to see again, there came a choky feeling in our throats. And when a little later he picked up a much beloved rag doll which Mrs. Baynes had made for him, sat down with it in his lap, licked its face all over for the last time and then carried it off to bed with him, we couldn't help feeling very sorry that little bears grow up into big ones. Of course our intelligence told us that he had no idea that he was going away, that his standing at the piazza post that particular afternoon was merely an interesting coincidence, and that the sadness of his expression was probably in our own imagination. Nevertheless, these things all tended to emphasize the fact that he was about to leave us and we were genuinely sad to think that we were going to lose him.

Early next morning a sledge drawn by two big black oxen stopped at our door. They were headed toward Lebanon, our nearest railroad station, eight miles away. After we had all let Jimmie give us a parting hug, I led him to a crate which had been made for him, and a few moments later the crate, with the bear inside it, was lifted on to the sledge.

"Gee!" cried the driver, and the great black oxen swung to the right, breaking out the runners and sending glittering ice splinters in all directions.

"Huish!" The powerful brutes lunged forward into the yoke, the sledge moved northward over the rough and frozen roads, and Lucy, her apron held to her face, stood crying as if her heart would break.

Two months later I went to New York, and naturally the first person I called on was Jimmie. I wanted to see if he remembered me—to know whether he could distinguish me from the thousands of other people who went past those bear dens every day. I told the director and he consented to go with me and help me to make a test of it. From a distance we could see Jimmy lying in a corner of the den, his head on his left paw and evidently fast asleep. According to agreement, the director went to the corner which was farthest from the sleeping cub and began to call him by name.

"Jimmie!" he shouted. "Jimmie! Jimmie! Come along, Jimmie! Come! Come!"

But the bear never moved. Of course he must have heard the sound, but the voice meant nothing to him. Then the director stepped back, and I began to call. Instantly Jimmie's head came up from his arm, and he scrambled to his feet. Then he came trotting along the inside of the pen and when he got opposite me he stood up on his hind legs and I gave him my hand through the bars. He grabbed it in both his forepaws and fairly gasped in his excitement.

"Ooah! Ooah!—Ooooah!"

Then he gave way to that queer, continuous, bubbling sob he often made when greatly stirred.

"Ubble-uble-uble-uble-uble-uble," he blubbered, and he kept it up until I thought I should cry myself.

It was very hard to leave him, but, of course, it had to be. Slowly

I took my hand from between his clinging paws and walked away, leaving him sobbing softly to himself.

About a year later I went to see him again. He had grown much larger and was easily holding his own with several other young bears who were occupying the same den with him. When I arrived some small boys, in defiance of the rules, were throwing peanuts through the bars. All the bears in the den were on the alert for them, but it is safe to say that Jimmie was getting three out of five.

I went as near as the guard rail would let me and called him by name. Again he came up, but with a look quite different from the one he had given me a year ago. He stood up on his hind legs and looked at me with a puzzled expression which seemed to say, "It seems to me that I have met you somewhere before, but I'll be hanged if I can remember just where it was or who you are."

The last time I saw Jimmie—and it was not so long ago—he was still at the Zoo. He had outstripped all his companions both in size and good looks, and was really a superb specimen. As he arose on his hind legs he was tall and straight, his eyes were bright, and his coat was long and healthy. He was the largest and handsomest black bear in the New York Zoological Park.

MY FRIEND TOTO

By *CHERRY KEARTON*

Illustration by Frank Shields

I

THE FINDING OF TOTO

SOME four years ago I was in Central Africa for the purpose of photographing wild animals in their natural surroundings —lions, elephants, leopards, rhinoceroses, hippopotami, and many other beasts, besides birds and even insects. I have always loved animals, and I have never felt any desire to hunt and shoot them. Instead I have devoted my life to watching them in their own "homes," and obtaining records with my cameras of what I see.

For this purpose I have traveled all over the world: throughout Africa, north, south, east and west, in India, Ceylon, Burma, Borneo, Canada and America. But always Central Africa has appealed to me more than any other country. And out of all Central Africa there are few places so fascinating as the lower slopes of the "Mountains of the Moon." They stand directly between Lake Albert on the north and Lake George on the south, while the immense Lake Victoria Nyanza lies some two hundred miles to the east. As one stands on these slopes the mountains tower over one to a height of nearly seventeen thousand feet, snow-tipped and wonderful. Around one is the jungle, wild and often impassable. Stretches of open country break through the tropical forests here and there, dotted with stunted trees; but for the most part, on the slopes of the mountains, there is nothing but close-growing vegetation, with trees sixty feet in height intertwined with creepers, where, except on the few paths laboriously cut by the natives, nothing but an elephant can force its way.

At the time of which I write, I was marching, with an expedition consisting of some twenty native "boys" or porters, through the Congo Free State, planning to go afterwards across British East Africa to Mombasa on the coast. Sometimes, when game was comparatively scarce, we would march each day for a week; at other times, when it was more plentiful, we would pitch our camp on a comparatively open spot and stay until I had exposed many hundreds of feet of cinematograph film and numerous photographic plates.

We had halted near the foot of the "Mountains of the Moon," which were clothed in everlasting mist; my tent was pitched, the baggage and boxes were safely piled, the porters were resting, and I had just returned from a short prospecting journey with my cameras, when I saw coming toward me an Englishman. It was an out of the way place to meet anyone but a native, but this man I knew was encamped a few miles away, shooting elephants. Our paths had crossed three weeks before, and I was not surprised to see him again.

As he came nearer I could see that he carried what looked like a bundle of some sort under his arm.

"Hallo!" I shouted. "What have you got there?"

"A chimp," he said, and he laughed. "The King of the Chimps, perhaps; or their Prime Minister. Too young for that, though. More likely an infant prodigy, with a great future before him."

I looked at the little fellow as I sat smoking. He certainly was a young chimpanzee, probably not more than one year old. He peered at me out of a pair of most intelligent eyes.

"He's a fine little chap," I said, and I put out a finger. The chimp at once extended his hand and took my finger gravely.

"He's a perfect gentleman, too," said the hunter. "Aren't you, Toto?"

"I can see he's quite a gentleman," I said.

The hunter let him loose. The chimp at once climbed on to my knee, looking up into my face with an expression which seemed to denote a real desire to make friends.

"He's quite taken with you, Kearton," said the elephant hunter.

"What are you going to do with him?" I asked.

The hunter laughed.

"Well," he said, "I'll tell you. We are off today to the coast. We're traveling light, and I may not come back. I brought him along to see whether you would care to keep him."

I looked again at Toto, smiling at him. The little fellow almost smiled back at me, looking just like a little Irishman. I can say without vanity—although as a matter of fact it is a thing over which I always rejoice—that most animals soon make friends with me. This one, I could see, would be no exception.

"He's a jolly good chimp," said the elephant hunter, "and far and away the most intelligent I ever came across."

I patted Toto on the head, and he proceeded to curl up against my chest, holding on to my sleeve while one arm crept round my neck.

Should I take him? I wondered. He might prove a tremendous nuisance. On an expedition such as mine the amount of extra baggage that can be carried was necessarily limited, and very few luxuries were possible. To carry a chimpanzee in such circumstances seemed absurd. Yet—well, I liked Toto at first sight; I was practically alone, since the native boys hardly counted as far as companionship went—and the idea of having a good-natured pet to play with appealed to me.

"All right," I said at last. "I'll take him."

. . . . .

I need not attempt to describe Toto. Whether or not he was handsome may best be judged from his picture. Certainly he had features which would not count for beauty in a man: a large mouth, a very flat nose, and protruding ears. Yet in spite of that, there was something very pleasing about him: something pathetic that called for sympathy, and at the same time something roguish that showed him a real companion, always game for anything "sporting" and always ready to share a joke.

He stood about two feet high. He had very long arms and big hands. He was surprisingly strong, active and quite untiring.

When the elephant hunter left me, I put Toto down on the end of my bed and went outside to call Mahomed, the native boy who acted as my cook, valet and gunbearer. I wanted Mahomed to build

Illustration by Frank Shields

Toto's portrait.

a sort of kennel in which Toto could sleep at night, something light enough to be carried on the march and yet strong enough to keep him secure. But when we returned to the tent we found that Toto had his own ideas on the subject. Chimpanzees build nests for themselves in the treetops: roomy, flat nests made of intertwined twigs and padded with dry grass. Toto seemed to have made up his mind already that he had come to my tent in order to stay there, and he was proceeding to build for himself a nest—on my bed. He had collected material from all round the tent; anything that resembled a stick, including my miniature telescope, had been carried into the heap.

I laughed at the sight. "He's determined to save you the trouble," I said to Mahomed. "But we'll have to do better for him than that. Go and get him some dry grass and make him a bed in your quarters."

When I began to clear my bed, Toto seemed to want to keep the things he had found, so I gave him the telescope to play with while I put the others away. He sat on the ground, and for an hour I heard no more of him except for the clicking of the telescope as he pulled it to and fro.

At last Mahomed returned, and Toto followed him quietly enough. A few minutes later I went out to see that he was comfortable. I found him curled on a bed of grass, looking at the native boys as they rolled themselves in their blankets. For some minutes he watched them with great interest. Then he realized that this strange method of covering oneself must somehow be superior to building a nest and sleeping on grass. If it were better for the boys, no doubt it would also be better for him. So he got up, quietly walked toward them, snatched one of the blankets and trotted away with it.

Naturally there was a great uproar then in the camp. The boy whose blanket had been taken was furious. Unfortunately, he made up his mind to get it back, and Toto was determined that he shouldn't. He grunted furiously as the boy chased him, and directly the boy's outstretched hand touched the trailing blanket Toto turned suddenly and bit him. A monkey's bite makes a wound which is uncommonly painful, and the boy did not risk letting it happen again. He retreated very sulkily and persuaded a friend to let him share a blanket for the night, while Toto departed with his booty and sat down on his bed, uttering victorious shouts.

The next night the same thing happened. But this time Toto got the worst of it. He was treated roughly by the porters, who, though they loved him, loved their blankets more. They lay in wait for Toto and gave him a warm reception. Repulsed and very unhappy, he walked over in the dark to my tent, grunted with irritation, and crawled on to my bed. There he sat jabbering, telling me no doubt exactly what he thought of those porters.

We did not know each other's language, but a sympathetic voice always means much to an animal, and after I had talked to him for a while he seemed pacified. It was late then, and I lay down, wanting to get to sleep. To my astonishment Toto crept in beside me. And before morning he had got the best half of my bed!

He was an affectionate little fellow. He put one arm round my neck and the other under his head, and lay there just like a child.

The next night I made him a little bed to himself in my tent, and ever afterwards he slept near me. He was happy there and as good as gold, but I knew that he regarded it as only the second best thing, for if ever I sat too long at the camp fire in the evening I always found that he had crept quietly into my bed and was lying there when I came, looking up knowingly as if to say, "Mayn't I stay, just this once?"

· · · · · ·

It did not take us more than a week, as may be imagined, to fall in love with each other. He wanted to go with me wherever I went. Sometimes this could not be allowed. On the first occasion, I thought I could trick him. After telling Mahomed to look after him, I crept out of the back of the camp, thinking that I had evaded him. But Toto soon smelt a rat. He seemed to guess which way I had gone, and slipping loose from the boy, he bolted and, taking a short cut, was close behind me before I had gone a hundred yards.

I stopped, talked to him seriously and firmly, and turned to lead him back to the camp. But Toto in those days was inclined to be "spoilt," and the idea of going back in disgrace did not appeal to him at all. He stamped and screamed, beat his hands against his head, and finally began to bang his head against the ground. Poor Toto! It was his first lesson in discipline, and he didn't like it.

· · · · · ·

Before Toto had been found by the elephant hunter, he had lived with his father and his mother, his brothers and sisters, uncles and aunts and cousins, in the trees of the forest. There were, so to speak, two quite different worlds in the forest: the world of the treetops, where the birds and the monkeys lived, and where it was bright and sunny and warm, and the world of the ground below, where lived the animals that could not climb, and where everything was dark and mysterious because the leaves overhead were so thick that the sun could hardly ever be seen. The monkeys of the upper world

did not often go down to the ground, for there was danger from
bigger animals and from snakes; but they looked down often
enough, and there they saw the mother elephants with their babies,
and heard them trumpeting whenever the children rambled out of
sight; they saw the okapi, with his zebra-like stripes, stealing warily
along, alert against attack; and the few pigmy black men who crept
through the forest with bow and arrows in search of something for
dinner. Now and then, too, in clearer places near a river, a hippo
would lumber along, or a small herd of buffalo would pass on its
way to drink.

And there, up aloft, Toto would have sat, watching and wondering, with all his small brain busy, while parrots and other birds in
all their varied colors shrieked from the branches beside him and
white-collared eagles hovered overhead.

That, probably, was the life of Toto before he came into the hands
of my friend, the elephant-hunter. I do not know how he was found.
But I think that his mother must have been killed by one of the
deadly poisoned arrows of the natives, and then Toto, not knowing
or understanding what had happened, must have climbed down to
the ground, missing the food that his mother would regularly have
provided. And so he would have been found at the foot of a tree, a
forlorn little object, who would certainly have been killed swiftly
enough if the hunter had not come to his rescue. Poor little Toto!
He was not to see his home again, nor swing as he used to do from
branch to branch of those African trees; and yet I think that he has
been happy, following me into very strange places, and finding at
any rate a friend who loved him.

II

TOTO STARTS HIS JOURNEY

I had many miles to travel on that journey through Africa and
much work to do. The moment the expedition halted I had to get
out my cameras, and as soon as the tents were pitched and I had
seen that all was in order I would take two of the native boys as

carriers and start out to see what animals I could find. Sometimes I went more or less at random, ready to unslip my cinematograph camera whenever anything attracted my attention, and at other times I would make for a particular place, which I had seen in the distance through my glasses and chosen because it seemed a likely piece of country in which to find hippopotami, for instance, or a particular kind of bird.

But now, wherever I went, Toto came with me, shambling along with that curious four-legged walk which apes use when there are no trees on which to swing and they have to travel on the ground. After the first few days, I tried the experiment of giving him something to carry, at first something of little value which could not easily be broken, but later, when I saw how careful he could be, something more precious. He seemed to realize then that he was helping me, and he would clutch the box of film or whatever I had given him tightly to his chest and hop along just a pace behind me, looking up every now and again with a quaint expression of pleasure and pride.

He was also helpful in other ways. His eyesight was far sharper than that of a man, and he proved himself an excellent scout. My own eyes are accustomed to the jungle, and I do not often need field glasses to find the animals which I then stalk until I am near enough to use the camera. But Toto's eyes were far surer than mine, and often he would give me warning and show me the direction to take.

Once, while we were out together, Toto and I were resting under a little bush near some rocks. Before sitting down I had, as I thought, made sure that there was nothing within sight that I wanted to photograph, so that I could rest without fear of missing valuable opportunities. Suddenly Toto stood upright, thumping his chest excitedly, and turning to me with a little grunt, as if to say, "Be careful! Be careful!" But I could see nothing. I examined every inch of the grass in front of us, but nothing was visible. I took my glasses and studied the ground ahead more thoroughly. Then, fully one hundred and fifty yards away, I saw four tiny dark specks just showing above the grass. They were the tips of the horns of a pair of deer.

In the jungle Toto was always on the alert. Probably he had

learnt caution from the dangers of life in his world of the treetops, when often a young monkey who strayed carelessly on the ground would disappear forever. Toto was suspicious of everything that he did not know for certain to be friendly. In particular, he was always terrified of snakes; and rightly so, for snakes must have ended the days of many of his young cousins at home.

It is no unusual thing in Central Africa to find on the ground the dried outer skin of a snake: for snakes shed a thin skin at regular seasons and glide away in all the glory of a freshly grown covering, while the discarded coat lies where it fell on the ground. But Toto did not know that, and to him a snake skin must contain a snake. I remember that once we came upon the thrown-off skin of a big puff adder. Toto very nearly trod on it. Then he bounded into the air, his hair quite literally standing on end. As time went on, Toto learned many things, but this, the snake which was no snake, was a mystery of Nature which was always beyond his understanding.

On another day, as we were going back to camp in the evening, Toto had wandered some ten yards in front of me, when suddenly a small snake slid out from behind a stone, passed right in front of Toto, and dropped into a crack between two rocks. Toto yelled with terror, then ran back to me, and stood, with his teeth chattering, holding his hand as if to show where he had been bitten. I examined it carefully, but could not see the tiny mark that would have been made by the snake's fangs. I made sure of this, and then told Toto that he was only frightened and that the snake had not touched him. He did not believe me. He had been so scared by the sudden sight of the snake that he was certain that he was hurt and probably imagined he was going to die. Knowing that this was not so, I tried to coax him to come back with me to camp. He would not come. I walked ahead, expecting him to follow. After a few paces, I looked back and saw the little fellow stretched out on the ground, convinced that he was too ill to move, and looking at me with piteous entreaty not to leave him. So I picked him up and carried him to my tent, where at last the sight of a bunch of bananas distracted his thoughts until he forgot his terror; and half an hour later he was sitting on my bed, playing as contentedly as ever.

But it must not be thought that Toto was a coward. He was very far from that. Of snakes he was always afraid. I never saw a chimpanzee that was not. And I don't think he had any particular friendship for crocodiles. Nor have I. But there was little else that he feared.

He did not walk into danger, and he always grunted his usual warning when we approached any animal that I had not seen, but I have never seen him scared into flight from a single animal, although on one occasion, at least, I, at any rate, would dearly have liked to have taken to my heels. This was when we were together one day at a considerable distance from the camp. I was looking for a suitable place to hide the camera and myself, so that I could take pictures of vultures, hyena and jackal.

A few yards away was a river, and a little dip in the ground near its bank was filled with water, either from a hidden channel joining it to the river or else from a spring. Round this pool were the tracks where many animals had come to drink, and it was there that I expected to get my photographs. A few thick bushes, making a little clump about ten yards across, stood close to the pool, and I planned to hide amongst them with my camera. I walked toward the spot, happily enough, thinking of the good pictures that I could obtain without great difficulty.

Suddenly something touched my arm. It was Toto. He stood beside me, gazing first at the clump of bushes and then at me. At first he merely stared, as if uncertain whether an alarm should be given or not; then he seemed to make up his mind, and he pulled harder at my sleeve as if to draw me away, giving several of his deep-throated, warning grunts.

I stopped. I knew by that time that Toto did not give the alarm unnecessarily. Undoubtedly there was something hidden among those bushes. Whether it was any animal dangerous to man I did not know, but it happened that I was entirely unarmed, and I decided to make certain what lay ahead of me before going any closer. So I turned away, getting to a greater distance from the bushes, while I worked round to the other side, where I hoped to find a gap into which I could look.

Toto kept close at my side, stopping after every few yards and standing upright to look behind him.

At last we reached the opposite side of the clump, and turning, I began to approach it again, rather more warily than I had done before. Suddenly I saw the leaves of the nearest bush move, and I stopped. Something was moving into the open from behind that bush . . . something yellow . . . a lion!

Several times I have photographed lions in Africa, but I would not go toward one without a weapon, although I should only use it in the direst emergency. But now I had nothing more effective than my camera tripod, and I quickly decided to retreat. In fact, I must confess that my main desire at that moment was to put five hundred yards between that lion and myself as quickly as possible.

But to have run would have been to invite pursuit. A man-eating lion will always attack if he thinks he has an easy victim. If I had turned to run, that lion would have been across my body, tearing at my flesh, before I had gone twenty yards.

I knew that my only chance was to face him squarely, and edge quietly backward as best I could. At first I stood perfectly still, staring. It was a painful ordeal. I have no idea for how long I stood there, perhaps for a minute, or a minute and a half; but to me it seemed almost a matter of hours.

Slowly the lion moved, taking a few steps backward. Then he turned and snarled, showing his fangs as if deciding that I was unworthy of royal attention. Slowly, I began to retreat. Toto all the time had stood firmly beside me, watching as I watched and waiting till I gave the word to move. Gradually we retreated together until we were nearly a hundred yards from that clump of bushes. Then at last I turned and hurried away, glancing back every now and again to make certain that there was no pursuit.

That night when I found Toto in my bed I did not turn him out.

. . . . .

This adventure was the second turning-point in Toto's life. When my friend the elephant hunter brought him to me and I agreed to take him, I gave but little thought to the future. At the moment I was busy in Africa and there I should remain for some months. I knew, vaguely, that the day would come when I should turn toward the coast and eventually go back to England, and if I gave the matter a thought I must have assumed that then Toto would be left behind. Without having troubled to consider the matter, I suppose that I intended to leave him in a forest where he might join a passing family of chimpanzees, and soon forget that he had ever known any other life than that of the treetops. A chimp's memory is long lived, but I hoped this little fellow, whom then I hardly knew, would soon forget and be happy, playing monkey games among the branches.

But now everything seemed changed. For one thing, we had had adventure together. We had risked our lives, and, without a doubt, now it was Toto that had saved mine. By every unwritten law of the African wilds, whether of white man, of native, or of beast, that should have prevented me from deserting him.

No, it was out of the question to keep Toto for a few weeks or months as a plaything and then to leave him to take his chance of whether he first found friends or enemies. But it was equally out of the question to restore him to his own family. For one thing, we were now fully two hundred miles from the spot where he had been found. But the more important objection was that Toto's family would not have received him at all in the way in which the Prodigal Son was received by his father. On the contrary, since apes know by instinct when one of their number has been in contact with human beings, they would have regarded him at the best as a stranger, while it is more than possible that, considering him a traitor to his race, they would have killed him.

To take Toto back was therefore unthinkable. Besides, I must confess that I no longer wanted him to leave me.

If he was not to go, only one thing was possible. He must come with me on my travels, out of Central Africa, through British East Africa, and so by way of Nairobi to the coast, then across the sea to Marseilles and eventually to England.

I considered this plan very carefully. The first part of the journey presented no great difficulties. We had already traveled over a hundred miles together, and I had grown accustomed to carrying Toto pickaback for mile after mile. At first he had clung desperately clasping his hands under my chin until I was nearly throttled; but gradually I had shown him how to balance with his legs at my waist and hold me tightly by the shoulders. Then we were both comfortable enough, and sometimes I would even forget all about him till he would suddenly lay his head on my shoulder and try softly to kiss my cheek.

Thinking the matter over, I had little doubt that Toto could safely be brought through the jungle and as far as Nairobi. But there we should have left the wild and open country behind us. Toto, of course, had never seen a house nor walked on a pavement. He had never seen a white woman, and the only men he had ever met were the elephant hunter, the native boys of my expedition, and myself. In the wilds, his pranks were amusing, but what would happen in a town?

What would other people, the people I was to stay with, say of him, and would they even tolerate him at all?

But if he was indeed to come with me to London, he must begin to get used to civilization some time, and the sooner the better. And as far as that went, he was already a very well-behaved little fellow. He was learning daily what might be done and what was forbidden. He was even learning manners and many becoming little habits. For instance, he had learned to wash.

This began one day when he sat outside the tent and watched one of the boys cleaning his teeth. The native did not use a brush as we do, but a little wooden stick with a frayed and fibrous end, which did its work exceedingly well. Toto picked this up when the boy laid it down and, like the perfect imitator that he was, put it into his own mouth, drawing it to and fro as the boy had done.

Doing this seemed to give him great satisfaction, and for several days he did it every morning. Then he began to realize that I did something a little different, and he decided upon an experiment. One morning I noticed him fumbling in my valise, and a minute later I saw that he had taken my toothbrush.

Now, though I had every desire that Toto should be well brought up, and should learn in time to wash behind his ears and clean his teeth three times a day, I preferred to keep a toothbrush, at any rate, to myself. So I chased him round the tent, took the brush away, and then gave him a new one, just as it was bought, in a little paper bag.

He put it at once into his mouth, and soon became entangled with the paper. In a few minutes, however, he got rid of this and settled down to the new experience.

He found the method of the white man considerably more difficult than that of the native. He had, as may be seen from his picture, a fairly large mouth; but that, instead of making the matter easier, rather added to his difficulties, because he was uncertain into which part of his mouth the brush should be put. First of all he brushed his tongue, and it tickled. Then he tried to eat it.

"Steady, old fellow," I said. "Watch what I do," and taking my own brush I held it up to attract his attention. Toto imitated me at once, holding the brush so that it scraped his nose and made him sneeze.

I laughed at that, and Toto, who always hated to be laughed at, flew into a temper, flung the brush on the floor, and stamped on it. But as soon as I tried to pick it up, he snatched it and began again, this time with greater success.

The next thing that interested him was my bath. He sat watching me at my morning tub, and then directly I got out he got in. He did not mind the water, but it puzzled him. At first he could not distinguish between wetting and drying. As soon as he was in the bath he picked up the towel and started to use it. Naturally the towel immediately got wet and he made little progress. He would rub his face with the sopping material, and then, feeling very damp and uncomfortable, would look up at me to make sure that I was not laughing at him. I think he knew that he was doing it wrong, without being able to decide what was the matter.

So I gave him a lesson, performing each operation very slowly while he watched me with an expression of extraordinary seriousness. He wanted to learn. There were many things in this strange way of life that he had come into which puzzled him, but he was determined to master them one by one. Now he saw me take first the soap and then the sponge; and then get out and stand beside the bath to dry myself. When I had finished he began, and so well had he learnt the lesson that he did it perfectly—almost. He made a lather with the soap and began on his face, spluttering uncomfortably, and then, with a piece of originality, he reached for his brush and cleaned his teeth. He was very methodical, and he seemed to think it right that everything to do with the face should be settled in one operation. Then he washed his hands, and next his feet, holding the sponge so that the water trickled on to them, exactly as I had done. But then he thought he had finished.

"Go on, Toto," I said. "Don't forget your body."

But he would not do any more. He became accustomed to follow me into the bath every morning directly I left it, but he would never wash anything besides his face, hands and feet, and then he would clamber out and dry himself.

Afterwards he would take a brush and a mirror and complete his toilet.

He was also learning to behave properly at mealtimes. When in the early morning I would call to the boy to get my tea, Toto would slip out of his bed, stand at the entrance to the tent and give a shout in imitation of mine. Then when the boy appeared, Toto would come too, holding his cup in one hand and the saucer in the other. He would stand patiently beside me till I was ready to pour out, and then he would hold up the cup for me to fill it.

He was fond of sugar, and if he did not think I had given him enough he would slip his hand up to the sugar basin, look imploringly at me, and wait until I gave him the word to help himself.

More than anything else he liked bananas, and however many I gave him he always wanted more. Sometimes he would help himself, and eventually I had to keep them in a locked box. But one day Toto watched me as I took the keys from my pocket, unlocked the case, tore off two bananas and gave them to him. A little later we were playing together by the fire when I felt a hand at my pocket. I went on with the game, pretending not to notice. Toto put his hand stealthily into my trouser pocket and drew out the keys. Wondering what he would do, I went outside the tent, and after waiting a minute to make him think I had gone away I looked silently in at the doorway. Toto was sitting in front of the banana box, trying one key after another in the lock until he found the right one. Then he took out a banana and began to gobble it up as fast as he could.

When I came in suddenly and caught him in the act, I think he was surprised that I only laughed and let him finish the fruit. But then Toto did not share my remembrance of a very small boy, many years ago, who stole the key of his mother's larder in search of strawberry jam . . .

Chimpanzees are not accustomed to regular mealtimes. They sit and nibble all day, taking a leaf from one branch and fruit from another. I gave Toto, from the first, four good meals a day, but it was a long time before he accustomed himself to the routine and felt satisfied. At first he would enjoy a meal with me and then slip out and invite himself to dinner with the porters, taking very good care that no one had a bigger helping of their mealie food than he did. But gradually he came to prefer eating only with me, and to feel that there were advantages in not running away directly our meal was finished. He would sit on a chair watching and imitating nearly everything I did. Sometimes he would read the newspaper, if it was mail day and one was within reach. He would prop himself up against the back of the chair and wrestle with the problem of unfolding the big sheet without overbalancing, until he could hold it outstretched in front of him exactly like a man in a West End Club.

One day he watched me in silence for a long while as I sat smoking. Then he came toward me and reached up to touch my pipe. "It's an evil habit, Toto," I said laughing. "You'd better keep off it."

But soon I found that he was serious. He wanted to smoke. So I gave him an old pipe, wondering what he would do with it. He went back to his chair, put the stem between his teeth, and leant back luxuriously, closing his eyes. For a time he seemed content, and for some days after that wherever he went he carried the pipe as if it was his most precious possession. Then he realized that I used to put brown grass into the bowl of mine and set fire to it, and he wanted to do the same with his. I let him try. The matches proved a difficulty, but at last he learnt to strike them and to light the top of the tobacco. But he did not realize the secret of the art of smoking and he was puzzled when the flame in his pipe died directly, while mine continued to send forth clouds of smoke.

It was constantly a problem for him, and often I felt that he was longing for me to show him how it was done. I tried to do so, but my drawing in of breath must have looked to him merely a matter of making faces; so that I roared with laughter when he began to imitate my expression.

Still, he played every evening with the pipe. Many months later, it chanced that he drew in his breath through his mouth while the pipe was between his teeth. He gasped. He choked. He coughed. But the secret was found, and from that night he exhausted his half-ounce of tobacco every week.

It was while Toto was playing with his pipe one evening, long before this discovery, that I finally made up my mind to take him home with me.

Pushing back my chair, I got up.

"Toto, old fellow," I said, "you shall come to London."

Toto looked up at once. Then he tucked the pipe into a fold of skin between his ear and his shoulder where he liked to keep it, climbed off the chair, and ran toward me, so that I felt that he approved of my decision and was eager to start.

III

TOTO'S JOURNEY

The forest in which Toto had been born was near the western slopes of the "Mountains of the Moon," just within the borders of the Congo Free State. A very few days after he came to me we had forded the river which formed the boundary, and as we climbed the farther bank we came into Uganda. At that moment Toto, though he did not know it, left his own country forever, and began his journey through foreign lands. At first there was little difference in the country through which we passed; there were the same stretches of forest and of open country, the same animals, the same birds, and always the mountains behind us, now growing more and more distant.

We marched the whole way, Toto riding pickaback. At night we pitched the tent as before. But when we came to a place where animals were very numerous and there was much work to be done with my cameras, I decided to stay there for some weeks, and therefore got the boys to build for me a grass hut after the native fashion, thinking that it would give me more space than I should have had in a tent.

During those days Toto grew restless. In all my care for his welfare I had forgotten to arrange for him to have any special amount of exercise. In his earlier days he must have spent many hours in doing gymnastics among the branches of the trees in which he lived. But lately he had lived a lazy life, crouching on my back during the day and sitting on a chair in the evening. When the grass hut was built and he came into it with me, its grass roof must have reminded him of more energetic days. My bed stood in the hut, and scrambling on to it, he found that he could reach the struts and rafters which supported the roof. Grasping these, he swung from one to another, round the hut, and then back to the bed, until I feared that the flimsy structure would collapse. I told him to stop, and pointed to a chair on which I expected him to sit. But instead of obeying he leapt once more at the roof. When I ran after him he slipped to one side, ran to the grass wall and plunged through it, leaving a considerable hole. Then he ran around outside and looked at me through the door, as if wondering what I would say.

"Come here at once, Toto," I cried, and he came in. But before I could catch him, he jumped again on to the bed, swung across the roof and disappeared through the hole again.

This could not be allowed. The wall of the hut shook every time he went through it. So, to stop him, I went outside, cut a large branch off a thorn bush and filled up the hole. Toto watched me all the time with so comical an expression that I felt that he was laughing at me and planning some new ruse to get his own way. And directly I returned to the hut he slipped outside, and a minute or two later I saw him diligently disentangling the thorns and clearing his entrance.

Then he came back into the hut, stood daring me to catch him, and directly I moved was off once more across the roof and out through the hole.

Without a doubt we both enjoyed the game. But it had to be stopped if anything of the hut was to be left standing, and once more I filled up the hole, fastening the branches this time more securely. Toto saw then that I meant business. But he wouldn't allow me to pretend that I was serious. He came and gave me a playful smack on the leg, as if to say: "Right you are, but it was rather a game, you know," and then he climbed on to his chair, picked up my empty rifle and began to play with it.

A few minutes later, after working the bolt to and fro several times, he came running across to me.

"Let's play at something else," he seemed to say, and picking him up I began to tickle him. Toto always loved to be tickled. He squirmed in my arms, screaming with half hysterical laughter, just as a small child would have done, trying to get away but always coming back so that I could do it again.

Toto was never bored. He would play for hours with some simple thing, or he would go out and join the porters as they danced round the fire in the evening. Anything like a romp appealed to him, from climbing to the top of my tent and sliding down the outside of it, to banging a native drum until even the boys would grow tired of the sound and would chase him across the encampment.

He was interested in everything, and whenever he met anything new he at once went to inspect it. Once he found a giant rat, fully three feet long from nose to tail, hiding in a hole at the foot of a tree. All that Toto could see of the rat at first was the tip of its nose and its whiskers, level with the mouth of the hole. So he took a stick and gave the rat a little poke. He probably imagined that this would induce it to come out of the hole. It did. The rat jumped out, bit

Toto on the hand, and leapt back to safety before Toto had recovered from his surprise.

Toto then retired for a couple of yards and considered what he should do next. At last he took a bigger stick, broke off its branches, and went forward to the fight again, confident, no doubt, that his superior weapon would bring him victory. But the rat was artful; it took two or three pokes in the face without flinching and waited until Toto forgot his caution and ventured too close for safety. Then it jumped out again and once more nipped Toto's finger.

The victory was clearly with the rat; and Toto, rather sore about the hands, decided that it was no use playing with people who were rough, and that it wasn't fair and he wasn't going to play any more.

He went and sat under a tree and felt rather sulky. Once or twice he looked round, hoping perhaps that the rat would be tempted to come out into the open and give him a proper chance. But the rat knew its business better. It ignored Toto, and settled down to wash its face.

. . . . .

When we had traveled some two hundred miles eastward from the "Mountains of the Moon" we approached the shores of Lake Victoria Nyanza. We pitched our camp near a native village, and waited until news should come of the arrival of the steamboat which was to carry us more than a hundred miles across the water. Fortunately, we had not long to wait, and three days later we moved down to the jetty.

Toto was not afraid of water, provided that it was not the home of crocodiles. He enjoyed running over the rough bridges and he liked bathing, although he found fording rivers when he was sitting pickapack and the water reached to my thighs, an experience full of terrors. But the sight of the lake did not mean very much to him. I think he hardly understood that the immense stretch of bluish white that lay ahead was water, and could not be trodden upon. In any case he had little time to consider the matter, for I carried him straight on board and put him down in the smoking room while I went to supervise the stowing aboard of our baggage. When this was finished I brought him on deck, and we stood together at the rail looking down on the shore. The natives were carrying bunches of little red bananas on to the ship, and Toto helped himself as they came up the gangway, to the great amusement of everybody on board except the owners of the fruit. Then he looked up at the funnels and the masts, longing no doubt to climb about them. But this was very strictly against the rules, and to keep him from temptation I had to take him below again, where he spent the next twelve hours alternately sucking at his pipe and dozing on the cushioned seats.

The next morning, when we reached the opposite side of the lake, Toto walked ashore happily enough, I suppose without the slightest idea of the immense distance that he had traveled in the night. But then a new surprise was in store, by far the greatest that he had yet encountered.

Standing near the jetty he saw a very large creature, bigger than an elephant, with a broad trunk turned upward and clouds of smoke coming out of it. Behind the creature was a long string of immense boxes. Toto had never seen anything like it, for this was the nearest point to his home to which the railway had yet been carried. The engine whistled, and Toto clung to me in terror, his arms holding very tight around my neck. I carried him into a carriage of the train and put him down.

He ran first to one window and then to another, mystified by everything. He could no longer see the strange snorting creature in front, and that, no doubt, calmed him. I expect it was then that he began to realize that after all this was not a new animal, since I had produced neither a camera to photograph it nor a rifle with which to protect myself.

A little later the train started, and Toto jumped to his feet at the first jolt. He looked out of the window and then peered up at my face, as if to say: "This is all right, isn't it?" and then, as I nodded consolingly, he settled down in a corner to enjoy the new experience.

He was scared once more when we got up steam and the jungle beyond the windows changed from a clear picture to a moving blur, but again he settled down, becoming greatly interested in the strap which hung from the window. Then the luggage rack overhead attracted his attention and in a minute he had climbed into it. That fascinated him. He sat on the bar, swinging his legs; then he sprang across to the opposite rack and back again.

"Quietly, Toto," I said, and then he stretched himself out at full length in the rack and prepared to go to sleep.

The journey by train occupied some twenty-four hours. We stopped frequently at little towns and native villages, and always Toto wanted to get out and go into the jungle. But this, of course, was impossible, although whenever we could Toto and I got out to stretch our legs on the platform, and then the natives and officials would gather around in amazement at the sight of man and monkey walking together. They would not have been more surprised, although more scared, if I had brought with me a lion or a hippopotamus.

At last the end of our train journey was reached, and I think we were both heartily glad. I long always for the open spaces, and find a prolonged journey by train indescribably tedious. Toto, of course, had the same feeling: it was one of many which he and I had in common. If I were a believer in reincarnation, I think I should be convinced that I had seen this world before from the point of view of a chimpanzee in an African forest, swinging all day among the branches with the sense of unexplored country all around me. At any rate, it would have been among the most delightful of all conceivable existences.

After leaving the train at Gilgil, we set out once more on the march, and Toto returned to his favorite position on my back. For some days we marched, and then it could be seen that we were again drawing near to civilization. The first sign was a far-outlying farm, owned by an English settler. It was good to meet a white man again and to enjoy the comforts that had been impossible in the many months I had spent in wilder places. I called a halt for my expedition, and turned aside toward the settler as he came out of his house to greet me.

In such a very lonely spot some sort of protection was needed, and for this purpose the settler kept five fierce-looking dogs who roamed constantly round the house and through the farmyard. Naturally, they growled at Toto as he approached, and Toto, always cautious, immediately picked up a stone in one hand and a stick in the other.

"Hello," exclaimed the settler, "that's a cheerful-looking pet you've brought with you. What is he going to do? I'd better call off the dogs."

"Wait a minute," I answered. "Toto's a match for all your dogs. Let's see what will happen."

I had no fears for Toto, for I had seen him in similar circumstances before. Standing upright, he advanced toward the house. The dogs growled and moved as if to intercept him. Toto stopped. Then he stamped his feet, threw the stone at the dogs and waved the stick threateningly over his head. The effect was instantaneous. The dogs stampeded and left Toto in possession of the field.

There were many other occasions on which Toto showed his skill with stones and sticks, and proved once again the military axiom that the proper method of defense is to attack. But it seemed that he had greater success when his enemies had the power of reasoning than when they lacked it. This was curious, but probably it showed what a large effect surprise, and a feeling that Toto was neither man nor beast but something uncanny and unnatural, had upon those who possessed the power of thought but had not had it cultivated to any strong degree. For instance, I have seen a dozen fully-armed native soldiers put to flight when Toto chased them with my walking stick, yet he certainly came off a bad second best in his encounter with the giant rat; and once he was severely defeated by no more terrifying opponent than a hen.

This was when we returned to Gilgil, an outlying settlement some miles from Nairobi. It was a desolate place, amid bare and uninteresting country, yet it boasted the distinction of containing an hotel. Unfortunately, this hotel was a very tiny affair; and when I arrived, every room was occupied and I had to content myself with an outhouse which was little more than a bare shed in a yard at the back. I fixed my bed in the room into which I was shown, and then began to explore. I opened a door, thinking it might lead to another room which could serve me as a sitting room, but found instead that it led into the stable of a tame zebra! A third door opened into the yard, occupied by a number of chickens.

There was, therefore, nothing to do but to make the best of things as they stood, and I got into bed and fell asleep. The next morning Toto awoke earlier than I did, and he, in his turn, went on a tour of investigation. He opened the first door, and immediately the zebra walked into the room.

This, of course, was the first time that Toto had slept in a house, and I am afraid his opinion of town life must have suffered a shock. He turned to the other door in a hurry, pulled it open and stepped out. Unfortunately, in doing so he nearly killed a young chick, and there was great indignation in the farmyard. The mother hen came to the rescue of her family, and I awoke suddenly with the idea that every fowl in Africa was screeching at the top of its voice. Also I was rather alarmed to see the zebra loose in the room and nibbling at my clothes. Before I could jump out of bed, Toto had retreated into the room again, banging the door behind him.

It was still before daybreak, and I am afraid Toto resented this uproar at so early an hour. Besides, he wanted to continue exploring the yard. So he opened the door once more, but banged it again when he saw the hen with all her ruffled plumage waiting for him outside. Again he opened the door, but this time more cautiously, protecting his body with it while he leaned round it and tried to strike the hen with his open hand. But he missed her and only saved himself from a sharp peck by jumping back just in time and slamming the door.

He made up his mind that next time he would be quicker; but when he tried smiting with one hand and shutting the door with the other almost at the same moment, his right hand was too quick for his left, with the result that the door was slammed on his fingers before he could withdraw them.

The injury was painful, and perhaps, as he sat on my bed ruefully sucking his hand, he forgot about the hen altogether. Or it may be that this was merely pretense, to save his pride when he decided that discretion was the better part of valor. At any rate, he made no attempt to open that door again.

IV

TOTO COMES TO TOWN

At last we reached Nairobi. I had sent one of my porters running ahead, with a letter announcing our arrival to my old friend Blayney Percival, the Game Warden of Kenya. In this letter I mentioned, without saying very much about it, that a chimpanzee was with me, that his name was Toto, and that I thought he would give my friend and his family a good deal of amusement. I thought that after this warning they would make preparations for us both, and I planned to reach town next day and go to Mr. Percival's house.

But I had no anticipation of the reception that was prepared. And it was not for me. It was for Toto.

I had forgotten, for the moment, that my boy could not be expected to deliver the letter and come straight back to me in silence. The natives of Africa are the greatest gossipers on earth, and this one had a tale worth telling. He could not keep it to himself, and he gave Mr. and Mrs. Percival a glowing account of the wonderful animal that was coming to share their house. I do not think that exaggeration is necessary with regard to the wonderfulness of Toto; his exploits are sufficiently remarkable in themselves. But the native, like many people who have a tale to tell, and certainly like all African natives, could not resist the temptation to "improve" on his news.

The first result of this was that Mr. and Mrs. Percival were thoroughly alarmed. They were a little uncertain, as I learnt afterwards, whether the number of apes that I was bringing was two or six. But they obtained a clear impression, at any rate, that all the animals were able to talk in several languages, that they carried weapons and were in the habit of using them at random, and that the expedition would enter the town with the apes carrying me in a litter.

The second result, which came from the story being spread not merely to my host and hostess but to nearly everyone else in the town, was that the entire population, or so it seemed, came out to meet us. As we drew near the first house of Nairobi, some hundreds of natives filled the main street, all agog to see the wonderful sight that had been promised them. I am afraid there was some disappointment over the affair. But that was not Toto's fault. He appeared to realize that he was the center of attraction, and, perched as he was on my shoulders, he did his best to provide entertainment.

The natives started a sort of cheer as we came along. Toto shouted in reply. Someone waved to us. Toto seized the hat from my head and waved it in imitation.

But that, I am afraid, was all. The thing fell rather flat. And by the time we reached the Percivals' house most of the crowd had melted away, and not more than thirty people were following us.

Mr. and Mrs. Percival both came out to greet us, and were soon reassured by the sight of Toto. He always made friends quickly, and now, directly I went up to the Game Warden and shook hands with him, Toto slipped from my back, went to Mrs. Percival, and held out his hand. Mrs. Percival is one of the most genuinely sympathetic people I have ever met. She wanted to laugh at Toto's imitation of me, but, as she told us afterwards, she felt that Toto was being very serious, and that to laugh would hurt him. Knowing him as I do, I think she was right. So she shook his hand gravely, gave him a little smile of welcome, and then led him toward her husband. She and Toto were great friends from that moment.

In expectation of more fearsome visitors, Mr. and Mrs. Percival had arranged for us to live in a wooden bungalow some sixty yards from the house. They now wanted us to come into other rooms, but I refused to upset the arrangements. After all, Toto was not used to the ways of civilized people, and his adventures in the hotel at Gilgil had proved that there were surprises in store for him. The little bungalow was much better than the tent and the grass huts he had known in the last few months, for I felt that it would be better for him to get used to things gradually. The grounds of the house were very extensive, and the bungalow stood close to a little wood which would make for Toto a fine playground.

Toto was now on holiday. For a while there would be no more marching and no photography. He had nothing to do all day but to enjoy himself, and this he did very thoroughly. He made friends at once with everyone on the estate. He played all sorts of games with Mrs. Percival's two little boys, riding on their scooters and rocking horses, playing catch-as-catch-can round the lawn, jumping over bushes in a furiously exciting race. Basil, the elder boy, wanted to teach him to play football, and without a doubt he would soon have become an expert if only he had understood that the rules of Rugby did not apply to the Association game. He would handle the ball as soon as it came near him, and then no one was rash enough to try to take it away.

But the occupation that seemed to give Toto more pleasure than anything else was sitting on the ground with little Jim, the younger boy, and making mud pies. This he would do for hours at a time. Jim would chatter to him all the while as if he had been another child, saying sometimes, "No, you mustn't do that, you must do it this way," and Toto, very patiently, would watch what Jim did and then give a perfect imitation of it.

Another game of the same sort consisted of trying to build a dam across a pond in the garden. Basil would build from one bank, while Toto, determined to give his aid where it was most wanted, would help Jim on the other. Jim would take command, and Toto obediently carried out the orders, scooping up mud with his hands, carrying it to the edge of the water, and laying it exactly where Jim directed. Then Jim would pat it into hardness and call for more, and Toto would stop watching him and race off again to the mudbank. It was delightful to see them, and I have little doubt that Jim, now grown to be a big boy of nine or ten, still remembers the games that he and Toto played together.

To Toto, those must have been among the most fascinating days of his life. He was surrounded by friends, all eager to play with him, and he would enter into the spirit of any game, whether it was with the white children, or the black servants, or the many animals that lived in the grounds. And it was not only in games that he participated. One day, as Mr. Percival and I came out of the house, we saw a group of native "boys" sitting on the ground, washing clothes. Taking his place in the circle, accepted apparently without question as an additional helper and hard at work, sat Toto. He was entirely absorbed in his task, washing a cloth with soap in a bowl of water, wringing it out in exact imitation of the way the natives worked, then wetting it with a cupful of clean water and wringing it out again.

And then there were the animals. One was a tame cheetah. These two were suspicious of one another at first, but Toto boldly "stood up" to the cheetah and tried to pat it on the nose at the first meeting; then they became friends. They would play a sort of hide-and-seek together in the long grass that covered a little hollow on the estate. The cheetah would go ahead and suddenly lie down so that it was entirely covered by the grass. Then Toto would try to find it, running here and there, and jumping into the air in his efforts to get a better view.

Also there were two Airedale puppies and a rather fierce-looking hyena. Toto would ride round the garden on the hyena's back.

Toto was very fond of being carried about, and I do not know what form of locomotion pleased him most. On the second day of our stay in Nairobi Mr. Percival and I took him out in a motorcar. He was fascinated by the steering wheel, and was allowed to sit on the driver's knee and hold it. We showed him the engine, and he wanted to put his hands into the middle of it. But the thing that he most enjoyed in a car was, I regret to say, to sit at the back, and, whenever a native came riding by on a bicycle, suddenly to reach out a hand and knock off the boy's hat.

On another occasion when we had gone out, Toto and I came back in a rickshaw drawn by a native boy. That was great fun for Toto, and he enjoyed it so much that the next day, in the main street of the town, he suddenly ran away from me, jumped into an empty rickshaw, and signed to the boy to start. The boy looked to me for orders.

"Take him round the town for half an hour," I said, and off they started.

At the end of thirty minutes I was waiting for Toto to return. But he did not put in an appearance for another two hours, and then it was in another rickshaw drawn by a different boy. The first boy, it appeared, had got tired of the amusement and pulled up; Toto had jumped down at once and climbed into another car, and so the afternoon had been passed, seven of the boys taking it in turn to give Toto a ride.

V

TOTO CELEBRATES CHRISTMAS

Even the most enjoyable of holidays must eventually come to an end. But when I talked of going, Mr. and Mrs. Percival and Basil and Jim all joined in begging me to stay. They would not hear of my leaving them, at any rate until after Christmas. They insisted that they could not spare me; that Christmas would not contain half as much fun if I were not there.

But it was not I who could not be spared.

For weeks past, as I knew, the boys had been making plans for a Christmas surprise for Toto. Toto was to be the center of all the jollity. Everyone wanted to give Toto a present for Christmas. And all the schemes would be ruined if Toto went.

So we stayed.

Christmas in East Africa is an even greater and more preoccupying occasion than in England. At home one makes quite a good pretense that it is purely a children's festival, and that one is only doing foolish things like putting on a colored paper cap and playing absurd games because the children are amused by one's doing so. But in East Africa one enters into the spirit of the thing. "Auld Lang Syne," when one is many thousand miles from home, takes on a new meaning. A Christmas pudding is a hundred times more interesting when it has been sent from England because there is someone there who refuses to forget you.

Perhaps it is because you are only a small group isolated in a foreign land. Or perhaps it is in rebellion against a feeling that because you are so far abroad Christmas will be a very small festival. But in any case you insist upon making it a big one. You let yourself go. You wear the colored cap because it is brightly colored and because it comes out of a Christmas cracker. You sing and laugh and dance and play absurd games, however old you are, simply because it would be absurd not to be absurd at Christmas time in Nairobi.

The celebrations lasted a week. First there were the decorations. There Toto was entirely in his element. Mrs. Percival stood on a pair of steps and her husband passed up the branches of evergreen; but before she could fix them Toto would come leaping round the room, from chair to table, from table to bookcase, and from that to piano, snatching the leaves from her hands and reaching with ease to all the apparently inaccessible places.

It was a great day for him. By this time he was growing used to spending a good deal of his time inside a house, and accepting all kinds of strange restrictions which prevented him from climbing on to the furniture. Now at last he was not only allowed to go almost everywhere he wished, but the more he climbed the more—actually —he was applauded! Only one thing was forbidden. The chandelier hanging in the center of the room had attracted him from the first. He wanted to swing on it; and now that discipline was relaxed he apparently decided that this day of days could fittingly be crowned by an exciting finale of gymnastics.

But the moment he climbed on the center table he was lifted down again. It was very disappointing. He tried again and again, choosing the times when everyone seemed preoccupied. But it was of no use. Each time, however quietly he had moved, he was seized just as he was about to jump up and catch the swinging lights.

In the end it was we who tired first of the struggle and tried to distract his attention. I picked up a sugar basin and offered him a lump. He had been getting rather cross at being so continually thwarted, and perhaps he planned to get his revenge, or perhaps he merely wanted to make sure of getting as many lumps as he wanted without interruption. In any case, he grabbed the sugar basin from my hand and raced out into the garden with it, ran to the nearest tree, a very lofty one, and before we reached the lawn was sitting on a branch sixty feet above our heads.

Mrs. Percival was genuinely distressed. The bowl was a valuable one, of antique cut glass, and she was certain that it would be broken.

I assured her that it was perfectly safe. Toto had often carried my photographic plates, and I knew the care that he always took. And I was right. Toto waited till he had eaten every lump of the sugar. Then he climbed down the tree, holding the bowl as if he was very well aware of its value, put it carefully on the ground, and hurriedly retreated to his perch.

On Christmas Eve we all went out to dinner at one of the hotels. Near the entrance of the dining room were some friends of mine, and I stopped for a minute to shake hands and speak to them.

Toto stood beside me. As I have said before, he was always very anxious to learn, and he was convinced that everything that I did was right for him to do also. I led him to our table and our meal began. A few minutes later some strangers passed us, going to take their places at the other end of the room. Toto immediately slipped off his chair, stood up and held out his hand, exactly as he had seen me do a short time before. His newly-made friends were certainly surprised, but by that time everyone in the town had heard of Toto, and no one would have missed an opportunity to make his acquaintance. In fact, many people passed our table that evening, I am certain, simply to see Toto get up and, with the most gracious air imaginable, shake hands with them. He was certainly the hero of the evening.

At the meal, as usual, Toto conducted himself very well. But he was always impatient when others were served before him, and if bananas or sweets were on the table, he always helped himself surreptitiously between the courses.

Afterwards we went to the house of some friends, and there in the course of the evening the gramophone was played. Toto was astounded. He looked all round the room, trying to find where the sound came from, and at last he made up his mind that, improbable as it must have seemed to him, it must come from the wooden box on the table. He examined it from every side, and then, like a kitten with a looking glass, he crouched down in front, springing up suddenly in the hope of catching whatever was hidden inside it. Finally he gave up the search, sitting on a chair in front of the instrument, and starting to sing whenever a passage particularly appealed to him.

On Christmas morning, when Toto and I reached the house, the
presents were already laid out on the breakfast table. There was a
little pile on each plate. Basil and Jim were standing by their chairs,
impatient of the rule which forbade any of the parcels being opened
until everyone was seated.

Toto walked solemnly round the table, as he did each morning,
shaking hands, and I think he was surprised that the boys paid less
attention to him than usual.

But a few minutes later everyone was seated, and the celebration
of Christmas Day began. Toto was on his usual chair, spoon in
hand, waiting very eagerly for Mrs. Percival to serve the porridge.
But the porridge bowl was not even on the table—there it stood on
the sideboard, and, instead of eating, everyone was untying parcels.
That was quite different from usual, but everybody seemed very
happy, and Toto had no intention of being left out of the fun. There
were parcels on his plate, too, and in a minute he had laid down the
spoon and was attacking the string with fingers and teeth.

The first parcel that he opened contained a square glass bottle of
sweets with a screw top, which puzzled him at first before he found
the way to undo it. Then he took out one of the sweets and ran to
give it to Mrs. Percival. After that he helped himself, and found the
sweets so much to his liking that he would not have opened the
other parcels if I had not reminded him.

The next contained several bananas. Toto was always well-
mannered—a credit, in fact, to me for the way I had brought him
up—and much as he loved the fruit he would not eat it until he had
broken one into two pieces and offered half to Jim.

The boys' surprise came next. This had been kept very secret, and
as a matter of fact I doubt whether otherwise it would have been
permitted. I was rather horrified when I saw it. They had made it
themselves, and it consisted of a mechanical monkey, painted in very
bright colors, on a stick. You pulled a string, and the monkey leapt
to the top of its pole. Basil explained, while Jim shouted in his
excitement, that they thought it would make Toto feel at home to
have a little monkey to play with.

If the representation of the monkey had been more lifelike, I do not know what Toto would have done. He might possibly have thought that he was being laughed at. But fortunately the boys were cleverer at mechanics than they were in art, and the figure balanced on the stick was as much like a red banana as a monkey. Consequently, when I pulled the string and the figure jumped, Toto shouted with laughter, and for weeks after that the toy was in close rivalry with his pipe as his most treasured possession.

Mr. Percival also had a game for Toto. Preserved cherries, he knew, were regarded as an especial luxury, and Mr. Percival put one into an empty wine bottle. The cherry was too big to be shaken out, and Toto was faced with the problem of how to secure it. First, he tried pressing one of his long fingers into the neck of the bottle: but the fruit was slippery and he could not keep hold of it. Then he set the bottle down on the table in front of him and considered it. He quickly made up his mind, and looked round the room for what he wanted. On the sideboard stood the remains of a cold fowl. Toto went to it at once, helped himself to a long, thin bone, and put this like a spoon into the bottle. Then he held the bottle upside down and slowly drew out the cherry, balanced on the end of the bone.

It was one of the cleverest things I ever saw him do. My host declared that there was not a native in Central Africa who would have had the intelligence to do it; and for my part I doubt whether many white men would have solved the problem so quickly and so effectively. As I have said, Toto was a genius among apes.

. . . . .

In the evening the Percivals gave a party to their friends. We were all very lively, exchanging stories, singing choruses, and dancing. Toto was rather obstreperous when we danced, and I sent him outside to play with the black boys. They were fond of him and gave him a very good time, but I was always his best friend, and every few minutes he would look in at the door to make sure that I was still there. Then he would go and have another game and reappear for another minute directly it was over.

At about nine o'clock we started some charades. We ransacked the house for clothes, and among other things we found the complete outfit of a Father Christmas, complete with beard and whiskers, which Mr. Percival had worn the evening before when filling the boys' stockings. This was allotted by general consent to me—for the reason, I am afraid, that my girth corresponded more than that of anyone else to that decreed by legend for Santa Claus. In a few minutes I was disguised and playing my part in the charade. Then Toto looked in. He could not find me. He ran round the room and looked behind various pieces of furniture without success. Then he decided that I must have gone into the garden, so he ran out, paying no attention to Mahomed's call to him to come back for another game. He could not find me in the garden; I was not on the stairs, nor in the kitchen. He explored the whole house and then came back to the sitting room. By that time he had made up his mind that I must be there after all, although he could not see me. People must have got muddled up in this day of excitements. If his eyes deceived him he would see what could be done with his sense of smell. So down he went on all fours, and in turn he smelt the ankles of everyone in the room till he came to mine. Then he gave a great shout, hit my leg with his hand and went dancing round the room.

We played a Christmas game in which everyone in the room has in turn to point to someone and say, "This is the one that I love best."

"There's no doubt whom Toto loves best," said Mrs. Percival, and then, as Mahomed came into the room at that moment, she turned to him and asked:

"Mahomed, why is Toto so fond of his master?"

Mahomed, it appeared, had many reasons to give, and he gave them at length, telling several tales of our adventures together. The most convincing reason of all, and the one in which apparently all the native boys believed, he kept till the last. "And, you see," he finished, "the master is Toto's father."

.   .   .   .   .   .

Toto at times showed a real sense of understanding when I in my turn needed help and affection. Never did he show this so appealingly as soon after this Christmas, when I was stricken down with a severe attack of fever.

Toto made himself my nurse. He would not leave me. All day he would sit beside me, watching with a care that seemed almost maternal, and anything that I wanted he would bring me. He would go to the medicine chest when I told him to do so, and bring the bottle of quinine, and then he would fetch a glass of water. When I wanted a book he would go to the shelf and stand in front of the eight or ten books that lay on it. He would put his finger on the first and look at me.

"No," I would say, and then he would touch the one at the opposite end of the row.

"No," I would say again, and he would touch all the books in turn till I said "Yes." Then he would bring the book to me.

In the afternoon he would lie down on the bed beside me, put his arm out as if to protect me, and go fast asleep.

When I began to get about again, I felt the heat very much at midday, and would go up to my room and throw myself on the bed, too exhausted even to remove my boots. The first time that this happened I fell asleep at once. When I awoke, I could hardly believe it when I found that my boots had been taken off and put on the ground while I slept. It seemed impossible that Toto could have done this, and so quietly that I did not wake. But the next day, directly I lay on the bed, I felt his fingers undoing the laces.

It may be that some who read this book will say that friendship between an ape and a man is absurd, and that Toto, being "only an animal," cannot really have had the feelings that I attribute to him. Some people may say that. They would not say it if they had felt his tenderness and seen his care as I felt and saw it at that time. He was entirely lovable.

VI

TOTO GOES TO SEA

Whatever illusions Toto may have had concerning the water he crossed on Lake Victoria Nyanza, he had no doubt at all that the open sea, when we reached it, was something entirely strange. Very soon after leaving Mombasa we were out of sight of land, and Toto would sometimes stand at the rail with me and gaze toward the far distant horizon; then he would look up at me with that strange and rather comical expression which meant that his brain was considering an insoluble problem.

"Where are the trees?" he seemed to be asking pathetically, and there was nothing that I could say to console him, for now he had left the jungle behind forever. Yet he was happy on the ship, for there were plenty of passengers to make much of him, and any number of opportunities for getting into mischief.

Necessarily, I had to impose certain restrictions on him. He could not be allowed to wander at will, or he would certainly have spent most of the day at the masthead, and I should not have been at all surprised to see him trying to swing from one mast to another by way of the wireless apparatus; or else he would have incurred the lasting displeasure of the Captain by leaving footmarks on that most holy of places, the bridge.

Consequently, I was compelled at times to lock him in my cabin. The first time that I did this I was surprised to meet him half an hour later calmly walking into the smoking room. I took him back, but was amazed to find the cabin door still locked on the outside. I thought that someone was playing a practical joke on me, so I locked him in again and went on deck, standing against the rail where I could watch the companionway. Ten minutes later I found Toto sitting on the rail beside me.

"Now, how did you get here?" I demanded, and I turned to catch him. He jumped away, ran for a few yards along the top of the rail, and then began swinging himself, hand over hand, down the rail, till he was hanging by one arm over the side. With his other hand he reached a porthole (that, as I guessed, of my cabin), and a second later he had scrambled through and was out of sight.

So that mystery was solved! I went down to the cabin, and there he was, very pleased with himself, and looking at me innocently, as if to say: "Well, you didn't really expect me to stay here, did you?"

I called the steward and had the porthole closed. Then I went out again, locking the door behind me. Suddenly it occurred to me that if I left the key in the lock some passerby might possibly hear Toto inside and turn it in a spirit of kindhearted interference; so I laid the key on the floor, just outside the door, telling the steward where to look for it if he needed to go into the room. I went to dinner, but I must confess that, knowing Toto as I did, I was not as much surprised as anyone else might have been to see him at the door of the saloon by the end of the third course.

Still, it was altogether a mysterious business, and I left him busy with a banana while I went to investigate. The door of the cabin, of course, was open. And I was not surprised to find the key now on the inside of the door. So that was how Toto had got out. The question was, how had he got possession of the key? I looked round the room. All seemed in order. Then, suddenly—as writers of detective stories say—my gaze fastened on a small white object on the floor.

But as a matter of fact, much as I should have liked to have used the fascinating methods of Messrs. Holmes, Poirot and Co., a magnifying glass was not needed, for I saw at once that the object was Toto's toothbrush. Still, it was a clew. Toto, as I have said, was essentially tidy, and he would not in the ordinary way have left any of his washing materials on the floor. It followed, then, that the brush had been recently used and for some unusual purpose.

Beyond that I am afraid I cannot speak with certainty, for there were no other clews. But as I thought the matter out I came to the conclusion that Toto, planning his escape from the first, must have heard me drop the key. He would then have looked under the door and have seen the key lying just out of reach. Perhaps he remembered his own cleverness in getting the cherry out of the bottle, and looked round for another chicken bone. The toothbrush caught his eye, and it would not have taken him long to angle for the key and draw it toward him. After that, unlocking the door would have been easy enough, and without doubt he would have decided that it was proper that a prisoner so clever at escaping from his cell should be rewarded with at the least, a banana. Or else it may have been that instinct, recognized in man, which demands that any great success should immediately be celebrated with food and drink. In any case I was inclined to agree that he deserved congratulation.

One of the things that made Toto a favorite on the ship was the fact that he made himself useful. He started a laundry. He began in a small way, just as all the magnates of business have begun. He found a bucket of water on the deck, and since any small quantity of water always suggested to him either drinking or washing, he looked around for something to wash. Nothing suitable being in sight, he went to the cabin and fetched one of my handkerchiefs. Then he fetched another and another. By way of putting up the capital for the business, so to speak, I furnished him with a piece of soap. His work was very successful. He washed the handkerchiefs until they were spotless and then spread them separately round a big coil of rope to dry.

Some friends of mine thought this an excellent idea, and soon half the passengers aboard were bringing their handkerchiefs to:

MESSRS. TOTO, KEARTON & CO.
The Lightning Launderers.   Handkerchiefs a Specialty.

Toto kept it up for nearly the whole voyage. As soon as the linen was dry he would take a little pile and hand one to each person who came up the stairway. The only disadvantage was that one could not be sure of having one's own property returned to one—a failing which I have noticed to be shared by a good many other laundries. But even that had its advantages here, for many idle hours on board ship were passed in the new game, which became very popular, of exchanging handkerchiefs until everyone had his own.

Toto also earned his living—the payment being usually in bananas and occasionally in sweets—by tidying the deck. In the early morning he would help the sailors with a mop, or turn the big water wheel. And on one occasion he gave a severe lesson in seemly conduct to the wife of a native noncommissioned officer. This lady was remarkably fond of oranges, and she spent the greater part of each day reclining in a deck chair eating them. But she did not take the trouble to throw the peel over the side. She pulled it off in little pieces and left them lying about the deck. Toto, who as I have already said was—to my credit—well brought up, sat down in front of her on the third morning, picked up every piece of peel and threw them over the side. Then he sat in front of her again, as much as to say: "Now let us see if you've learnt to be tidy."

Unfortunately, the lady had not. She smiled pleasantly at Toto, took another orange and began to peel it. When she dropped the first piece of the skin on the deck Toto pounced on it and threw it overboard; then he sat down again and waited for the same thing to happen. It did. But I am glad to say that at last the lady took the hint, and the next morning she was observed to be carefully placing the peel, bit by bit, in a neat little bowl brought with her for the purpose.

Just after we passed out of the Suez Canal and entered the Mediterranean, Toto caught a chill, the result of a careless sailor having let a hose drip on to his blankets. Our ship boasted a doctor, but not a "vet." Neither the doctor nor myself felt very certain how to treat an extremely active ape with a cold in the head, and perhaps we were not as successful as we might have been in fighting his entire disregard for the danger of standing in draughts. In any case, in two days Toto developed pneumonia and was dangerously ill.

For three days I thought the poor little fellow would slip out of life quietly, with just a sigh and a pathetic look in his eyes as he lay in my arms. Yet I was determined that he should not, if anything that my affection for him suggested could possibly save him. And there was no lack of volunteers for the task of nursing him when I needed a rest. The news that Toto was ill went round the ship, and I had countless offers of assistance. Ladies would warm their own blankets on the radiators and bring them to my cabin; but the thing that touched me most was when the lady of the oranges, who had been rather offended at Toto's reproof of her, came and begged me to let her nurse him.

It was difficult to express my sense of thankfulness when at last Toto was out of danger. On the morning of the fifth day he looked quite disgusted at being offered nothing more exciting for breakfast than a bowl of bread and milk, and from that moment he rapidly got better.

When we reached Marseilles it was possible to bring him ashore, but I knew that it would be dangerous, and indeed reckless, to try to take him straight to London. He was in no condition to stand the long railway journey, and besides, there was the fact that it was still early in the spring, and the weather in England would certainly be damp and possibly foggy. To have taken him home then would have meant the probability of a relapse, and that I could not risk.

But I had to get home quickly now myself, and to stay two months in Marseilles was out of the question. So I went to the beautiful Zoological Gardens there and asked the Director if he would keep Toto for me until I could come back in the summer to fetch him. The Director very kindly agreed, and the next day I took Toto to the Zoo and introduced him to his new friends.

I think that in that strange way that animals have of feeling what is before them, Toto knew that we had come to the moment of parting. He took an instant liking to the Director, but he would not smile, and he looked very sad indeed. As a parting gift I gave him the dark velvet bag into which I used to put my head and shoulders and hands when I developed plates in the open. He wrapped himself in it, and I felt, as perhaps he did, that it was a garment of sadness.

"Good-bye, old chap," I said.

VII

TOTO COMES HOME

It was on a warm day in the early summer that I came back to Marseilles. During the past two months I had had many letters from the Director of the Zoological Gardens, telling me how Toto had refused to be comforted at first, but that as the days went by he had begun to make new friends and to take an interest in all that he could hear and see of the life of the other animals around him. The last report had shown that he was now thoroughly enjoying himself: so much that the Director said, "I doubt if he will want to leave us."

I thought that I knew Toto better than that. I felt sure that he would rejoice to start on his travels once more with me. But even I did not anticipate the welcome that he gave me.

I first saw his cage when I was about seventy yards away from it. Many people were watching him, and I have no doubt he was enjoying himself in showing off his cleverness, for "playing to the crowd" was one of the many human failings in which he shared. Whether he heard me, smelt me, or saw me, I do not know; but suddenly he stopped playing and looked down the road toward me, watching intently. Then he gave a great shout, waved his head from side to side, and started racing round and round the cage in delirious excitement, screaming with delight at the top of his voice. The spectators, of course, enjoyed the sight, but Toto had no thought for them. Round and round the cage he went, up to the roof, down to the swinging trapeze, round the walls, up to the roof again, yelling at the top of his voice. And then I opened the door and entered the cage.

He was at the far corner near the roof at that moment. One jump took him on to the trapeze, sending it swinging perilously, another brought him to the floor at my feet, and then he was in my arms, hugging me with all his strength.

It was, perhaps, one of the happiest moments of my life, and certainly, I think, the happiest of his. He would not let me go. One long arm stole round my neck, and I have no shame in saying that I kissed him; not on his great mouth, which was now extended more than ever in a grin of almost hysterical joy, but on his funny, squat, flattened little nose.

Suddenly he tore himself away, ran to his nest, dragged out the tattered remains of my developing bag, laid them at my feet, and then climbed back into my arms once more. I felt that I was a Prodigal Son, and that he was bringing me the greatest of his possessions.

. . . . .

I had intended leaving him at the Zoo for one more night, before we took the train to Calais. But I saw that I could not go away again, leaving him uncertain when I would return. So I took him with me, there and then, and we went to the station. But traveling was not to be as simple for him in France as it had been in Africa. There were regulations to be consulted, officials to be satisfied, before he could be allowed to board the train. And I was firmly told that in any case he could not be regarded as a passenger and travel with me. I protested, but it was useless. I suggested that if he was not a passenger, at any rate he did not come under the heading of either "luggage" or "goods," and asked that an exception might be made to the regulations of the State. But no, it was clear that he counted as "live stock," along with a crate of chickens, a pig and a dog for companions.

Argument was of no avail, and I had to let him go. But I soon discovered that however he was classed, he was not to lack company, for when the train stopped and I went to see him I found that all the officials on the train had gathered in his compartment and were enjoying the entertainment which he was only too ready to give them.

The journey by taxi across Paris provided a half-hour of great excitement. Toto wanted to sit with the driver and hold the steering wheel, but it was impossible to convince the driver that he had often done this before, and could quite safely be trusted. So he had to sit at the back of the car with me. But if the steering had been entrusted to him entirely we could not have had more hair-raising escapes than we did on that drive. The taxi drivers of Paris are notorious, and the traffic regulations are beyond the comprehension of an Englishman. I am told that a driver is considered cowardly and incapable if he does not have at least one collision a day: if that is so, the proportion of courageous and competent drivers in Paris must have considerably increased that afternoon. All eyes were turned in our direction, and once, as Toto stood up on the seat and waved to the crowd, I saw four cars settling into one glorious heap beside us. Passers-by, gendarmes, drivers, everyone turned to watch Toto, and I can only regard it as the result of a kindly Fate that our driver at any rate, whatever others may have done, did not kill anyone during that half-hour.

. . . . .

In the train beyond Paris I left Toto in a van near the engine, in charge of the guard. The van was empty except for some fruit baskets, and I congratulated myself on the fact that he would have plenty of room. I felt that after our recent excitements I needed a rest, and decided that the first necessity was luncheon. No sooner had I started the meal, however, than someone rushed along the corridor and stood in front of me shouting in French. But I am no linguist, particularly when the other party to the conversation is in a state of excitement, and all I could catch was "Gorilla! Gorilla!"

I appealed to the Englishman opposite to me for a translation.

"Your gorilla," he told me, "is on the roof. He has broken loose."

I ran down the corridor toward the van where I had left Toto. The train was traveling at sixty miles an hour, and although I knew Toto's sureness of foot, I did not imagine that he could stand for long on the roof of the moving train. But the guard would not let me in. It was all right, he assured me. Toto was not on the roof. He had not been there. Certainly he had broken loose, but the guard had been energetic and had caught him in the van behind the tender of the engine. All was safe. But it would not do to unlock the door.

So, reassured, I went back to my meal.

When we reached Calais several things happened. In the first place, a crowd collected out of nowhere, eager to see the wonderful gorilla, who, rumor said, had helped to drive the engine. And then, when I reached the door of the van and let Toto out, there was the dirtiest object I have ever seen. The energetic guard had rescued

Toto from the coal tender, but he had forgotten to lend him a clothes brush. He was black all over: hands, feet, face and body thick with coal dust.

That was bad enough, but there was worse to come. A man was on the platform to receive three baskets of fruit that had been put into the same van as Toto. And Toto had been loose in that van for ten minutes before his escape was discovered. Consequently the three baskets of fruit did not arrive quite in the condition in which a well-conducted railway might be expected to transport them. Two of the baskets were open but practically untouched. As for the third—well, the owner said that it had contained very fine bunches of grapes.

· · · · ·

When we got aboard the cross-Channel steamer I took Toto below for a wash. He needed it. There was the usual row of basins, in front of one of which stood a young man with his head down and his hands busy lathering his face. Toto walked quietly up to the next basin and set to work with the soap.

Without looking up, the young man felt round where the cake ought to have been, and then when he could not find it he turned to look for it. Instead he saw beside him a chimpanzee entirely self-possessed and very busy rinsing the lather off his face.

I thought that young man was going to collapse from sheer fright. "Well, I'm jiggered!" he exclaimed, and forgot to dry himself in the excitement of watching Toto.

But Toto went on washing. He was far too polite to take any notice of the ill-behavior of eccentric fellow passengers.

· · · · ·

Toto received almost a royal welcome at Dover, and on the train he added to his popularity by shaking hands with nearly three hundred people as they passed along the corridor. Ladies brought him tea; biscuits, sweets and fruits were literally showered on him.

At last we reached London!; we hustled through the station as quickly as an excited crowd would permit, climbed into a taxi and drove to my house in St. John's Wood.

I was glad to be home again after the adventurous journey. So, I think, was Toto. He settled down in an armchair at once, and when he looked up at me I told him his journey was finished.

"This is Home, Toto" I said, "for me and now for you."

VIII

THE PASSING OF TOTO

But I was wrong. Toto was soon to leave me—forever.

He spent several weeks in that house, and I think he learnt to love it as much as any home he had ever had. It was, for him, an exciting house. Particularly, he liked the staircase. He would rush up the stairs, two steps at a time, and then come sliding down the balusters, like any schoolboy just home for the holidays, till he came to the landing. Then he would scamper along the passage, climb on to the rail again, and come sliding down to the hall. Then up the stairs again, and down the rail once more.

He liked being in the garden. He was particularly happy when I took him out and photographed him. He would fetch and carry for the other inmates of the house, he would watch the operations of cooking with the greatest interest, and he learnt to help at washing plates and dishes. He played with the dog, children came to see him and play with him, and he made many lasting friendships. Every-one adored him, and I most of all.

But the time came when I had again to go abroad. I could not take Toto with me, and there was nothing for it but to leave him at the Zoological Gardens in London. He had been happy at Marseilles, I knew, and I knew that he would not be any less happy or well cared for in the hands of my own countrymen. And it would not, I imagined, be for long.

We said good-bye. It was another sad moment, and Toto was very affectionate, very dear. He did not want me to go, and I did not want to leave him. But I looked forward to seeing again his joy when I returned.

Alas! I was not to see it.

When I came back I was greeted with the news that he was dead. Once again he had caught pneumonia, and despite every care he had died.

I can only hope and trust that he thought at the last of the friend who loved him.

THE WILD BULL

By ALEXANDER FINTA

With JEANETTE EATON

NO SOONER did the wild geese cease to fly when there befell me one of the most perilous adventures of my entire life. What led up to it was a situation in the animal world of Ecseg which was one of the herdsman's most severe trials.

So far we have said little enough about the cattle on the ranch. But, indeed, although I myself had had nothing to do with them and had been occupied only with the horses, the herd of bullocks, cows, and bulls involved a large part of the labor of the *puszta.* Moreover, a considerable number of them remained to be cared for all winter. Now the cows and bullocks were so tractable as to be no problem to their caretakers; but the young bulls, restless with pent-up energy after long weeks of standing around in the *karám,* were an everlasting nuisance.

Such fighters as they were! Just as soon as they were released from their pen for exercise or a drink at the wells, a hot fight was sure to be started. It was exciting enough to see those wild rushes and the locking of long sharp horns. But it was a spectacle to be viewed only at a distance. I was always warned not to let my boy's curiosity lead me too close to the scene of action. Naturally the belligerent animals hurt one another very badly and it was always a temptation to every cowboy to try to prevent a battle. A fatal temptation, for many a man has died at Ecseg for his attempt to interfere! The only result of his senseless risk was a pause on the part of the antagonists just long enough to finish off the intruder, then on with the fight again!

Sometimes it happened that one of the bulls would receive a bitter lesson from his sparring partner. Then with roars of fury he would try to compensate for his lost victory by picking a new fight. Often such an animal would challenge one bull after another until he was forced by exhaustion to yield. Occasionally the maddened warrior would be cornered by all the other fighters acting in concert and would be chased from the *tanya*. From then on, the misguided beast was forced to be an outcast, for whenever he attempted to rejoin his fellows they set upon him and drove him off. Distraught by the humiliation of losing every battle, the outcast bull would either rush off to the swamp, where he perished in the quagmire, or else in the direction of some farm, where he broke fences, ruined haystacks, attacked other animals, and often killed human beings.

This destructive force incarnate was as soon as possible checked by a shot. But it took a brave man to risk the peril of shooting the mad bull. If one bullet did not succeed in stopping that stormy heart, the man who fired it was in grave danger of his life.

At Ecseg we had a bull which had earned the name of Duhaj, which means fighter, because almost from the time he was a calf he had been continually at war with his companions. Finally he carried his thirst for battle too far, began to lose fight after fight, and was ultimately cornered and ousted from the herd. He lived thereafter in the swampy territory, whence he would make forays into farm-lands and into remote parts of the *puszta*. Every few days the cowboys would bring in dismaying news of his depredations. One haystack he tore to pieces and scattered to the four winds, and was just starting on another one when the ranchmen decided they must end his career. A haystack, especially this winter when we had more than our usual number of animals to feed, was indeed a serious loss.

One night after the evening soup the bull's sentence of death was passed. My uncle Miklos was due to return shortly, and his men were afraid of his anger. "He will call us all cowards," said Joe soberly, "if we do not kill Duhaj before he does any more damage."

Discussion of the best way to execute the criminal was protracted until a late hour. Uncle Miska viewed every possibility. At last, however, a plan was laid and I was made the pivot of it. Yes, it was I who was to be placed on the top of the haystack in question to watch and wait for the arrival of the marauder. From that point of vantage, out of reach of his cruel horns, I was to kill Duhaj with a long-handled pitchfork.

Readily I agreed to undertake the task. Indeed, I was immensely pleased to be chosen for it, and I saw myself well wrapped in my sheepskin coat, snuggled into the hay, smoking at ease and waiting the arrival of the outcast bull. When he came thundering up I should strike him down boldly and rid the *puszta* of his vicious presence. Happily I went to bed and revolved this picture of success before my dreamy eyes.

Next morning the weather was beautiful—mild, sunny, and windless. As we gathered about after breakfast, one of the men said, "It is too warm today for Sandor to wear his big sheepskin coat. He must leave it home."

"No," replied another, "he will need it up there on the haystack. Perhaps he will have to wait some time for Duhaj to come."

"Yes, and then a wind might blow up," added a third.

Thus with the passion for arguing about trifles so typical of the herdsmen, they hotly debated the question of fur or no fur. At last someone said that my uncle Miklos might arrive that very morning and if I had been sent out without my coat and caught a cold it would go hard with them all. That point carried, and when I mounted Mocskos it was with my big sheepskin cloak about my shoulders.

Quite a party rode with me the half-mile from the *tanya* to the big haystack, visible at some distance because of its snow-covered top. Uncle Miska rode ahead and looked carefully about to prevent our being surprised by a sudden rush from the wild bull. Finally he gave us the signal that all was safe for the time being, and we dashed forward at a gallop. At the haystack everyone dismounted speedily and began preparations in all haste, goaded by fear of Duhaj.

One of the men, named Jóska, had brought a long strong cord. He flung this over the haystack in such a way as to make a pulley for hauling me aloft. When it was secure, he knotted one end about my chest. "Up you go!" he cried. "Remember, if you kill the bull put your hat on the handle of the pitchfork. We shall see it and gallop back here!"

"Yes, do that, Sandor!" cried all the others.

Feeling very important and much elated, I agreed to show the signal of victory. It never occurred to me that I might fail, such is the confidence of boyhood. In a twinkling I was hoisted up to the snow-capped mountain of hay. First I cleaned the snow from a place near the edge. Then by means of the pulley rope I pulled up my heavy cloak, and after it the long-handled iron pitchfork—my only weapon against the dangerous enemy. Finally I waved farewell to my impatient companions below and an instant later saw them galloping off.

I didn't feel a bit lonely, however. I busied myself making a deep hole in the hay to ease my position and then practised jabbing the pitchfork at the imaginary bull. Without his presence the practice went marvelously. At last, laying the pitchfork lengthwise near the edge of the stack, I lighted my pipe and sent up clouds of blue smoke to show the herdsmen, waiting near the *tanya,* that I was merely on guard and that the bull had not yet arrived. Pipe after pipe I smoked and still no bull arrived. Somewhat bored, at last, I decided to take off my heavy coat and was just struggling with the clasp which fastened tightly round my neck when I perceived, quite far away, the approaching bull. It was an agitating appearance, and at once I laid hands on my pitchfork and assumed a majestic pose, ready to plunge it downward.

Duhaj, however, came on slowly and I could only wait with nerves strung tight. At a short distance from the stack he stopped and, uttering a mighty roar, stabbed the ground with his beautiful long horns, and then to mark his anger he tossed his head high in the air. With his breath he made quite a large cloud around him in the morning air and had the steamy sound and look of a locomotive. Now and then he stopped this exhibition of fury and scanned the horizon. Then he moved to a new spot, dug deep holes with his strong feet, and flung the earth backward and so high that it flew almost as far up in the air as I was myself.

It was an interesting spectacle to watch the rage of the fine young bull. But it unnerved me. Already I had a stiff arm from standing so long with the heavy pitchfork poised, and when I tried to limber it up with a few passes I evidently must have made some sound, for suddenly Duhaj became aware of me upon the haystack.

Up to that second his anger had been more pictorial than real. But now with a terrible bellow, more savage than the roar of a lion, he bounded forward and flung himself against the haystack.

"Here is the moment upon me!" I thought in great excitement. "I must do it now!" And I lifted my pitchfork, waiting for the bull in his deep rage to get into line beneath the spot where I stood. At last he reached the place most favorable for my blow. I concentrated all my strength in the swing of my weapon and lunged downward toward the back of the roaring beast. Perhaps my nervousness, or the stiffness of my arm, caused my miscalculation.

At any rate, the mighty thrust missed its aim and I stabbed only the air.

The shock of meeting no resistant surface was tremendous. But what began instantly to follow was infinitely worse. The speed and power of my action, and my inability to recoil from that far-flung stroke, had swung me out from my firm resting place. Suddenly I felt the hay, and with it myself, begin to slide downward. In vain I struggled to recapture my footing. Slowly, inevitably, I was being swept along with the toppling crest of the haystack. Giddy and sick as the horrible moment lengthened, my mind refused to face what awaited me below. It escaped in dreams that were swifter than pulse beats—dreams of lying in bed smoothed by my dear mother's hand and of sitting secure and at peace before the fire in the *tanya*. Yet with each fraction of a second I was slipping, slipping to perdition.

My coat! My fine sheepskin coat was forgotten up there in the hay! That thought jerked me back to the present. Then indeed I realized my situation. For my heavy fur garment was tightly clasped about my neck and it was floating—floating together with my body in the air. Instinctively I grasped it and even as I realized that I was lost, that nothing could save me from the infuriated great beast who waited only to gore me, I landed. And I landed exactly on his head!

He had been holding it high in amazed and stupid concentration. He had ceased to bellow and even to move, in his astonishment over the descending avalanche. Those long, cruel horns had been lifted stiffly upward. But with the very bump of landing I realized two things—I had fallen directly on his skull and my coat on each side had been pierced by the sharp horns in such a way that I was fastened tight to my incredible resting place. There I was! Escape was impossible.

For half an instant Duhaj and I both remained motionless. The surprise of our meeting paralyzed us in equal degree. But it was I who recovered first. In a twinkling I flung an arm about each of the mighty horns and with the same movement twisted my legs about the great head. This action dragged my heavy cloak across the bull's eyes so that he was completely blinded. That astounded animal, unable to follow the swift turn of his destiny, stood help-less under the impact of my weight, confused by the sudden darkness.

These things he had not willed and could not comprehend. At least, however, something untoward had happened to him. The instant that he realized it fully he uttered a roar of fury.

The sound almost caused me to faint. It is one thing to hear a bull's roaring even at a slight distance away. It is quite another to hear it from the first box of the balcony immediately above the mighty organ itself. Yes, I assure you, it is an absolutely unique experience in sound to have a bull let out his terrific bellow just between the legs of the listener.

More and more ferociously he uttered his ear-splitting protest. The violence alike of his gusty breath and of the movement of his muscles lifted the offending cloak and swung it up and down. A watcher would then have been afforded a glimpse of my legs clasped around the head of Duhaj. They were trembling like the strings of David's harp, but they clung on in desperation.

Now the bull began to back. He moved slowly like a ballet master executing a difficult rhythm for his pupils. One step after another he took backward, and held his head as carefully as though he were carrying, not a deadly enemy, but a precious burden. As he moved, he lifted his voice from the depths of his angry heart and let it burst in air. From a distance Duhaj might have looked like a strange and impressive leader in a funeral march—a march pro-ceeding backward. But it was my sorrow to see everything from too close a range for appreciation. My only thought was this, "How long can such a situation last?"

Whenever the maddened animal caught his breath between bellows, he reached up with his prickly tongue and tried to lick my thighs. At a moment less fraught with terrible danger I would have found that tongue ticklish, but as it was I only shrank in discomfort and resisted the efforts to dislocate my firm position. My response was a sharp kick at his mouth. I could move my boots with a swing like that of a pendulum and to do so gave me a new sense of how well entrenched I was on the head of Duhaj. Yet at every instant the same question rose before me: "How long? How long will this keep up?"

Not at such a deadly moment can one realize any elements of good luck. But fortune really favored me in misfortune. In the first place, it is always better to fall between a bull's horns than upon them. In the second place, it was so mild and clear on that morning that sound carried a long distance. Consequently the wild and mighty voice of my partner in catastrophe was plainly audible half a mile away at the *tanya* and aroused among the herdsmen a sense that something was wrong. Hastily they called a conference, as I afterwards learned, and then, mounting their horses, they galloped for the haystack.

Some distance away, however, they halted cautiously. With eyes of anguish I saw them come slowly forward, giving every sign of fear and astonishment. Feeling their presence, Duhaj suddenly stopped his infernal bedlam, and that gave me my opportunity. Uncle Miska was not quite near, and at the top of my lungs I yelled to him. To my own ears the sound was higher and shriller than any I had ever uttered. The effect was most unexpected. Like flying devils, the entire troop dashed off again. I could see them halt, wheel, and burst into excited talk with gestures of agitation.

In despair, I said to myself, "I make a mistake to yell so loud. They think the bull is finishing me, that he is goring my stomach, and that nothing but my death will satisfy him. They are saying to one another, 'Who will be the next victim?' And that is why they dashed away."

But in a little while they came back at a snail's pace. They came so close that I could see how pity for me struggled in their eyes with terror of Duhaj. It must have been a strange spectacle, indeed, this reversed bull fight in which it was the bull and not the toreador who wore the cloak. Perhaps it was the view of his fine sheepskin coat so carefully mended and now put to so astounding a use which drew Uncle Miska near enough for me to hear him say, "How did you get into this?"

How, indeed! Even in my peril the foolish question excited such anger in me that I shouted in my loudest voice: "Help! Help!" Action first and explanations later, in Heaven's name, I thought!

Once again that unexpected roar from me going off like dynamite from the shrouded crest of that plunging animal scattered the herdsmen. In panic they dug their spurs into their horses' flanks and sped away. Then once again my sinking heart revived to see them, as if for very shame, turn back on their course and ride within speaking distance of me.

"Boy, are you dying?" cried Uncle Miska.

"No, no!" I cried, hastily, and this time not so loud.

"Are you hurt?" asked old Miska.

"No."

"Be brave!" came the answer. "Hold everything together until we come back!" With that the entire group galloped off and disappeared from sight in the direction of the *tanya*.

What had he meant by holding everything together, I wondered. It seemed to me that it was I who was held with no will of my own, attached firmly to a maddened bull, and the horror of it was at once increased by bellows, redoubled in fury, which surged up from below the soles of my boots. Fortunately for my state of mind, I soon saw, like a snowy cloud in the distance, the cowboys racing back to their comrade in danger.

Now Uncle Miska dismounted. Stealthily and carefully he crept toward the animal, Duhaj sensed this approach, and still holding me stiffly aloft, ceased roaring and gave the effect of listening beneath his heavy veil of fur for what was coming. My watchful eyes beheld my rescuer take from beneath his gabardine the old gun, the gun inlaid with gold and silver, which had provided us with so many dinners of wild duck. As I saw the old hunter with foxlike cunning inch along behind the bull, I called out, "What are you doing?"

"Be quiet," returned he in a whispering tone meant to escape the victim's notice. "I am going to shoot the beast under his tail and save you."

"What do you want to do, shoot me?" I cried out in anguish. "Those miserable iron nails are all right for boot soles and for shooting duck—but for killing a mad bull—why, you're crazy, Uncle Miska! Simply crazy!"

"Listen, boy," argued the small man. "It isn't loaded with boot nails, but with my penknife."

"Your penknife?" For an instant I thought his surprising invention a clever one. But the next second I was in imagination following the course of that penknife from the bull's tail into his stomach, out through his backbone and straight into me! "No, no," I yelled; "that won't do at all!"

"But I am the best shot in the county!" protested Uncle Miska. "We all agreed that if I get a good shot into the tail it will bring instant death!"

A swift vision of the animal falling forward and carrying me with him to end as a mass of broken bones brought from me another, "No, no! No shooting!"

Apparently thinking me in a delirium from strain, Uncle Miska merely lifted his famous rifle and took a step nearer the rump of my terrible steed. His disregard of my fate drove me frantic. "Uncle Miska," I howled, "I see from here that your hand is trembling! Do not shoot! Do not shoot!"

The William Tell of Ecseg stopped still. His eyes dropped to his arms and, probably because of my foolish interruptions, they actually did begin to tremble. Snatching my opportunity, I suggested that he recharge his gun and fire the penknife with its blade closed. The idea was worthy of this fantastic debate which went on with the mad bull between us.

Uncle Miska, more and more nervous, would have none of it. "In that case," he argued, "the explosion of powder might make the blade fly open in the muzzle of the gun and then all would be finished!"

As he spoke, Duhaj, with a fresh eruption of roars, began to sidle toward the sharpshooter. He had barely time to leap upon his horse, and the very next minute he and all the others had sprinted off toward the *tanya*. I had to cling on as best I could in an agony of suspense. It seemed hours before I caught sight of the herdsmen again, and I could not imagine what delayed them from the rescue.

In time, of course, I learned that upon reaching the hut the riders had the shock of beholding in front of it my uncle Miklos. Just returned, he was looking about in the bewilderment of finding every man on the place away. It had never happened before and his uneasiness was confirmed by one glance at the faces bent down upon him. They spelled disaster.

"What on earth is wrong here?" cried Uncle Miklos. His eyes were fixed upon old Miska, who was as pale as death.

"An outcast bull! It is Duhaj who was beaten by the others, driven off the *puszta* and is now on the rampage."

Uncle Miklos stared incredulously from him to the others. "What? That's all! That's *all*? And for that nothing every man of you left the *tanya*?"

"Yes, boss, that may sound like nothing. But Sandor is fastened on the head of this mad bull. That's the reason we are in such a hurry!"

One of the herdsmen told me afterwards that upon hearing this news Uncle Miklos staggered as if he were swooning. His emotion revealed the fact that, although he had never shown me sign of preference, never petted me at all, he had been pleased by my prowess on the ranch and, beyond the mere claim of kinship, really loved me well.

As soon as he could get his breath again my uncle shouted: "Get a scythe! Quick! Get a scythe and sharpen it!"

Meanwhile, beside the haystack far away I was finding my situation going from bad to worse. During the endless period since my fall I had been able now and then to ease the ghastly strain on my arms which gripped so tightly the bull's horns, by letting my body rest upon the stretched folds of my stout sheepskin cloak. Now, however, to my horror, I observed that the stitching had begun to give way exactly along that center seam which once in vengeance I had slit with my knife.

"Oh, Nemesis!" I wailed, soundlessly. "If the seam gives away and the cloak falls in two pieces the bull will regain his sight again! And then what?"

The answer turned me faint. My arms no longer had the power to hold my body firmly in place. I was sinking into the folds of a cloak which was gradually ripping apart. Giddiness such as had attacked me as I slid from the haystack overcame my sense of reality. Monstrously I fancied that Uncle Miska had planned all this, had sewn the cloak with rotten thread and then deliberately sent me to my doom between the horns of a mad bull. What brought me to was a sudden glimpse of white figures flying toward me from afar. Like a dream came this vision of rescue, but it lent some vigor to my exhausted mind and frame.

This courage was quickened by a sudden recognition. That first horse belonged to my uncle Miklos! He must have returned! He would save me! My joyous eyes beheld him now plainly, and saw how intrepidly he galloped almost beside the roaring bull. Without stopping to fling his reins to one of the cowboys, he sprang from his horse and rushed forward. My heart leaped up in new confidence to watch.

"Boy," he yelled out, "keep your head and your strength! It won't be long now!" Over the din of bellows, that stern loud voice carried conviction to my very soul.

Suddenly he flung back his gabardine and out flashed the sharp scythe, glittering in the bright sunlight. Uncle Miklos rolled up his shirt sleeves and, with eyes warily watching every backward move of the bull, he stepped with measured deliberation to the animal's left side and struck the pose of the attacker. So fearless and majestic was his attitude, that even with my life at stake, I thought of the high priests of old who in the era of Hungarian mythology went solemnly out to kill as a sacrifice the *taltos,* the sacred white horse.

There was one moment of hesitation—one moment of judging in

which direction lay the heart of Duhaj. Then, holding his scythe on a level, uncle Miklos ran straight against the bull. With all his might he pushed that sharp blade, and it plunged from the side up into the chest itself, cutting the heart in two. The next instant my rescuer had leaped to the animal's head and snatched me up in the air, cloak and all. Duhaj had stopped backing. His roar was hushed. And at this signal of victory the cowboys leaped from their saddles and rushed to help extricate me from the horns of the stricken beast.

Slowly, slowly as strength left his legs, mighty Duhaj sank to earth. Voicelessly he collapsed upon the ground and lay stretched in death. And at last I was lifted from my long imprisonment. At long last I was free again!

Above me bent the face of Uncle Miklos, and in his eyes were tears. But with a joyous ring in his voice he said to me: "All right, boy! All right now!"

I tried to smile in return. But the herdsmen had set me on my feet and something strange was the matter with my legs. They would not straighten out. That long-continued nervous gripping about the head of the bull had cramped them and stiffened them so badly that I could not stand without support. Clinging to the arms of the herdsmen, I took a step.

All the men at once burst into a hearty laugh. "Look at Sandor!" they shouted in high glee. "His legs are curved like pretzels!"

"He walks like an orangutan, on the sides of his feet!" roared Jóska.

Old Miska smiled pleasantly to have another than himself the butt of the cowboys' mocking. But as I hobbled painfully, infinitely exhausted, to the place where the horses were tethered, I felt they might have been more tender-hearted about a companion so narrowly escaped from death. I did not realize what now I know, that these jokes were just a means of letting off the pent-up anxiety which had possessed every man on the ranch until the moment when Duhaj fell to earth. In jesting, moreover, each cowboy concealed his envious admiration of the bold courage with which my uncle Miklos had delivered the mighty stroke that saved my life.

A COWBOY AND HIS PONY

By WILL JAMES

With Illustrations by the Author

I 'LL NEVER forget the day when, finally, the war came to a sudden end and the armistice was signed. I was by the stables a-trying to get one of the spoiled horses into his stall when I hears a commotion and noise and hollers like I've never heard before or since. Thousands and thousands of soldiers was war-whooping and acting like as if they'd kick a hornet's nest. I had no idea of what the commotion was about, but it sure looked and sounded exciting, so I saddled the horse I'd been trying to lead in and lined him out toward the parade grounds. I never seen so many crazy-acting fellers in my life as I did when I got there, and when I got the news of what they was acting up about, that the war was over, I went just as crazy-happy as any of 'em did. I layed both spurs on my spoiled horse's neck and drug 'em back, and while he tore holes in the parade ground with every jump he made, I whooped and fanned like I never whooped and fanned before.

The first thing I thought, with the news that the war was over, was my getting back to the range, to home and free to roam again, and it was no wonder I got wild. It was no wonder anybody got wild, we was all going to home. . . .

But it took some few weeks after the armistice was signed before anybody begin to leave for home. There was a lot of men to handle and things had to be done in a regular way. It was a week or so after the day of the good news that I received some bad news. I was told that I was in a department where I'd be the last to be let go, on account of handling the horses and waiting till they was disposed of and so on, and that I might have to stay in the army for another three months or so longer. That was sure some bad news for me. But now that the war was over I made up my mind to get out, and long before three months' time too. I got to thinking of many ways on how that might be done, and finally I stumbled onto one way which I figured would turn the trick.

I sent a long telegram to the old feller I'd worked for before coming in the army. I knowed he wanted quite a few horses broke and that on account of the war taking most of the riders, he'd had a hard time getting anybody to do that for him. I told him I'd break his horses and ride for him for forty dollars a month and for as long as he wanted me to, if he'd only get me out of the army right quick. He'd been paying seventy-five a month for that. I knowed I was making quite a promise, but it was sure worth it to me to get out of the army. I was sort of desperate.

I told him to get a petition up of the stockmen of that country, also the stock Association to make a holler and say they was needing their riders. That was sure enough the truth.

It was about a week after I sent the telegram when I heard from the old man. His answer sure sounded fine, and he said he'd go to work on the petition right away and do all he could. . . . A couple of weeks later I was told to report to the Captain. He asked a few questions which I was mighty glad to answer, and then I was sent out to get an examination, to see if I was fit as I'd been when I entered the service. I knowed that if I wasn't they might hold me and see what was the matter with me, so, when I went in the building for that last examination, I sure stepped lively and done some graceful prancing around.

The next day I was handed transportation and a honorable discharge. I folded the papers neat, put 'em in my pocket and then I grinned at the Captain. "I'm sure getting away with something," I says to him. "What's that?" he asks.

"Six days of Kitchen Police," I says.

I'd been handed them K. P.'s before I went in special duty and I'd never been called on to serve them after that.

"Don't crow too much," says the Captain. "You're under army rules and orders for three days yet."

"That would still leave me three days to the good," I says.

He laughed and put out his hand for me to shake. "Well, I'll let you get away with the whole six of them K. P.'s . . . "

That same night I got on the train, and with my saddle by my side, I was heading back for the cow country again.

I met the old cowman in the same desert town where he'd hired me near two years before. He didn't recognize me when I went in the lobby of the hotel where he was stopping. I had my uniform on and that made quite a change from the way he'd been used to seeing me. We was both mighty glad to see one another and him and me celebrated quite a bit that night. Just him and me. That was my homecoming reception after the war. There was no sweetheart to greet me, and no wife and mother that most of the boys had to fall into the arms of when they stepped off the train.

But I'd never knowed nor thought of such bliss and, as it was, I felt I was as happy as any man. And something else came up which made that reception all that I could wish it to be. That was along the next morning, when me and the old cowman started for the stables to get the horses and ride out. I walked in there and, as is my habit, I went to looking over all the horses that was in the stalls. The stocking hind feet of a horse caught my eye, so did his color. Some picture away back in my mind was trying to make itself fit in as I went on to sizing up the horse. I went in the stall, looked at his head, and the picture begin to fit more. But, I thought, it couldn't be, not after all this time. I untied the horse, led him out of the stall and looked at the brand on his thigh. It had been worked over, but I could see the original brand there. It was the brand that had been on good old Smoky, and the horse *was* Smoky.

"What's the matter with you there?" hollers the old cowman as he hears me letting out a whoop.

"This is my horse Smoky. Stole from me four or five years ago."

The stable man came up about then and heard what I'd just said. He asked me, if it was my horse, where did I get him in the first place, where was he stole from, and many other questions, and when I answered 'em all and showed him the original brand made by a stamp iron, and how it had been worked over by a running iron, he seemed convinced that mouse-colored horse was mine sure enough.

"This boy has worked for me long enough so I know he wouldn't lie about that horse," says the old cowman. That settled it.

"Well," says the stable man, "I'm not out anything on that horse. I only paid twenty-five dollars for him and I cleared more than that from renting him for the last six month." He looked at me and asked, "Did he ever buck with you?" I said "Some. . . ."

"I thought so," he went on, "because up till about a year and a half ago he was the toughest bucking horse in this country, and that's saying something. He was took to all the big rodeos as a final horse and he throwed many a good rider. Then for no reason that anybody could tell of, he quit bucking. I got him about a year after that and he's never bucked since."

Well, that was sure news for me, to hear of Smoky's bucking record. I was proud of him for that, but it hurt me to learn that after he quit bucking he was rented out as any common livery horse and for anybody to ride. . . . I soon forgot about that, tho. Now I was happy to have him again and I just wanted to go away with him to where both him and me belonged, back to the range.

I didn't ride Smoky out. He was looking old and weary and he wasn't in the good shape I used to keep him. I led him behind the horse the old cowman had brought for me, and when I got him to the main camp I begin shoving hay and crushed barley to him. Hay and grain was expensive because that had to be shipped into the country by rail and then freighted out of town by teams. The old man had got quite a few tons of hay and some grain freighted in for the bronks I was going to break for him. He'd wanted to keep 'em while I was breaking 'em. I paid for Smoky's feed and I was mighty glad to do that. I floated the old pony's teeth, got him condition-powders and got his hoofs in shape. Poor shoeing had caused 'em to contract pretty bad.

In a month's time I had him looking slick as a whistle. His hide had loosened up and begin to shine like it always had before he'd been stolen from me. I kept him around for a few weeks longer, and every day, after I'd get thru stomping out my string of bronks, I'd go to looking him over and wondering what more I could do for him. The old man used to say that he'd seen plenty of cowboys act like daggone fools over a horse but that he'd never seen such a big daggone fool as I was over that old smoke-color horse.

"You'd think he was a ten-thousand-dollar race horse," he'd say.

"A heap more than that to me," I'd come back at him.

Will James

He was the toughest bucking horse in the country.

[See page 96]

I took a lot of pains putting new shoes on Smoky one day, and when a bunch of mixed horses came at the spring to water, I turned him loose with 'em. The feed was good and strong where that bunch ranged, but it was mighty rocky, and I shod Smoky so he wouldn't get sore-footed while going back and forth from range to water. A sore-footed horse never picks up much fat. There was colts and yearlings in the bunch, and when I turned old Smoky loose he begin to buck and play, just like them colts and yearlings did. He mixed right in with 'em, and soon the bunch went to running, over one ridge and another and out of sight. Smoky stopped and looked back just before going over the last ridge, and he acted like he would turn back. But soon he went to playing again and headed for the bunch and wide open range.

I got to see him every day or two after that, when him and the bunch would come to water. He'd leave the bunch then for a time and stick his head over the corral fence where I was always busy edducating one bronk or another, and he'd nicker a hello to me. I'd always have crushed barley in a morral (nose bag) and ready for him when he came, and while he'd chew away on that, I'd get to feel his slick hide and talk to him. Often the bunch he was with would water and leave before he got thru eating his grain, but he didn't seem worried about that, and when I'd take the morral off his head and turn him out of the corral he'd sometimes stick around for an hour or two, just as though he wanted to confab with me.

Smoky was a great horse. If any man ever said a word by mouth, that pony done near as much by the way he'd cock his little pin ears. I knowed the language of them ears mighty well. I'd seen a lot of country over them, and if ever I was dubious about what was ahead while riding in dark nights, I could tell by the feel of 'em if I should go ahead or turn back. My hand on his neck would tell me a lot of things his horse-sense knowed, and that way him and me talked to one another.

I never rode Smoky after I found him again at the livery stable. He'd done his work, I had more than plenty other horses to ride, and now all I wanted to do was to have that pony around, see him once in a while and see him feeling good. . . . If I'd ever caught anybody riding that horse during that time I think I'd been mighty tempted to sight down on that hombre and pull a trigger.

Sometimes, when old Smoky would come to water with the bunch, then to the corral for his grain, he'd stick around so long afterwards that I couldn't keep him company. I'd go to work on my bronks and sort of forget he was there. Pretty soon I'd hear squeals and poundings on the earth, I'd look out thru the corral to see him playing and bucking all by himself, and then he'd throw up his tail like a wild one and hit out to catch up with the bunch. The bunch might be three or four miles on the way back to their range, but I knowed he always caught up mighty easy, because he was right with the same bunch every time they came to water.

In a couple of months' time I had two fine strings of bronks lined out and ready to be put to work. A young feller had come along one day, and he was hired to take the first string I had started and keep 'em going till they was well edducated to the ways of the range cow. I kept the second string for myself, and now, being I'd broke all the horses the old man had wanted me to, I went back to range work, from one spring to another, branding, getting cattle back in the hills after the tanks got to be more mud than water, and driving back cattle that had drifted.

The old cowman's herd was bigger than it had been when I worked for him before, and now he always kept a rider to help me. This rider and me seldom rode together, we could do a better job watching the cattle by being separated. As for the old cowman, he couldn't ride much any more. He'd stopped a couple of bullets once in a fight over some range, and even though that had happened a long time before and the wounds had healed, there was times when he'd feel pretty stiff in one leg and hip. He could hardly get on a horse, and riding was mighty painful to him. As he told me, he was sure glad when the war came to an end because he'd had to do most of his own riding during that time, with just an Indian kid to help him, and he couldn't of rode much longer. He'd been mighty pleased to get my telegram from the army, and he never held me to my offer to ride for forty dollars a month. He paid me ninety dollars and gave me charge of the outfit, and all he'd do himself would be to haul grub to me and the other rider once or twice a month, and stick around and cook for a few days. He spent most of his time in town, in the hotel lobby, smoking cigars and talking to old-timers like himself.

I took Smoky along with me to whatever camp I'd go to. I'd take him along so I would have his company and so I could take care of him. Another reason was that I was afraid somebody might steal him again. Then being I'd sometimes be away from the main camp for a couple of months at a time, I thought of his shoes wearing off, him getting tender-footed and me not around to put new shoes on him.

There was about twenty springs that me and the other rider had to watch and where the cattle came to water. I'd stay at one spring from one to two weeks at a time, and all Smoky had to do was hunt for good grass and shade in the hills around the camp. There was most always plenty of that, and with his little feed of crushed barley twice a day and all the few leftover biscuits which he bummed me for, he was sure what I called in shape. Maybe not in shape to jump right out and make a long run or anything like that, but in shape to dodge all the diseases that catches onto weak animals. I don't know if anybody has ever seen a horse chew on a beef bone before but I have seen Smoky do that many times. Maybe that's what made him so brainy. He'd pick up an old bone with some meat still on it and roll it in his mouth like he sure seemed to enjoy it. It wasn't the lack of salt that made him do that either because there was plenty of salt blocks at every camp where there wasn't alkali licks.

I always had from ten to fifteen head of horses in my string. I liked lots of horses, specially in that rocky country where, if they was rode steady, they'd get sore-footed even with shoes on. I'd hobble 'em for night, and sometimes for the day, and shove 'em up a hill and above where cattle would generally go. There was always good bunch grass on top of the hills.

I never hobbled Smoky. He was free to go as he pleased all the time, and never left a camp where me and my horses was at. When I'd move from one spring to another I'd leave him poke along behind and travel to suit himself. If he wanted to graze a while he'd

stop and graze and then catch up on a high lope. Sometimes I'd
pass bunches of horses, and if they was close enough, Smoky would
run to one side to rub nostrils with 'em. I'd keep on going with my
string of horses till there was many times when I left him a mile or
two behind. But pretty soon, and after he was thru sizing up the
bunch he run acrost, I'd see him stir a dust and here he'd come
a-bucking, a-playing and a-running.

Smoky was like a big spoilt old kid, with nothing to do but eat
and play and stick his nose into whatever I was doing when I was
around camp. He was more company to me than I can tell, and during the two years I worked for that outfit and while he was around
he made this cowboy mighty contented and pleased to stay in that
one country. I never stayed so long in one country, not since I was
left alone. But now I somehow didn't care to drift no more. It was
mostly because I didn't want to take Smoky on any long trips, and
I sure didn't want to leave him behind.

Something else held me there. I didn't want to leave the old cowman. A few times he dropped some hints as to how he'd like to
turn his whole outfit, cattle, horses, range and all, over to me and
have me run it on shares of the calf crop. He'd remark as to how I
was young and that I ought to make a start for myself and have an
interest in the outfit instead of just plain wages.

"I've got to turn this outfit over sooner or later," he said once,
"and I'd just as well make it soon, because all I can do now is hold
down a chair in the hotel lobby and talk to old has-beens like myself. That last trip I made out with the grub and while the wet
snow was coming down sure didn't help my bum hip and leg any."

I couldn't quite answer to the old cowman's talk. I still had it in
mind to have a little spread of my own, but I didn't care to have it
in the desert so much. I liked the desert, it was sure wide open and
a fine country to ride in, while riding for wages, but for a place to
make my start and home I couldn't think of any other country than
where I was born and raised—a rolling country covered with a thick
carpet of grass, plenty of good running water in every coulee, tall
pines, cottonwoods and quakers for shade, where cattle that are not
sore-footed graze in big herds instead of little scattering bunches; the

old home of the buffalo, and where elk, deer and antelope still roamed.

Till I got to that kind of country, I wasn't thinking much on making a start. As it was now, I was happy to just be working for wages, handle the outfit for the old cowman that way, and keep Smoky rested and feeling good.

I liked my job there, it was paying me better wages than I ever had before and I had a responsibility that made it mighty interesting for me. This was my third job where I had full charge of an outfit. I liked to have the say as with such jobs. I liked to see pleased looks on the owners' faces when I done something well, like pulling cattle thru drought and disease, bringing in a likely beef herd when shipping time come, and the many other things that a good cowman can appreciate. This old cowman I was working for was one of the best I ever seen and the most appreciative of what I done for him.

Like with most all cow outfits I'd ever rode for, my working hours wasn't very regular. They're less regular with desert outfits on account of water holes being far apart and where riding is mostly done from permanent camps. It's not like riding for prairie outfits and where the roundup wagon follows the works. While riding for the old cowman I'd sometimes be in the saddle twenty out of twenty-four hours, with nothing to eat during that time. That would be when a snow or rain storm would come. Cattle would then drift to fresh range and where there was no spring water. I'd have to see that they didn't drift too far, so they could get back to the springs again when the snow and rain-water was all gone. Cattle that I'd sometimes miss would barely make it in to the springs and when they did, if I wasn't around to watch 'em, they'd near kill themselves with water. A few would, once in a while. Sometimes big thirsty herds would drift in to troughs that could water only fifty head at a time, and many a time, after a long day's ride, I'd have to get up in the middle of the night, get on a night horse that I always kept up, split the herd and scatter it to other springs. It was hard work to get the thirsty cattle away from the troughs, and sometimes the sun would be high when I'd get back to my camp. I'd heat up some coffee then, swallow a cold biscuit, catch a fresh horse, and go a-hunting for more cattle that was holding out on far-away range and feeding till thirst drove 'em in.

With such work that has to be done, a cowboy can't form no union and go by no union hours. If a rider was to quit when a certain hour come and there was work still to be done, he wouldn't be no cowboy, and in some countries there wouldn't be no range cattle. . . . Sunday is no day of rest for the cowboy, and there's no celebrating of holidays. They're just days like all others.

But it wasn't always long hours in the saddle. There was whole weeks at a time when I'd ride out of camp after sun-up and could easy get back in the middle of the afternoon. That was when there was no water in the flats and cattle watered at the springs. Before leaving camp in the morning, I'd always wrap a big can of tomatoes with gunny sack and plant it by the spring or slip it under a trough where water would drip on it. When I'd get back from my day's ride the first thing I'd do was to open up the can, sprinkle a little salt on the tomatoes and take the whole canful down. That was sure what I called refreshing. Then I'd ride to where my horses was hobbled, change to a fresh one, ride back to camp and go to cooking me a bait. My day's work was done, unless cattle came to water and there was calves in the bunch that needed branding.

I sure always liked them late afternoons and evenings at the camps. Everything was sure peaceful, and I'd stretch out either on my bunk or under a cedar tree, looking at saddle-makers' catalogs and old magazines or at the distance. When dark come I'd light a candle and draw a bit by it. I thought I was getting to draw pretty good about that time, but no new ambition of trying to be an artist came to me.

I don't know how long I'd kept on with the desert outfit. I figured to stay with the old cowman for as long as he wanted me. Then come a time when, as the old feller seen I wasn't right anxious to accept his outfit and running it on shares, he begin talking about selling out to a big neighboring outfit. He'd heard of some place where there was hot mineral waters that would keep the stiffness out of his hip and leg and he was wanting to sell out, take the money and go to making himself a permanent camp by them waters.

Finally he did come to a deal with the neighboring outfit and sold out to 'em. The old cowman drove up in a buckboard to tell me about it one day and say how he hated to leave his little outfit go— also to make me a present by handing me a bill of sale for two of the best saddle horses he had.

Well, after the old man bid me good-bye and as I watched him drive away, I got a sudden hankering to drift. Smoky and the hobbled horses came in to water as I got to thinking on the subject, and I talked things over with him. I decided then that I'd just as well stay where I was, one place was just as good as another, and besides, I didn't want to have Smoky knocking on the rough trails he would find while following me around.

But I found it hard to stay. I wasn't boss of the little outfit no more. The foreman of the big outfit took charge of everything and my wages was cut down to what the company allowed the cowboys, sixty dollars a month. Besides, I was asked to trade three of my broke horses off and take green bronks in their place. . . . That last didn't go so well with me, because after I broke that string of bronks for the old cowman near two years before and got 'em gentled, I hadn't broke any other. I'd been riding only them, and for the past year or more not a one had bucked to speak of.

Any rider that's fighting bronks steady will tell you that he don't want no broke horses in his string. Riding a horse that broke gentle will cause the rider to sometimes be off his guard when he's on a wild one, and he'll maybe get throwed off or struck or kicked. As for me, and now that I'd been riding horses that I'd gentled, I'd drawed the line on bronks. I'd decided that I was thru with the rough ones, and the main reason was that I was getting scared. I'd been hurt and took thru some mighty tight places by many of 'em. I'd lost a considerable of my nerve and now, instead of getting to be a better rider all the time, as most people would think, I'd passed the peak of my good riding and was going downhill.

The rougher and more dangerous a game is, the younger a man is when he quits it. Mighty few bronk fighters that's been at the game steady and hard are still at it when they're thirty years old. I know many that didn't know what it was to be scared of a horse or anything under the sun, but as bones was smashed now and again, skin was peeled and months was spent laying and waiting for that to mend and heal, a rider would gradually begin to get more careful as he went back to riding each time. And when a bronk fighter begins to get careful as he handles his bronk is when he better quit or what he thinks is apt to happen most likely will, and too soon.

I'd had horses fall with me in every way, shape or form, while running, stampeding, or bucking, at night or day, while the sun shined or while the stars was hid by dark clouds and lightning played, in the thick of cloudbursts, hail and blizzards. . . . I'd rode stampeders that swept me off in the thorny brush of the South, run off the side of tall Northern mountains, and bucked in places where a man couldn't walk. My breath had come short many a time. I'd been kicked and struck, rolled over the top of and dragged, and, as happening after happening accumulated and left me with scars, my mind begin to tally back to them many happenings as I'd climb a big snaky bronk; and come a time when my spur rowel rang and sounded like a warning tune as I stuck my foot in the stirrup.

That was the fix I'd got to be in when the company handed me three big husky bronks to snap out and keep in my string. I took 'em, and outside of getting my saddle tore up pretty bad as one fell over backward and got wedged between some rocks, I got along pretty well with 'em. But I didn't care to ride bronks no more. I was thru and all the interest I had in 'em was to see that none got me under and that I missed the hoofs that came my way.

There was one thing I was glad for as I kept a-riding for the company and that was that I was left to stay on the same range which had been the old cowman's. I knowed that range and camped at one spring and then another the same as while he owned it, and I was left alone about as much as before.

Everything was going pretty good. I'd got the three bronks so they'd quit bucking and also quit their snorting and spooking at every move I made. They was fast getting gentle and to doing good work, and now things was pretty near the same as they had been.

One evening, after I'd tied up one of the bronks for a night horse, I happened to look up a draw where I'd took the hobbled horses up thru, and sees old Smoky all by himself and poking along down toward camp. I'd never seen him leave the bunch during the evening, before. I laughed as I watched him come and I says to myself, "That old bum wants another biscuit."

But Smoky didn't want no biscuit. He refused the one I held out to him, and for the first time. He didn't seem to want anything, and there was a kind of a faraway look in his eyes. I thought then that he was sick. I felt of his ears, but they was warm, and I couldn't find any signs of anything being the matter with him. I figured he just wanted company, and after I talked to him a spell I went to making some cedar kindling to start the morning fire with. I didn't pay no attention to him while doing that, and when I got thru I looked to see him laying down by a cedar tree and with his head propped against it. I went to him again then to watch for signs of sickness, but he was breathing easy and regular and he seemed all at peace. He sure didn't look sick, and he was round and fat as a butter ball.

I squatted by him, rolled me a smoke, and while taking the burrs out of his foretop I went to talking to him. He seemed to enjoy that a whole lot, he liked me to rub his ears too. I sat by him there thru the whole evening and till dark come, and then after one more pat on his slick neck I left him to go into the cabin and crawl in between my soogans. There was a long ride ahead for me on the next day.

It was sure some surprise when, waking up the next morning, I looked out the opened door to see Smoky still laying where I'd left him the night before, still in the same position and with his head propped against the tree. He looked asleep, but I jumped out of bed into my boots, pulled up the pants they was always left inside of, and hit out to Smoky's side. He didn't move an ear nor open an eye when I came near, and as I layed a hand on his neck it felt cold . . . with the cold of death.

Old Smoky had just went to sleep thru that. I don't think he ever felt a pain or that a muscle even twitched when he drawed his last breath, and far as I know he might of passed away while I was talking to him the evening before.

I didn't go on that long ride that I'd planned on. Instead I dug a deep hole right by where Smoky layed, rolled him in and buried him, and stacked rocks on his graves so the coyotes wouldn't dig him out.

Smoky's going made me feel down-the-mouth quite a bit, and now that I couldn't do no more for him, I wanted to ride and ride, in one straight line and for many miles. It was noon that day when I caught the two horses the old cowman had made me a present of. I put my bed on one, my saddle on the other, and taking the hobbles off the other horses, I started 'em out of the corral and turned 'em toward the headquarters of the company. It was late that night when I got there. I asked for my time check the next morning and rode on again, a-looking ahead for new ridges to cross.

WILL JAMES
—'30

BUDDY, SEEING EYE PIONEER

By DICKSON HARTWELL

Illustration by Caroline Thurber

The Seeing Eye is the name of a philanthropic school, located near Morristown, New Jersey, at which dogs are scientifically trained to guide their blind masters. The institution was the outcome of an experiment conducted soon after the first World War by Mrs. Dorothy Eustis and her husband, George Eustis, on their estate, Fortunate Fields, in Switzerland.

The thoroughness of the training of both dogs and their blind masters at The Seeing Eye is exemplified in the following story of Buddy and Morris Frank.

THE Dogs of The Seeing Eye are not unlike their masters in their variations of personality, temperament and size. They are completely different from their masters in that all of them must meet rigid standards for intelligence and performance, which, in terms of human understanding, are just two or three points short of genius. There are usually about a hundred dogs at The Seeing Eye at one time and they have much the same attitude toward doing their jobs as a candidate for a position on the freshman football team has toward the varsity squad.

When they leave the school with their blind masters they begin to adapt the fundamentals they have learned to widely divergent conditions. One will guide its master about a farm in a quiet rural countryside, going into a small town once a week on Saturday nights. Another, the guide of a salesman of household appliances, will be with his master on the sidewalk, calling on block after block of housewives, continuously throughout the working day. Still another dog, whose master is a commuting lawyer, will find itself using bus, taxi, train and street car, and amassing a broad knowledge of the intricacies of a large county courthouse. Another will find itself on the campus of a large university—a campus where there are no sidewalks but only smooth pathways with no identifying curbs to mark intersections and tell a blind man where he is. These are the everyday problems to which dog and master together gradually adjust themselves. These conditions, like the weather, or the rules of play in football are accepted for what they are and treated accordingly. They do not affect the spirit, the character or the individuality of the dog any more than the regulations, or the condition of the playing field, affect the individuality of an athlete.

But with their individual differences, Seeing Eye dogs have certain common features which run like a backbone through their character. There is a vast difference in the detail of their makeup, but there is a true likeness in fundamentals. In these fundamentals Morris Frank's beloved Buddy was typical of all Seeing Eye dogs.

Man, even with his capacity for mental creation, a few years ago could not have imagined a guide for the blind such as Buddy was. Considered merely as a substitute for eyes, in getting a man from place to place, Buddy was magnificent. When she guided Morris past a building they had entered once before, no matter in what city it was, she always slowed imperceptibly but enough to indicate to him alone that here was a place where he might have some business. When they went into a hotel she headed first for the desk, realizing that it was both a place for registration and a source of information. When getting off a train she would stand near Morris's bags until a porter picked them up, and then, at the command from her master to go forward, would follow those bags, guiding her master to wherever the porter took them.

In an office building Buddy knew an elevator button from a wall decoration. She knew the significance of a uniform—whether on a policeman, doorman, elevator starter, bell boy or Boy Scout. When there seemed to be doubt in Morris's mind she would guide him over to the nearest uniform and stand there until he got his directions. An especially neat piece of guiding was as exhilarating to Buddy as a long run around the end is to a fast halfback. Third Avenue and Twenty-third Street was one New York intersection which she especially enjoyed. There was heavy traffic at this crossing complicated by two street car lines. But the real zest came from the Elevated which ran above Third Avenue.

Occasionally when Buddy was in the center of this intersection, picking her way carefully across with Morris beside her, with a crashing roar an express train would thunder overhead, blotting out sounds on which Buddy depended for her own and Morris's safety. Then her ears would go fully forward and her eyes would dart back and forth, alert not to miss a moving thing. After an experience of this kind, when Morris returned to the nearby hotel where he often stayed when in New York, Buddy would jump around him to show how pleased with herself she was for the fine job she had done. If they went home to The Seeing Eye at Morristown, Buddy would go the rounds of the offices; to Mrs. Eustis, Jack Humphrey, Will Ebling and other members of the staff, tail wagging, eyes shining, nudging them with her nose until they gave her a pat on the head or some other sign that she was recognized and her splendid qualities fully appreciated.

For Buddy was a truly great dog. It is not difficult to find in her a character which is both rich and noble and yet possessing those endearing qualities which all people, in defense of their frailties, commonly describe as human. Buddy had unusual opportunities and made the most of them. She had the undoubted advantage of extensive travel and she was constantly meeting people of superior intellect. It may have put her on her mettle but she invariably rose to the occasion.

Buddy could measure her rights in mathematical fractions which carried to three places beyond the decimal point. She could measure to an even finer degree how far she could advance beyond the limit of those rights and still not be challenged. She was astute, always conscious of her own natural charm, and ready to use her wiles to enhance its effectiveness when the occasion required.

Though ordinarily regal in appearance and attitude, there were times, while not guiding, when Buddy would permit herself the commoner's luxury of being a tramp. When in one of these moods and out slumming, she was not above a roll in the muck or the thorough inspection of a neighborhood garbage can. At other times she was a downright thief. If someone set down a tray of canapés or cookies near her, she could silently filch half a dozen without seeming to move her head. Buddy would steal her hostess blind, as the saying goes, but she would never beg. Buddy had character and with it dignity. She knew that begging was mean.

On matters in which there was a possibility of doubt Buddy was her own supreme court. She would never have refused for a moment to obey Morris Frank on anything she felt was really important or clear-cut. But on things that she considered trivial, mere whims of her master, or open to reasonable interpretation, she did exactly as she pleased. When Morris was endeavoring to make a particularly good impression on an audience, which was not infrequently, Buddy might completely nullify his efforts by screwing up her face into a look of ferocity and barking at the audience at inopportune moments with all the menace she could muster. She enjoyed hearing Morris apologize for her, explaining that shepherd dogs weren't at all fierce really, that Buddy just liked to bark to show she was present.

Buddy must have enjoyed those feeble attempts at an explanation. She wanted to bark because she wanted to bark. It amused her to bark. And as far as getting recognition for her presence, she could tell, if her blind companion could not, that every eye in the audience was focused on her, whether she barked or not. It was she they had come to see. In order to watch her they would tolerate what her sometimes stuffy master had to say to them.

There were some people who twitted Morris, telling him that Buddy was spoiled, and that he ought to be more firm with her. Buddy wasn't spoiled; Buddy was smart and knew her role. If she climbed up on a silk bedspread in a house where she and her master were staying it was because in her position she felt is was important that she should. Of course ordinary dogs should sleep on the floor. That was because they were ordinary dogs. If all dogs were to climb on beds, no one would have them around and that would be very bad for dogdom.

But it was practically mandatory for Buddy to be on a bed because it helped to show people that there was a difference in dogs, just as there was a difference in people. People who were important; people who had done things; people who had shown capacity for leadership were accorded privileges as a matter of course. Buddy was all these things. She maintained the propriety of her position by making certain that there were no errors of omission on her part.

Buddy would have lived up to her royal blood with any master who did not completely crush her spirit. With Morris Frank it was perhaps a little easier than it might have been with another because, as Morris had been told the first day he met Buddy, he did not own her; she owned him. Morris did nothing in particular to encourage Buddy's assumption of sovereign privileges nor did he do anything consistently to discourage it. He was somewhat in the position of an aide-in-waiting who often found it necessary, if somewhat trying, through constant repetition, to explain patiently to crude commoners who had lived too long in a democracy, the full meaning of the phrase "The Queen can do no wrong."

Morris claimed for Buddy certain gifts which verge on the supernatural and probably had no basis in fact in even such a remarkable dog. Whenever Morris went to a clothing store to pick out a suit of clothes, he would feel the texture of the several offered for his selection and discuss each of them with the salesman. Then when the time came to pick out one, he would call Buddy over and let her sniff carefully at each. The one she sniffed at the longest was the one he decided she thought was best for him and that was the one he would buy. Whatever Buddy's capacity may have been for judging either the style, color or cut of men's clothing, even Morris's worst enemies wouldn't have said of him that he wasn't well dressed.

During their first years together Morris was also inclined to judge people by Buddy's reaction to them. If Buddy was obviously hostile, it would take a good deal of tact, persusion and charm to put Morris in a frame of mind which could be described as anything more than coldly civil. If Buddy was friendly and showed approval when meeting someone, Morris would welcome him as a bosom friend. This inclination could be as quickly dissipated, however, if any annoyance was shown at Buddy's unexpected exuberance. Such a reaction Morris was inclined to put down as a lack of good breeding or, if in his more tolerant moods, merely to a lack of understanding of who Buddy was.

But Buddy's tendency vigorously to express her friendliness finally got out of bounds. Whenever she felt particularly affectionate, which occurred frequently, Buddy would greet an unsuspecting friend by jumping up and putting her front paws against his, or her, chest and making a valiant and usually successful effort to plant a kiss on whatever uncovered portion of anatomy came within reach. Occasionally Buddy would thus express her attachment for some lady in a fragile evening dress.

Prodded into action by several persistent friends, Morris finally decided that something had to be done to cure Buddy of jumping up on people. He reached this decision with reluctance and, because he was a sensible young man, with trepidation.

It is very simple to stop a dog from committing the malfeasance of which Buddy was guilty. It was also a very kind and considerate thing to do. For, from the animal's point of view, once this method of greeting people becomes a fixed habit, any punishment seems harsh and unwarranted. But in polite society—in Buddy's social circle—jumping on people causes an immediate and continued diminishing of popularity. This, too, a dog finds difficult to understand when its intent is so friendly.

In breaking the animal of the practice, when it jumps up on a friend who has been forewarned what to do, the friend merely inches his foot forward and steps lightly on the dog's hind feet. The resulting discomfort comes as a complete surprise to the animal, which, ever trustful of man, blames the discomfort on the fact that its front paws are not down where they should be. As a consequence, after two or three repetitions, the dog ceases to jump up.

In order to break Buddy of the habit, Morris asked his cousin to undertake the small task of stepping on Buddy's toes the next time she jumped up on him. The cousin obligingly agreed and when opportunity afforded, did so. To his great amazement, Buddy did not immediately jump down. Apparently she was not aware of the formula. She merely took his wrist firmly in her teeth and held it until he took his foot off her toes. A cure was affected all right, but it wasn't the one which Morris had anticipated. Thereafter, the cousin kept his feet well curled up under him. Buddy kept greeting people by jumping up on them and nothing further was done to

Buddy Fortunate Fields, pioneer of all Seeing Eye dogs.

A portrait by Caroline Thurber

teach her otherwise. It was less work, Morris reflected, to mould the world to Buddy than Buddy to the world.

Morris learned from experience to make only the most considered statements when he lectured on The Seeing Eye. Once when he was speaking at a convention, he made the unqualified statement, in answer to a question, that Seeing Eye dogs never engaged in fights with other dogs—they were too well educated!

After the talk, Morris went to the check room, got his hat and he and Buddy went about their business. A score of people from the audience followed to see what happened when he got out on the street in traffic. Suddenly a fox terrier joined the crowd, yapping at Buddy as if to challenge the right of the big shepherd to walk on its block. When Buddy didn't respond, the terrier became courageous and finally got close enough for Buddy to retaliate. She nipped a piece out of the terrier. The terrier yowled murder. Immediately some of his lecture audience pounced on Morris.

"I thought you said your dog didn't fight," they challenged.

"Well, I don't call that a fight," Morris replied. "Do you?"

They agreed it wasn't.

Morris had silenced his onlookers but thereafter he was careful to qualify his claims regarding Buddy's capacity to resist annoyance.

Morris maintained that Buddy was so peaceful that she must have some Quaker blood in her. "Why, she's only been in ten fights in her life. That's one a year and that's a lot less than I've had," he said.

Because Morris and Buddy worked together as smoothly as if they had been cast from one mold, not infrequently people thought that he received a special training or that perhaps he could "see a little." On one occasion a lady in a Queen Mary hat stopped at The Seeing Eye and wanted to be shown about. Though it was not during visitors' hours, because she was an older person and had come a long way Morris courteously took her around himself, explaining as they went along how the organization functioned.

After a bit, she asked if she could see some of the blind students working with their dogs. Morris politely told her that it was impossible and mentioned the school's inflexible rule against placing the students on public exhibition. But to be obliging, Morris walked with the lady out to where she could see the kennels—from a distance. That special privilege, he felt, ought to satisfy anyone. But the lady was not satisfied.

"I think it's outrageous," she said, "to come all the way to this school and then find that you are not able to see even one blind person."

"But, madam," Morris replied. "I'm blind."

The woman looked at him closely for a minute then said, "Oh, no, you're not. Your right eye looks perfect."

The opening was too inviting to ignore. As Morris said later, he could have driven a chariot through it.

"It ought to be," he replied. "It cost me $25.00."

Many a dog has at one time or another been credited with saving his master from fire, and sometimes along with him a whole house full of people. Buddy is no exception. One morning in an Eastern hotel, Morris was awakened by Buddy licking his face, in the cold dark hours before dawn. It was obvious that Buddy wanted something and though normally she would have been good for several more hours, Morris naturally assumed that she wanted to take a walk. He took up the telephone on the table beside his bed and called the porter. He got up to get Buddy's leash and when he opened the closet door, a cloud of smoke billowed out at him. He gave the alarm. But by the time the hotel fire staff had reached his room, Buddy had guided Morris down to the lobby and safety. The linen-room on the floor below Morris's room was ablaze and was rapidly being consumed when Buddy's sensitive nose was aroused to the danger of fire. Ever afterward Buddy was a hero at that hotel.

Buddy lived up to her position in the dog world by proving she was equal to the ordeal by fire. She also showed she was equal to the ordeal by water. Morris enjoys swimming and will plunge into anything bigger than a bathtub. Ordinarily, when there was room in a pond for both of them, and even if there wasn't, Buddy would come in after him. When he was in deep water, she would swim around him in circles, standing by, as it were, in case of need.

Morris's friends thought this stunt of Buddy's was "cute" rather than practical, especially whenever Morris swam in the friendly atmosphere of Mr. Ebeling's lake at Openaka. But on one occasion when Morris had been swimming alone for an hour or so in a large lake he unexpectedly found that all at once he was exhausted. As he started to swim ashore, he suddenly realized that he had lost his sense of direction. He didn't know where the nearest shore was!

There was no sun and he could not learn his direction by feeling its warmth on his face. The light breeze he dared not trust; he knew the vagaries of the wind. He knew that even if his fading strength held out he might swim in circles for hours without ever touching the shore. For a moment he was panic-stricken, then he remembered and relaxed. "Buddy," he called. "Come."

And Buddy paddled over and Morris reached out and felt her shaggy coat and took hold of the tip of her tail.

"Buddy, forward," Morris commanded, and then swam along behind her as she paddled off.

In five minutes, Buddy had him back exactly at the place where they had entered the water together. Buddy never got any Carnegie medals for heroism—she just did her job.

Yes, Buddy just did her job. Her life was filled to the brim with happiness of a kind few are privileged to know, the joy of appreciated service. Now Buddy II directs Morris Frank's energetic steps, and Buddy has gone to whatever special heaven is reserved for the faithful and the brave in heart. But her spirit still guides.

Hundreds of other guide dogs outside the spotlight that followed Buddy are today, and every day, doing their jobs. From the deserts of Arizona to Montana's Little Big Horn; from fog-wrapped Puget Sound to the deep blue water of Florida's Boca Grande; day in and day out these devoted animals joyfully lead men and women out from the bondage of blindness into a world where the only barriers are those of space and time.

They and those two-score people of The Seeing Eye and the thousands of that organization's members who make possible this great humanitarian achievement have begun a new chapter in the history of freedom. The first page is now written. Through endless tomorrows the record will grow—the record of animal sagacity combined with human intelligence—the story of dogs against darkness.

SHIPPING WILD ANIMALS

By CHARLES MAYER

Illustration by Frank Shields

ELEPHANTS are easily trained, and, when they once get the idea of what is expected of them, they will do it over and over with little variation. A trick or a certain kind of work immediately becomes a habit with them. In fact, they can form habits more rapidly than any other animals I have ever seen.

In Burma there are large lumber mills, and elephants are used for rolling the logs into position for the saws. Pushing with their heads, they run the logs up two inclined skids to the platform. Two elephants do the pushing and a third elephant acts as boss. The boss need not be an especially intelligent animal; he is simply taught that the log must go up the skids in a certain way and that the two pushers must be kept even. In his trunk he carries a few links of anchor chain, which he uses as a whip. If one elephant falls behind, the boss gives him a rap with the chain. When the log is on the platform, the pushers turn and plod back for another. The boss elephant is quite unimpressed by his authority, and the others show no resentment when he swings the chain on them.

When the whistle blows, the elephants know that it is time to stop work and eat. It makes no difference if they have a log within a fraction of an inch of the platform; the boss drops his anchor chain and gets out of the way, and the pushers step to one side, letting the log crash down again. Then, without the least expression of interest, they turn for the stalls. Because they obey signals so mechanically, the engineer steps out, when feeding time comes, and looks up and down the runway to see if an elephant crew has a log on the skids. If so, he waits until it reaches the platform before he pulls the whistle-cord.

The great weight and bulk of elephants sometimes make difficult the problem of handling and especially of shipping them. They are usually hoisted over the side of the ship in slings, but that method takes much time and labor, not to speak of very strong tackle. I did not evolve a new one, however, until the refusal of the captain of one of the British India Steam Navigation Company's boats to take a consignment of elephants for me put my ingenuity to the test.

I was under contract to send fifteen large elephants to Madras, and I had arranged with the company's agent at Singapore for three shipments of five each. The animals were the remainder of the Trengganu herd and I was anxious to see them shipped, for I was still sick with the fever. The doctors had told me that the best thing I could do was to leave the country and recuperate, and any delay in disposing of the animals meant a sacrifice of either money or health.

The first five elephants, together with attendants and food, were waiting back of the sheds at *Tanjong-Pâgar,* the docks at Singapore, to be put aboard. At the last moment the chief officer came with the message that the captain refused to take them.

I went to the captain's cabin and found a stout, red-faced and apparently good-natured Englishman. He was just out of his bath, wearing pajamas and idling about in his cabin until the ship was ready to get under way. I thought it a good time to approach him, and I took care to be quite calm and cool, although I was raging inside.

I showed him my receipt and the bill of lading given me by the agent. He replied that the agent was not captain of the ship; he didn't care what agreement the agent had made. So long as he was captain, he'd run his ship to suit himself, and all agents could go to the devil, for all he cared. And, moreover, he'd not carry elephants— not for anyone. I explained my position and told him it would mean a financial loss if I failed on my contract to deliver the elephants.

"Look here, Mayer," he said, "I've handled elephants at Calcutta and I've always had a lot of trouble with them. If I load these elephants, it means that I have to rig up extra gear, and I won't do it."

"Captain," I replied, "I'll load those elephants without using a foot of rope. I'll put them anywhere you say, and you won't have to rig up a bit of gear. And I'll unload them at Madras the same way. Will you say the word?"

"I don't think you can do it," he answered, "but I'm enough of a sportsman to give you a chance."

That was all I wanted. I got out before he could ask me how I was going to work, for I couldn't have told him.

The elephants were to go in the bow and they had to be taken there through a seven-foot passage from amidships. The smallest of the elephants measured fully seven feet and the largest more than eight. I decided that we might as well try the largest first, and I asked that the electric bulbs be removed from the ceiling.

After some coaxing and prodding, we got the first elephant up the gangplank. The others followed obediently. Then I asked the chief officer to clear the cabins along the passage, for I was afraid that someone might open a door and frighten the elephant. A frightened, stampeded, eight-foot elephant in a seven-foot passage would give Singapore enough excitement to last for a year. The chief officer sent the people from the cabins and locked the doors.

The elephant balked at sight of the passage. I was at his head, talking to him and coaxing him, and two attendants were behind, prodding. We made him kneel and then urged him forward. At last we got him into the passage. It was a tight fit. His sides scraped the walls. I gasped at the thought of what would happen if he suddenly became afraid. He would try to stand up, of course, and then wedged in, he would begin to kick and lunge his way out; and the other four, who were close behind him, would do the same. "And then, good-bye, steamship," I said to myself. Slowly we made our way forward, with the five elephants hobbling along on their knees. I stayed close to the head of the first, talking to him and petting him. Finally we came to the end of the passage, and I drew the first deep breath in fifteen minutes. I took the venture simply as a matter of course, and I didn't say anything that gave the captain an idea of what my emotions had been in that passage; but Ali looked at me and I looked at Ali, and there was no need of words.

I washed and went to the captain's cabin for breakfast, while the men secured the elephants in their quarters. The captain said, "Mayer, that was the quickest and slickest thing I've seen, but what shall I do with those animals at Madras?" I knew that there were no docks at Madras and that all freight was unloaded into lighters, but I answered, "My men will attend to them."

When the ship reached Madras, the attendants opened the doors and simply backed the elephants overboard. They hit the water with a great splash and a roar and came up blowing like whales. They were swimming, of course, for elephants swim better than any other land animals I have ever seen. The attendants approached them in row-boats, and, jumping on their back, rode them to shore. By the time they reached land, they had completely recovered from the excitement of falling overboard.

The captain returned to Singapore, enthusiastic over this new way of handling elephants, and I had the pleasure of shipping my last consignment to Madras on his ship. He advised me never to take an agent's word for what the captain will or will not do, and after that experience, I always saw the captain first and the agent second.

In the collecting and trapping of wild animals one must not think that all animals so caught are fit for zoological or show purposes. Such is not the case; often, after trailing animals for days and after having trapped them, I found them old, scarred, mangey, with broken tails and in numerous ways unfit; and although I rarely killed, except in self-preservation, I would kill off all such as were not fit.

All animals I sold and shipped were at the time of embarkment, healthy, sound, and in good condition. As I never carried with my outfit any preparation for the curing of skins, I usually allowed the natives to have them, although I often presented good specimens to the Raffles Museum at Singapore that were mounted and catalogued as donations from myself. In one exhibit a group of eight orang-utans, from babies to full grown, and a baby elephant were well mounted and always came in for the particular notice of visitors.

I was having a busy week at my animal house in Singapore, getting a lot of animals recaged and ready for shipment to Melbourne, for Mr. La Souef, Director of the Melbourne Zoological Society, who was then on a visit to Singapore with his wife, when one day a messenger came from the Sultan of Johore, inviting Mr. and Mrs. La Souef and myself to call the following day.

As Singapore is an island of fourteen by sixteen miles, and separated from the mainland by the Straits of Johore, at the extreme southern point of Asia, or the Malay Peninsula, it really meant but a few hours, sixteen miles by rail to Kranji and by ferry across the Straits about a mile to Johore.

Back of the jail at Johore were built eight large, strong, iron cages, in which were kept all tigers, leopards and smaller cat animals that were caught throughout the state of Johore and sent to the Sultan for him to present as gifts or sell as he saw fit. I eventually had first call on all animals so caught.

On the following day, arriving at Johore, we were met by Dato Muntre, the prime minister, and introduced to Sultan Ibriam, who was at that time a young man and with whom I was very well acquainted. After showing Mr. and Mrs. La Souef through his palace and grounds, we came to the cages back of the jail, which contained three tigers, two black and one spotted leopard. The Sultan, pointing to one cage which contained a beautiful specimen of tiger, young, beautifully striped, and a bright golden yellow, said he wished to present that tiger to the Melbourne Society as a gift, and, turning to me said, "Tûan Mayer, you can get him whenever you wish," knowing I was Mr. La Souef's agent. Mr. La Souef was delighted and thanked the Sultan in his and the Society's name, promising to put his gift in a prominent place in the Melbourne Garden.

On our return to Singapore, I had quite an argument with Mr. La Souef regarding the flimsy, unsuitable cages he was having made to suit himself, and every time I ventured to point out the inadvisability of certain cages being built under his directions, he would invariably say, "Mr. Mayer, you may be right. I also am right, and I have handled animals longer than you." As the animals were his and he insisted on having his way, I simply carried out his instructions. His idea was to build large, roomy cages from the cheapest of wood (siraih), having a space between the floor and the cross section holding the iron bars, to clean out the cages and to hand in food.

I never would think of shipping an animal in such a cage. First, it is too large and roomy, giving the animal too much play to break the cage; and it is weakened by having a space between the floor and the cross piece, unless made of heavy and strong wood. I always caged animals for shipping in small narrow cages or boxes of heavy wood; sides of wood, but bars at each end and no space. When food or water was to be given them, the food was cut up small enough to be passed between the bars, and a drinking pan was nailed to the floor of the cage. When cleaning out the cage on board the steamer, both front and rear covers were taken off and the cage flushed with water, at the same time giving the animal a bath. The bath in some instances, and according to the animal, would be dispensed with, but never with cat animals.

I returned to Johore the following day with a transporting cage, and with Ali and the assistance of a few of the prisoners from the jail, soon had the tiger safely boxed and on his way in a bullock cart to my animal house in Orchard Road, there to be recaged in the cage Mr. La Souef was having built under his directions, by my Chinese carpenter who built all my cages. Taking me aside he said: "Tûan, etn, Orang bon-yer, gee-har sat-tu Jam remow pe-char" (Sir, that man is very foolish, the tiger will break his cage in an hour). I said, "Never mind, make the cage as he wants it, that is his lookout."

Well, the cage was made, the tiger moved into it, and a few days later we loaded the shipment on board the steamer, ours being the last thing to be put on board. As the steamer was to sail at midnight, we had no trouble in placing the cages on deck, and, as space was limited, I suggested to Mr. La Souef to let me arrange the placing of cages and animals. But no, he would see to that, and told the captain that he would like to have them placed as he wished. They were on the forward deck, in a circle about the hatch, with the smaller animals and deer facing the cages on deck, on the hatch itself. Can you imagine placing deer in crates facing tigers in none too strong boxes?

I bade Mr. La Souef and his wife bon voyage, and wished him success in landing his shipment. Mr. La Souef was a personal friend of the owner of the steamship company (the McAllister Line) who was a patron and also a director of the Melbourne Zoological Society. As Mr. La Souef had taken the trip with his wife, as guests of the owner, Captain Edwards of the vessel used diplomacy, said nothing, and allowed Mr. La Souef to have his way; but before going ashore, I said to Captain Edwards, "Watch out, there is going to be trouble before you get to Melbourne." "Never fear," he replied, "Mayer, I'll kill or dump the whole lot over the side if anything starts, friend of the boss or not! I have my other passengers to look to." I said good-bye to him hoping to see him on his return trip, when I would hear the news, if any.

The shipment consisted of the following, not counting the tiger, the gift of the Sultan of Johore: two small orangutans, twenty monkeys, one sun bear, one honey bear, two civet cats, one binturong, four crown gora pheasants, one black leopard, one clouded leopard, spotted and looking like an ocelot, one female tiger, two samber deer, two mouse deer; in all fourteen cages and three crates.

At five o'clock the following morning, I was awakened by a hammering at the gate and the calling of "Tûan! Tûan!" Looking out, I saw a native boatman. "What do you want?" I called.

"Tûan, etu re-mow, pe-char, sanken, mon lorrie" (Sir, the tiger has broken his cage and wants to run away).

"What tiger? Where?" I asked.

"The tiger from the steamer," he said.

"Well, what do you want me to do? The steamer left last night. I am through with it."

"Te-dar Tûan" (No, Sir), he said, handing me a letter, "the tiger is in my lighter and is tied to one of the buoys in the harbor." He begged me to get the tiger, as no one was near or on the lighter.

The letter, which was from Mr. La Souef, written before the steamer sailed, stated that the tiger presented by the Sultan of Johore had broken his cage and was in danger of getting clear away. The captain had had a sling put about the broken cage, after the ship's carpenter had nailed a few boards to cover the hole the tiger had made and partly strengthened it; and had hung the cage over the side of the ship, telling Mr. La Souef that if he did not get some kind of a boat or lighter to put the cage in, he would drop tiger, cage and all into the water. And as this happened at about half-past eleven at night, things did not look very bright for Mr. La Souef. He begged and prayed the captain to let the carpenter or himself get nails and

Frank Shields

He would have broken out and escaped.

[See page 123]

boards, but the captain was firm. They finally got the head stevedore of the dock to let him put the cage in a lighter, which they did, and then towed the lighter out in the harbor, everyone leaving it as soon as it was tied to a buoy. Mr. La Souef then told them to notify me, which they did. There I was, with instructions to get the tiger, recage it and ship by next steamer, eighteen days later.

I asked the boatman where the lighter was. Taking Ali and four natives with ropes, boards, nails, etc., we went down to the docks, and there, out in the harbor tied to the buoy, was the lighter with a fleet of small boats surrounding it at a good distance. I called a sampan and told the owner of the lighter to follow. As we neared the lighter, we could hear the growling and the tearing of wood, and getting alongside and cautiously climbing up, I looked in.

There was the cage with the tiger's head through a hole that it was trying to make larger. Fortunately the cage had been strengthened by the ship's carpenter, otherwise he would have broken out and escaped before I could have been notified. By that time the docks were lined with people. The story had spread that there was a lighter in the harbor, filled with wild animals that had broken out of their cages and were fighting and killing one another, and that those that could escape would jump into the harbor and make for the shore. Then someone called Police Headquarters and four European officers came down to the dock with repeaters.

Ali and I dropped into the lighter, calling to the natives to pass the boards, nails and hammers, and assuming that there was no danger, we took each an end of a board and carrying it to the top of the cage passed it over until it covered the hole the tiger had his head out of. As Ali and I held the board, my men nailed it and then another; so, soon we had him fairly well secured; that is, he was in the cage again, snarling, biting and scratching. Calling to the owner of the lighter to come aboard with his men and row his lighter to the docks, we went to work and nailed board after board against and over all weak spots. There was no need to tell the boatmen to hurry; they never rowed faster. Arriving at the docks, and after telling the inspector just what had happened, we got the cage on the bullock cart and soon had the tiger safe at my animal house. Three weeks later I shipped him aboard in a good strong cage, in charge of the captain, but as the steamer was steaming up the Yarra river into Melbourne, the tiger died. An autopsy showed he died of a fractured skull, and later I got the full particulars.

It seemed that when the tiger first attempted to break out of his cage on board the steamer, and the carpenter was ordered to get some boards and cover the hole he had been tearing, as the head showed against the opening the carpenter struck it with his hammer. The deer and smaller animals became terrified, and in their endeavor to escape, the deer's legs got through the slats in the crates; they broke their legs and had to be killed. This I was told later by Captain Edwards, who said it all happened within a few minutes, Mr. La Souef running about like a madman, begging this and that, getting in the way of everybody, but no one paying any attention to him; and what with the excitement among the passengers, the roaring of the tigers, barking of the bears, chatter of monkeys and crying of the smaller cats, and the frantic efforts of the deer to break through the crates, he was only adding to the confusion and disorder, until Captain Edwards ordered the water hose brought into play to quiet the animals. He told the carpenter to get some boards and nail up the opening the tiger had made, then having a sling put about the cage with the tiger snarling and biting and tearing at the opening it had started, but which was now covered by the planks, swung it over the side of the ship and there it hung. The captain then had the cages taken off the hatch and placed against the side of the steamer, telling Mr. La Souef that if he did not keep quiet he would have the whole shipment put over the side and dumped into the harbor.

That was the story Captain Edwards told me on his return trip to Singapore, and he laughed heartily over the way he said Mr. La Souef was hopping about in his pajamas.

My bill against the Society for services, paying for the lighter the tiger was put into from the steamer, labor, recaging, feeding for twenty-one days, and enough food for eighteen to twenty-one days' voyage to Melbourne seemed to Mr. La Souef an overcharge; and my bill of £50 all out of proportion, as the tiger was a gift from the

Sultan of Johore and not purchased. I insisted, and drew on him for that amount, at the same time resigning as agent for his Society, telling him that although he was an older man, he had still to learn the art of caging, recaging and shipping animals, not receiving them, and that had he not insisted on having things done his own way with cheap material, and had left it to me, what happened could not have happened, as barely one-third of his shipment landed alive.

KING COBRA TAKES THE STAGE

By RAYMOND L. DITMARS

IT was a king cobra which backed me into the most embarrassing situation in thirty years of handling animals.

This Indo-Malayan reptile is the world's largest poisonous serpent. It attains a length of fifteen feet—and is occasionally a yard longer. It is slender, however, really whiplike, extremely active, and fearless to the point of insolence. If stirred to anger, it will attack with a rush. It is the most intelligent of all serpents, and I have more respect for its indicated thought, reasoning, and bravery than for some of the big, four-footed animals. I have protested against its importation—and also the African mamba—unless consigned to the few institutions competent to care for it.

If a serpent comes under my care, its dangerous nature never arouses any feeling of antagonism. I feel we had a hand in taking it from its natural home. The reptile can't be blamed for showing its most devilish aspect in the changed environment of captivity. My thought is to calm it down, to make it feel content, or its life as a captive may be short. Then, again, there is another thing to consider. Such specimens are valuable. They must be kept alive and in good condition, if the expert's reputation is to be sustained.

Hence a king cobra, dangerous as it is, receives the same care as the other serpents, even to the extent of superficial surgery, if the same is needed.

King cobras have trouble in shedding the transparent plates over their lidless eyes. These plates, or caps, should come away when the skin is cast, but often stick over the eyes, and the snake becomes partially blind. Several years ago we had a big fellow in this condition, and by suspending a net on a big iron ring from the ceiling of one section of his double cage, then pulling the partition door and waiting for him to glide under the net, we managed thus to catch him. I went into the cage on that occasion, pressed down his head (through the net) and grasped him by the neck. The caps were

TAYLORVILLE C.U. No. 3
WEST SCHOOL

removed by working a pair of tweezers through the net, but the big cobra nearly twisted free, after thrashing most of its body outside the ring. I vowed to myself that never again would I attempt to hold a king cobra.

Quite recently the operation was repeated with another big specimen—a fourteen-footer—now several years in the collection. About a year past, it had failed to shed the cap over its right eye. They shed their skins every six to seven weeks. It was my hope that with the next shedding the obsolete cap would adhere to the one coming away with this skin, but when it was shed the eye looked duller than before. We realized there were now *two* old caps adhering to the right eye. The trouble continued through *seven* sheddings.

As the normal eye of the king cobra is of a brilliant hue, like new copper, and the majestic creature is remarkable for the intensity of its stare, the serpent was badly disfigured from what appeared to be—and was—a blind eye. The caps had accumulated to such a thickness that the afflicted eye was dull white, with no sign of pupil.

The headkeeper and I had tried various devices to assist the big cobra. The cage quarters, as is necessary with all king cobras, were double. There was a sliding partition door. Closing this, we would go into the empty cage and put down layers of heavy burlap sacks, moisten them thoroughly and weight them down with rocks. When the partition door was opened, the cobra would go through and do its best to rub the eye plates off against the bags.

As the bags didn't work, we tried bundles of brush, bound loosely together. The serpent appeared to wait for new devices and would start in to try them at once. For the first time, there appeared to be a friendly understanding between a king cobra and ourselves. We had the snake so interested and self-conscious about its eye, that at times it went around the cage rubbing the offending caps against sharp corners and doing its best to get rid of them. I thought of something, which gave a group of visitors a laugh, and made me wish I hadn't tried it.

It occurred to me that the straw jacket of a wine bottle might be a good thing for the cobra to crawl through and rub his head inside. To obtain this I visited an establishment which did not appear to be in accord with a much debated constitutional amendment. I figured, however, that the procuring of a straw container for the reptile was entirely legal, and placed it in the cage before the building was open. The cobra tried this, too. It didn't work. The cobra worked about half his body through it, then coiled up for a nap. This was disconcerting, as a straw bottle container, decorating the middle of a cobra, elicited remarks.

It was necessary to take a long rod and poke the cobra on the tail. This caused him to shed the straw jacket and evince the first irritability I had seen from him in weeks. Something radical had to be done—but I wasn't going to get hold of him. Going back to my office I got a sheet of drafting paper and drew the plan of a device which looked as if it might solve the problem.

The plan called for a wooden frame that would make a low and narrow cage, just about fitting the cobra when coiled. It was to be thirty inches long and eighteen inches wide. The height was specified as eight inches. The sides were to be of strong wire mesh, with one-inch openings. At one end was an upright sliding door, controlled by a cord and automatically locking when it dropped. The tricky part of the device, and that upon which its successful operation depended, was an extra top, within the top itself. This extra top was loose and movable. It was attached to two vertical rods, extending through the actual top. The inside, or bottom, of the movable top was to be covered with a pad of heavy felt, an inch thick.

This will give the reader an idea of the plan. With the cobra in the compact quarters, the top of the operating cage could be pressed down upon the serpent, holding the reptile so it could barely move. The disfiguring eye cap could then be removed with surgical tweezers.

The cage was made and set against the closed partition door. It was covered with a blanket, to make it look like a snug retiring place. Then the partition door was opened.

The king cobra, always ready to try anything once, glided over to take a look at the device. Deciding that here was a nice nook to go in and take a nap, he coiled inside. Headkeeper Toomey was keeping an eye on the situation, and coming along the passageway saw a foot of green tail protruding from the box. He slid the cage door open slightly and poked the tail with a long rod. The tail was drawn in; then the head of the cobra peered out to see what Toomey was up to. Deciding that the disturbance didn't amount to much, the serpent again retired within the box. The cord of the sliding door was released, and the door dropped down and locked.

At the end of the reptile house is a big room with a glass ceiling. We sometimes use it as a photographic gallery. The cage was carried to this room, as I needed plenty of light for the delicate operation. We were very careful in carrying the cage, in anticipation of the cobra becoming enraged and biting against the wire mesh. There was a chance, if we were careless, that its fangs might hook through and scratch us.

Strangely enough, it was not enraged, but extremely curious. It peered through the sides, and at us. We didn't waste any time. My secretary had come in to see the job. She held an extra pair of spatulate tweezers I might need.

The movable top was pressed down. Fred Taggart, an athletic member of the reptile-house staff, did that job. The cobra was pinned so it could do little more than wriggle here and there. Its head was forced against the netting by one of the body coils. The troublesome right eye was outward and in a fine position for working upon it.

An operation of this kind must be carefully done. A slip of the tweezers might injure the eye, which was delicate from being long and abnormally covered. The first step was to grasp some of the loose epidermis around the edge of the cap, and in that way to lift it off. In treating an occasional python with this trouble, the cap is thus readily removed, but the caps on pythons' eyes are thinner than with cobras, and again, we never permit them to accumulate. There is no problem about treating a python. The creature has no poison. All you have to do is throw a blanket over him, then tiptoe into the cage with several husky assistants, and fall on him.

The accumulated layers of caps on the king cobra's eye didn't lift off. It was necessary to go deeper, at the rear of the eyeball, and pry under the combined cap. A few seconds' examination convinced me the cobra would never have been able to rub it off. Using a scraping and prying motion of the tweezers, I loosened an edge of the cap, so I could firmly grasp it. A rolling move of the instrument now brought the cap away and the actual operating was over.

My thought immediately reverted to the condition of our valuable specimen. It had been held in severe restraint. At the touch of the tweezers, it exploded a hiss, approaching a snort. At each move of the instrument its reaction had been a similar hiss. This was not surprising. There is no more "touchy" creature in the world than a king cobra, nothing alive more liable to resent restraint. But it had not struggled, and this surprised me.

"I can't see through it. It's like tortoise shell."

My secretary was holding the cap to her eye, was moving her finger in front of it. She said she could dimly see a shadow of the finger.

We carried the operating box back to the big cage, placed it inside, and pulled up the sliding door at the end. The cobra glided out. A dozen visitors stood outside the cage wondering what was going on. The cobra reared, higher and higher. For a moment his body swayed slightly, in the unique movement of cobras, large and small. Then, posed like a gigantic candlestick, he became motionless, with the exception of the head, which turned slightly to one side, then the other, as he surveyed the group outside his cage. To me it looked as if he were testing his vision, and the proud pose hinted of returning assurance of his power to dominate, like other examples of his kind I have seen. Walking out to the front to get a look at him, it was gratifying to note that both eyes matched, in the curious glittering stare of his kind.

Back at the office, with tweezers and sharply pointed scalpel, I quickly separated the layers of the cap. They were as smoothly fitted, one over the other, as layers of onion skin. There were seven of them, representing seven successive sheddings of the skin. Placed in a row, they looked like hollow glass beads, cut in halves. They were cemented to a sheet of paper and marked with data.

On the evening following the operation, the headkeeper decided he would try the king cobra with his weekly snake—the big fellow being a strict cannibal. It was a day ahead of the scheduled feeding, but Toomey wanted to see if he had been much disturbed by the operation. If a snake is in any way out of sorts, it won't eat. Toomey placed a five-foot gopher snake in the cage. Not long after, he was pleased to see nothing but the tail of the gopher protruding from the cobra's mouth, like an elongated cigar.

Hunting me up among the animal buildings, Toomey told me that everything was well, and, reminiscing a bit, remarked about the king cobra not having missed a scheduled meal in a year. He figured an average of a five-foot snake a week, or approximately two hundred and fifty feet of serpents consumed in a year's time.

This goes to show that I am well acquainted with king cobras; and it serves as a prologue for my most vividly remembered king cobra episode.

Occupying the cage next to the serpent of the eye operation was a thirteen-foot king cobra transient. This one had been a guest several months, awaiting completion of its suite in the new reptile house of the National Zoological Park at Washington. Dr. W. M. Mann, Director of the National Zoo, had been very anxious to obtain a king cobra, as the reptilian star for his new building, which was costing about a quarter of a million dollars. There was a rumor that several were on the way from Singapore, escorted by a highly competent man.

They arrived in New York and I bought two of them: one for the government institution, and the one having the trouble with his eye.

They were taken from the steamer to the animal farm of Henry Bartels, near Jersey City.

While these serpents were in strong teakwood boxes, with observation ports covered with netting, I considered it a hazardous thing to trust them to an express company. We hunted around for some large and heavy burlap bags, placed each box in a bag, and tied the bags securely. I drove the snakes to the park in my own car. The idea of placing the boxes in the bags seemed safer, in case of an accident.

These were the largest king cobras I had seen, but both of them were very thin. Dr. Mann was delighted to know I had purchased a specimen for him, but was worried about their condition. It meant careful attention in feeding and spraying them with tepid water, to induce shedding of dry, wrinkled skins. Both had badly bruised snouts, from striking at the wire netting of the shipping boxes. They were seething with nerves and rage, and would swerve and dart at the merest shadow. It took a couple of months to calm them down, soften their old skins, and spray them so their bruised snouts healed, as well as the scars of nooses, inflicted by the native hunters. They were lightly fed at first, then the food "stepped up." They were both blooming with health and rounded to graceful outlines before the new building in Washington was ready. Dr. Mann was delighted. A spacious cage, with sloping tree and tropical plants, was being made ready as a feature exhibit for his specimen.

Modern animal buildings are complicated in their lighting, heating, and automatic devices. I had expected to ship the cobra to Washington during the autumn, and one of the teakwood boxes, in which the serpents had traveled, was to be encased in stiff and heavy wire mesh to guard against it being broken in an express car by something dropping on it. But the autumn passed by and the winter was well along when Dr. Mann mailed invitations to the opening of his new building, and requested that I get his king cobra to his zoo not later than the morning of the day set for the reception.

Here was something to think about. The weather was cold and freezing. A tropical snake cannot endure a temperature around the freezing point. Dealers had received whole shipments of them dead from carelessness in setting crates on a pier, or the weather changing while reptiles were in transit on express wagons. There wasn't going to be any hazard of this kind with Dr. Mann's king cobra. That reptilian star wasn't going to be out of my sight from the time it left our park to the moment it was delivered to its new quarters. So Toomey and I got together for one of our conferences, which range from the crating of deer to restraining the orangutans from smashing their skylights.

We decided there was but one thing to do. That was to get the cobra into a deep cloth bag and place the bag in a heavy satchel. I could take the satchel to the National Zoo without any more trouble than carrying ordinary baggage.

Weight was not a bothersome factor. King cobras are slender. While the specimen for the new building was about thirteen feet long, it was not over two inches in diameter at the thickest part. We estimated its weight to be around fifteen pounds. Our plans were simple, and Toomey started to get things ready.

The first thing he hunted up was a bag about five feet deep of tough white material. We had several of these. They are called millers' bags, and are the kind I always take when going out on a rattlesnake hunt. For the mouth of this bag Toomey made a frame looking like a box kite. He fastened the bag around this with thumb tacks. This formed a short tunnel leading into the bag, which was attached to the border of the partition door.

A piece of sash cord was fastened to the front of the cage, a turn taken around the mouth of the bag just below the "tunnel," thus forming a tying loop, and the end carried through the slightly opened door. Toomey pulled the partition door and went on a tour of inspection among his animal buildings. He had pictured what he would find when he got back, and his visualization of the cage was quite correct.

Coming back to the cobra cage, he found the king cobra had disappeared, and the bag bulging slightly. He yanked the cord, rolled back the door, and went into the cage. Cutting away a section of the cord, he tied the bag securely. The course of this procedure I afterwards learned from Toomey. Busy with a versatile mail, and making marginal memoranda for my secretary, who was away, I heard a step at the door. Looking up, I saw Toomey entering, carrying a bag. He was the same calm Toomey I have known for twenty-five years.

"Here's your cobra," he remarked. "You'd better label it."

He put the bag in a corner of the office. It reared a foot or so, then became as motionless as if it were a dust cloth, covering a model.

Toomey's remark about labeling the bag related to an old rule of the reptile house. We never put a poisonous snake in a bag without immediately tying a warning tag on the bag.

In this instance, I decided on an additional precaution, and flicking off the cover of my secretary's typewriter, inserted a sheet of our formal letterhead.

"We'll take another precaution in this instance, Toomey," I said, and tapped off the following:

> "This bag contains a living cobra. It is being taken
> to the National Zoological Park, in Washington."

I showed this to Toomey.

"You're going to put that in the satchel with the bag?" he asked.

"Yes. There's one chance in a thousand of somebody grabbing the wrong bag. I'm thinking of that chance."

We got out a sole-leather traveling case, which had been with me on two trips along the Mediterranean, in Brazil, and in Central America—had traveled many thousands of miles. It had withstood the rough treatment of baggage slings, been shot down slides, and banged by luggage smashers of at least six nations. It was tough, and nothing had happened to it beyond a dimming of its originally glossy surface. In this the king cobra was placed, with the emergency memoranda. The leather case locked at both ends. No snake on earth could have bitten through the walls of that container.

As my train left at night, I took the cobra home in my car and had dinner. Then I was driven to the railroad station in a heated automobile, the cobra case reposing on the rear seat. A porter took the traveling case at the station and carried it to the car. I had engaged a full section. The sleeping-car attendant stowed the case under the berth in the usual way. Feeling pretty tired, I went to bed at once.

As a rule, I sleep soundly on trains, but I woke up on this one, feeling chilly. They must have turned off the heat, for the car was cold. It took a minute or so to get my senses. The first thing I thought of was my overcoat, folded on a shelf at the foot of the berth. I reached for this and pulled it open, over the bedding. This bit of action brought me to my senses and I thought of the king cobra. It was decidedly too chilly for him—and what was to be done? It took a minute to think it out.

I'd been cooled off in sleeping sections before, and the overcoat had always remedied matters. Well, here was the overcoat and I'd be all right again in a few minutes, so the best thing to do was to share the protection with the cobra. The only difference it would make would be to shorten the berth.

Taking a look up and down the aisle, which was deserted, I ducked out, slid the case from under the berth, pushed the covers all the way down to the foot, placed the satchel at the extreme end of the berth, and pulled the covers, and the overcoat, back over it. There was a little readjusting to do, as the height of the satchel shortened the blanket so it wouldn't come up to my chin, but this was regulated by yanking the covers along a bit. By taking an oblique position, and doubling my knees a little, sleep soon returned. I was wakened by a pulling of the covers. I had arrived at my destination.

A taxi whisked me and the cobra to the National Zoo. Dr. Mann sent for William M. Blackburne, superintendent of the collections. Blackburne is the dean of America's "boss animal men." No abler chaperon for a big collection of wild beasts can anywhere be found. By keen and sympathetic observation, years of study, and by intuition, he is the ideal in a position of the kind.

He unlocked and slid back the rolling door at the rear of the king cobra's quarters, and I had a chance to look inside. It was like a glade in a jungle. There was no difficulty about liberating the cobra. The deep cloth bag was lifted from the case and placed in the cage. Then the bag was twisted beyond the portion where it was tied. The cord was cut, and we quickly closed the door. Blackburne shoved a bamboo pole through an auxiliary port in the door and prodded the bag. The cobra glided from it and reared to motionless pose in his new home.

They were all much interested about the way I brought the cobra down, and as I was to give a lecture at the United States National Museum as a part of the ceremonies of opening the new reptile house, they suggested that during the discourse I explain to the audience how their feature exhibit had arrived. It was that explanation in the auditorium which provided the whirlwind finish of this story.

Ascending the steps to the rostrum of the classic structure, which is the master scientific institution of the nation, and facing an audience of assembled scientists and guests, I swung into a prologue to lead the five motion-picture reels so critically assembled in my laboratory for this occasion. The reels were straight scenes, with no titles, so my talk was running without a break. The lecture was a third over, so I had my gait. A sheet of memoranda for the introduction was crumpled in my hand. I thoroughly enjoy a lecture when it develops to this stage, and was putting over my points, when a shadowy form loomed beside me. There was a voice: "Don't forget the king cobra."

I nodded, and swung along. There was a reel to come, elucidating the habits of cobras. I would tell the story then. The scenes of the reel flashed on and the method of bagging and delivering the cobra was explained.

Right there the seed was sown for a newspaper story which was to appear all over the country, from coast to coast. This was apparent from clippings which came in fat envelopes from a press-clipping service. Had I sensed the effect of that story, I never would have told it.

Along with the clippings came a lengthy and most emphatically protesting letter from a high official of the sleeping-car corporation. He stated he had received many letters of bitter complaint. He took the point that I had violated railroad rules and ethics, exposed the passengers and the train crew to grave danger, and shocked the traveling public. Moreover, I was forbidden to ride in the cars of his corporation if I ever again attempted to repeat the procedure.

A letter of this kind is liable to make a scientist see red. As I read it, the thoughts crowding into my mind were of *real* hazards I had willingly assumed, in handling hundreds of poisonous snakes to extract their venoms, in perfecting snake-bite serum. Right at the time I was extracting, every few days, the venom from a series of Indian hooded cobras to turn this over, and gratuitously too, for some important experiments going on in the United States and

France, in applying certain elements of the poison in minute and adulterated form, in the treatment of a tragic human malady.

In my mind, there had been no danger in the transportation of the king cobra. The serpent was of great value and the property of a government institution. I was responsible for getting it to them on time—and in good condition.

Calming down, in an endeavor to analyze the official's points of protest, I answered his letter in detail, stating the facts, and taking exception to some of his statements. I went into detail about our care in shipping dangerous animals in containers carefully designed to eliminate hazard, and cited past acceptances of the railroads, as carriers, of precariously packed specimens, which had escaped in express cars. I assured him that the transportation of the king cobra had been extremely exceptional, occasioned by unique conditions, and promised that I wouldn't do anything of the kind again.

There was no answer.

One thing possibly resulted from this letter—or it may have been purely incidental. I was visited by several gentlemen representing the railway shipping interests and asked about what I considered a properly built and safe container for traveling snakes. We had a long talk. I insisted upon boxes an inch thick, and the whole covered with strong wire mesh to reduce or eliminate possibility of escape if the boxes were broken during shipment.

One point brought out in the newspaper stories was unfair to the cobra. It was intimated that the serpent wheezed and hissed all night, and a passenger in a near-by berth thought somebody was snoring. This was not the case. It was unfair criticism of my reptilian companion. As an immediately adjacent passenger, his conduct was of the best. He slept silently, rustled no newspapers after hours, didn't explosively cough in a crowded washroom, or splatter the mirrors with a toothbrush.

Despite the explanation of the sleeping-car official that he had received many letters of complaint, I received but one, other than his own.

LEOPARDS AND RHINOS

By CARL E. AKELEY

Illustration by the Author

THERE is a general belief firmly fixed in the popular mind by constant repetition that the ostrich is a very stupid bird. A man might well expect easy hunting of a bird that tried to hide by the traditional method of sticking its head in the sand. But I found that the ostrich, like other African animals, did not always realize its obligation to tradition or abide by the rules set down for its behavior. I went a long way into the waterless desert of Somaliland after ostriches. We were just across the Haud and were camped in a "tug" or dry stream bed, where by digging we could get water for our sixty men and the camels. During two days of hunting in the dry bush of this desert I had seen many ostriches, but none of them had put its head into the ground and left its big black-and-white plumed body for me to shoot at. On the contrary, in this my first experience with them I found them exceedingly wary. They kept their bodies hidden behind the bush. Only their heads were exposed, each head only about large enough to carry a pair of very keen eyes and much too small to serve as a target at the distance that they maintained. As a result of being continually outwitted by them for two days I began to think ill of the man who originally started the story about their stupidity.

With the difficulties of the chase firmly in mind, I set out early on the third day to see if I could get a specimen. Concluding that the smaller the party the better the opportunity, I took only a mule and my pony boy. When only a half mile from camp I met an old hyena who was loafing along after a night out. He looked like a good specimen, but after I shot him, one look at his dead carcass was enough to satisfy me that he was not as desirable as I had thought, for his skin was badly diseased. I had very good reason to think of this very hard later in the day. A little farther along I shot a good wart hog for our scientific collection. Leaving the specimen where it lay, I marked the spot and continued in search of the plume-bearers.

Soon after this, I climbed to the top of a termite hill about eight feet high to look the country over with field glasses. As I held the glasses to my eyes while adjusting the focus, I suddenly realized that the letter S that I was focusing on was the head and neck of an ostrich and that there was a second letter S beside it. The birds remained perfectly motionless, watching, and I did likewise, locating their position meanwhile by the termite hills which were nearly in line between us. Suddenly the heads ducked and disappeared behind the bush. I dropped from my perch and ran rapidly to where they had been, but found only their trail in the sand.

When I had given up tracking them and was about to start farther afield I came into an opening in the bush that was about thirty yards wide and two hundred yards long. Near the center of the opening was a dense green bush a dozen feet in diameter. A beautiful cock ostrich broke into the clearing at full speed just below the bush and as I raised my rifle he disappeared behind the bush. I held ready to catch him as he passed out from behind it on the other side, where there were fifteen or twenty yards of clear ground before he would reach cover again. I stood there ready with my gun up until I felt foolish. Then I ran quickly to the bush expecting to find him just on the other side. He was nowhere in sight, but his trail told the story. As he had come into the open he had seen me, and when behind the bush he had stopped short, as indicated by a great hole and swirl of sand where he had caught himself by one foot, had turned at right angles and run straight away the length of the clearing, keeping the bush between himself and his enemy. I have not known many animals to do a more clever thing than this. I got one shot at him later—putting my sights at three hundred yards—but the bullet struck in the sand between his legs.

We returned to camp later in the afternoon, and after a little rest and refreshment I started out again with only the pony boy and carrying the necessary tools to get the head of the wart hog that I had shot in the morning. We had no difficulty in finding the place where I had shot him, but there was nothing to be seen of the pig. The place was strewn with vulture feathers, but surely vultures could not make away with the head. A crash in the bushes at one side led me in a hurry in that direction and a little later I saw my pig's head in the mouth of a hyena traveling up the slope of a ridge out of range. That meant that my wart hog specimen was lost, and, having got no ostriches, I felt it was a pretty poor day.

The sun was setting, and with little to console us the pony boy and I started for camp. As we came near to the place where I had shot the diseased hyena in the morning, it occurred to me that perhaps there might be another hyena about the carcass, and feeling a bit "sore" at the tribe for stealing my wart hog, I thought I might pay off the score by getting a good specimen of a hyena for the collections. The pony boy led me to the spot, but the dead hyena was nowhere in sight. There was the blood where he had fallen, and in the dusk we could make out a trail in the sand where he had been dragged.

Advancing a few steps, a slight sound attracted my attention, and glancing to one side I got a glimpse of a shadowy form going behind a bush. I then did a very foolish thing. Without a sight of what I was shooting at, I shot hastily into the bush. The snarl of a leopard told me what kind of a customer I was taking chances with. A leopard is a cat and has all the qualities that gave rise to the "nine lives" legend. To kill him you have got to kill him clear to the tip of his tail. Added to that, a leopard, unlike a lion, is vindictive. A wounded leopard will fight to a finish practically every time, no matter how many chances it has to escape. Once aroused, its determination is fixed on fight, and if a leopard ever gets hold, it claws and bites until its victim is in shreds. All this was in my mind, and I began looking about for the best way out of it, for I had no desire to try conclusions with a possibly wounded leopard when it was so late in the day that I could not see the sights of my rifle. My intention was to leave it until morning and if it had been wounded, there might then be a chance of finding it. I turned to the left to cross to the opposite bank of a deep, narrow *tug* and when there I found that I was on an island where the *tug* forked, and by going along a short distance to the point of the island I would be in position to see behind the bush where the leopard had stopped. But what I had started the leopard was intent on finishing. While peering about I detected the beast crossing the *tug* about twenty yards above me. I again began shooting, although I could not see to aim. However, I could see where the bullets struck as the sand spurted up beyond the leopard. The first two shots went above her, but the third scored. The leopard stopped and I thought she was killed. The pony boy broke into a song of triumph which was promptly cut short by

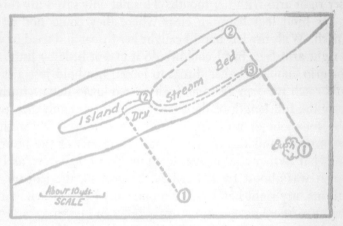

The dotted line indicates Mr. Akeley's movement during his encounter with the leopard. The dashes show the route taken by the leopard. At position (1), Mr. Akeley fired into the bush. Of the three shots fired at position (2), two went above the leopard and the third inflicted only a skin wound. The hand-to-hand combat took place at position (3).

another song such as only a thoroughly angry leopard is capable of making as it charges. For just a flash I was paralyzed with fear, then came power for action. I worked the bolt of my rifle and became conscious that the magazine was empty. At the same instant I realized that a solid point cartridge rested in the palm of my left hand, one that I had intended, as I came up to the dead hyena, to replace with a soft nose. If I could but escape the leopard until I could get the cartridge into the chamber!

As she came up the bank on one side of the point of the island, I dropped down the other side and ran about to the point from which she had charged, by which time the cartridge was in place, and I wheeled—to face the leopard in mid-air. The rifle was knocked flying and in its place was eighty pounds of frantic cat. Her intention was to sink her teeth into my throat and with this grip and her forepaws hang to me while with her hind claws she dug out my stomach, for this pleasant practice is the way of leopards. However, happily for me, she missed her aim. Instead of getting my throat, she was to one side. She struck me high in the chest and caught my upper right arm with her mouth. This not only saved my throat but left her hind legs hanging clear where they could not reach my stomach. With my left hand I caught her throat and tried to wrench my right arm free, but I couldn't do it except little by little. When I got grip enough on her throat to loosen her hold just a little she would catch my arm again an inch or two lower down. In this way I drew the full length of the arm through her mouth inch by inch. I was conscious of no pain, only of the sound of the crushing of tense muscles and the choking, snarling grunts of the beast. As I pushed her farther and farther down my arm I bent over, and finally when it was almost freed I fell to the ground, the leopard underneath me, my right hand in her mouth, my left hand clutching her throat, my knees on her lungs, my elbows in her armpits spreading her front legs apart so that the frantic clawing did nothing more than tear my shirt. Her body was twisted in an effort to get hold of the ground to turn herself, but the loose sand offered no hold. For a moment there was no change in our positions, and then for the first time I began to think and hope I had a chance to win this curious fight. Up to that time it had been simply a good fight in which I expected to lose, but now if I could keep my advantage perhaps the pony boy would come with a knife. I called, but to no effect. I still held her and continued to shove the hand down her throat so hard she could not close her mouth and with the other I gripped her throat in a strangle hold. Then I surged down on her with my knees. To my surprise I felt a rib go. I did it again. I felt her relax, a sort of letting go, although she was still struggling. At the same time I felt myself weakening similarly, and then it became a question as to which would give up first. Little by little her struggling ceased. My strength had outlasted hers.

After what seemed an interminable passage of time I let go and tried to stand, calling to the pony boy that it was finished. He now screwed up his courage sufficiently to approach. Then the leopard began to gasp, and I saw that she might recover; so I asked the boy for his knife. He had thrown it away in his fear, but quickly found it, and I at last made certain that the beast was dead. As I looked at her later, I came to the conclusion that what had saved me was the first shot I had fired when she went into the bush. It had hit her right hind foot. I think it was this broken foot which threw out the aim of her spring and made her get my arm instead of my throat. With the excitement of the battle still on me I did not realize how badly used up I was. I tried to shoulder the leopard to carry it to camp, but was very soon satisfied to confine my efforts to getting myself to camp.

When I came inside the *zareba,* my companions were at dinner before one of the tents. They had heard the shots and had speculated on the probabilities. They had decided that I was in a mix-up with a lion or with natives, but that I would have the enemy or the enemy would have me before they could get to me; so they had continued their dinner. The fatalistic spirit of the country had prevailed. When I came within their range of vision, however, my appearance was quite sufficient to arrest attention, for my clothes were all ripped, my arm was chewed into an unpleasant sight, and there was blood and dirt all over me. Moreover, my demands for all the antiseptics in camp gave them something to do, for nothing was keener in my mind than that the leopard had been feeding on the diseased hyena that I had shot in the morning. To the practical certainty of blood poisoning from any leopard bite not quickly treated, was added the certainty that this leopard's mouth was particularly foul with disease. While my companions were getting the surgical appliances ready, my boys were stripping me and dousing me with cold water. That done, the antiseptic was pumped into every one of the innumerable tooth wounds until my arm was so full of the liquid that an injection in one drove it out of another. During the process I nearly regretted that the leopard had not won. But it was applied so quickly and so thoroughly that it was a complete case.

Later in the evening they brought the leopard in and laid it beside my cot. Her right hind foot showed where the first shot had hit her. The only other bullet that struck her was the last before she charged and that had creased her just under the skin on the back of the neck, from the shock of which she had instantly recovered.

This encounter took place fairly soon after our arrival on my first trip to Africa. I have seen a lot of leopards since and occasionally killed one, but I have taken pains never to attempt it at such close quarters again. In spite of their fighting qualities I have never got to like or respect leopards very much. This is not because of my misadventure; I was hurt much worse by an elephant, but I have great respect and admiration for elephants. I think it is because the leopard has always seemed to me a sneaking kind of animal, and also perhaps because he will eat carrion even down to a dead and diseased hyena. A day or two before my experience with the leopard, someone else had shot a hyena near our camp and had left him over night. The next morning the dead hyena was lodged fifteen feet from the ground in the crotch of a tree at some distance from where he was killed. A leopard, very possibly my enemy, had dragged him along the ground and up the tree and placed him there for future use. While such activities cannot increase one's respect for the taste of leopards, they do give convincing evidence of the leopard's strength, for the hyena weighed at least as much as the leopard.

The leopard, like the elephant, is at home in every kind of country in East Africa—on the plains, among the rocky hills, among the bamboo, and in the forest all the way up to timber line on the equatorial mountains. Unlike the lion, the leopard is a solitary beast. Except for a mother with young, I have never seen as many as two leopards together. It is my belief that like the lion they do their hunting at night almost exclusively, and I am quite sure that this is their general habit despite the fact that the only unmistakable evidence of day hunting I ever saw myself in Africa was done by a leopard. I was out one day in some tall grass and came upon the body of a small antelope. As I came up, I heard an animal retreat and I thought I recognized a leopard's snarl. The antelope was still warm. It had evidently just been killed and the tracks around it were those of a leopard.

One of the leopard's chief sources of food supply consists of monkeys and baboons. I remember a certain camp we had near the bottom of a cliff. Out of this cliff grew a number of fig trees in which the baboons were accustomed to sleep, fairly well out of reach of the leopards. They were, however, not completely immune, and we could hear the leopards at the top of the cliff almost every night, and once in a while the remnants of a baboon testified to the success of the leopard's night prowling. Besides monkeys and baboons, leopards seem inordinately fond of dogs. A pack of dogs like Paul Rainey's can make short work of a leopard, but on the other hand a leopard can make short work of a single dog and seemingly takes great pleasure in doing so. One night in a shack in Nyiri, a settler sat talking to his neighbor, while his dog slept under the table. Suddenly, and quite unannounced, a leopard slipped in through the open door. Confusion reigned supreme for a moment and then the men found themselves on the table. The leopard was under the table killing the dog, and somehow in the excitement the door had been closed. One after the other the men fled out of the window, leaving the dog to his fate. A traveler had a similar but more painful experience with a leopard at the Dak Bungalow at Voi. Voi is a station on the Uganda Railroad where there was, and I suppose still is, a railroad hotel of a rather primitive kind known as the Dak Bungalow. One night a man was sleeping in one of the Bungalow rooms and, hearing a commotion outside, he started out to see what it was. As he passed through the open doorway on to the porch he was attacked by the leopard that had evidently come stalking his dogs.

Leopards are not particularly afraid of man. I never knew one to attack a man unprovoked except when caught at such close quarters as the case at Voi, but they prowl around man's habitation without compunction. I had a camp in Somaliland once where the tents were surrounded by two thorn thickets—the inner and outer *zareba*. A leopard came in one night, killed a sheep, dragged it under the very fly of my tent on the way out, jumped the *zareba,* and got away. Fifteen years ago, when Nairobi was a very small place, the daughter of one of the government officers went into her room one evening to dress. As she opened the door she heard a noise and looking she noticed the end of a leopard's tail sticking out from under the bed with the tip gently moving from side to side. With great presence of mind the young lady quietly went out and closed the door. Nairobi had many possibilities of thrills in those days. It was about the same time that a gentleman hurrying from town up to the Government House one evening met a lion in the middle of the street to the embarrassment of both parties.

．　．　．　．　．

There are some phrases in Tennyson's "Charge of the Light Brigade" that put me in mind of the rhinoceros, or "rhino," as everyone calls him in Africa.

"Theirs not to reason why, theirs but to do and die."

But it is stupidity, not duty, that keeps the rhino from reasoning. He is the stupidest old fellow in Africa. I know that many experienced hunters likewise consider him one of the most dangerous animals in Africa. I can't quite agree with this. Of course, if he runs over you, not only is it dangerous, but it is also likely to be fatal. It is also true that as soon as he smells a man he is likely to start charging around in a most terrifying manner, but the rhino is never cunning like the elephant, nor is his charge accurate like that of a lion, nor is the rhino vindictive like the buffalo or the leopard. Most men's estimates of the relative dangers of African animals are based upon their own experiences. The animals that have mauled them worst or scared them worst they hold most dangerous. I have been mauled by an elephant, chewed by a leopard, and scared half to death a dozen times by lions, so that I have the very firmest convictions about the dangers of these animals. On the other hand, I have twice been caught by rhinos in positions where an elephant, a lion, or a leopard would have had me in no time, and both times the rhinos left me unmolested.

When I first went to Africa I had the same experience as everyone else. Rhinos getting wind of me would charge me and to save myself I'd shoot. I suppose I had stood off twenty of these charges with my rifle before I discovered that if I did not shoot it would not necessarily be fatal. I discovered the fact, of course, quite by accident. I was going along the bank of the Tana River one day with my camera. My gun boys were some distance behind so as not to disturb any animal that might afford a picture. Suddenly I was set all a-quiver by the threshings and snortings of a rhino coming through the bushes in my direction. I very hastily took stock of the situation. There was nothing to climb. Between me and the thicket from which the rhino was coming were about twenty-five feet of open space. Behind me was a 30-foot drop to the crocodile-infested waters of the Tana. The only hope I saw was a bush overhanging the brink which looked as if it might or might not hold me if I swung out on it. I decided to try the bush and let the rhino land in the river, trusting to luck that I wouldn't join him there. The bushes were thrust aside and he came full tilt into the opening where he could see me. Everything was set for the final act. He suddenly stopped with a snort. His head drooped. His eyes almost closed. He looked as if he were going to sleep. The terrible beast had become absolutely ludicrous. While this was going on I felt a poke in my back. I reached behind and took my rifle from the gun boy who had come up with equal celerity and bravery. I drew a bead on the old fellow but I could not shoot. A stupider or more ludicrous-looking object I never saw. I began talking to him, but it did not rouse him from his lethargy. There he stood, half asleep and totally oblivious, while I, with the gun half aimed, talked to him about his ugly self. About this time my porters came into hearing on a path behind the rhino. He pricked up his ears and blundered off in that direction. I heard the loads dropping as the porters made for the trees. The rhino charged through the *safari* and off into the bush.

At another time, somewhat later, three of them charged me when I was sitting down and unarmed. I couldn't rise in time to get away or reach a gun, so I merely continued to sit. This time they didn't stop and doze, but they went by on both sides ten or fifteen feet away. Such a charge was much more pleasing to me and apparently quite as satisfactory to them as one in which they were successful in their attack. These experiences have led me to think that in his blundering charges the rhino has no clear objective, as a lion has, for instance. Even his blundering charge is dangerous, of course, if you are in the way, but I firmly believe that the rhino is too stupid to be either accurate in his objective, fixed in his purpose, or vindictive in his intentions.

This does not mean that a lot of people have not been killed by rhinos. They have; but I do believe that compared with other African animals the danger of the rhino is generally exaggerated. When he smells something, he comes toward the scent until he sees what it is. As he can't see very far, no man with a gun is likely to let him come within seeing distance without shooting. So the stupid old beast goes charging around hoping to see the source of what he smells and in addition to getting himself shot has made a reputation for savagery. In fact, he has blundered around and been shot so much that old rhinos with big horns are growing scarce.

I remember coming up over the top of a little rise one day and seeing across the plain an old rhino standing motionless in the shade of a solitary acacia about two hundred yards away.. The usual tick birds sat on his back. It was a typical rhino pose. As I stood looking for more entertainment, a second rhino came mouching along between me and number one. Number one evidently heard him. The birds flew off his back, he pricked up his ears, and broke into a charge toward number two. Number two reciprocated. Their direction was good and they had attained full speed. I longed for a camera to photograph the collision. But the camera would have done me no good. The collision did not happen. When about twenty feet from each other they stopped dead, snorted, and turned around, number one returning to doze under his tree and number two continuing the journey which had been interrupted. I suppose that rhinos have acquired the habit of charging whenever they smell anything because until the white man came along they could investigate in this peculiar manner with impunity. Everything but an elephant or another rhino would get out of the way of one of these investigating rushes, and of course an elephant or another rhino is big enough for even the rhino's poor eyes to see before he gets into trouble.

The coming of the white man with the rifle upset all this, but the rhino has learned less about protecting himself from man than the other animals. Man went even farther in breaking the rules of rhino existence. The railroad was an even worse affront than the rifle. The rhino furnished some of the comedy of the invasion of the game country by the Uganda Railway. In the early days of that road a friend of mine was on the train one day when a rhino charged it. The train was standing still out in the middle of the plain. An old rhino, either hearing it or smelling man, set out on the customary charge. The train didn't move and he didn't swerve. He hit the running board of one car at full speed. There was a terrific jolt. My friend rushed to the platform. As he reached it the rhino was getting up off his knees. He seemed a little groggy but he trotted off, conscious, perhaps, that railroad trains cannot be routed by the rhino's traditional method of attack.

MY FIGHT WITH A CATAMOUNT

By ALLEN FRENCH

Illustration by Frank Shields

MY guide, Alaric, and I had gone in after moose to the country beyond Mud Brook, in Maine. There its watershed between the east branch and the west is cut up into valleys, in one or another of which a herd of moose, in winter, generally takes up quarters. It was not yet yarding time, for the snow was still only about four inches deep, making it just right for the moose hunter who is at the same time a sportsman.

Our task was a slow one; we had to examine each valley for moose tracks, tramping up one side and down the other, or as we usually managed it, separating at the valley's mouth, each taking a side, meeting at the end and then, if unsuccessful, taking the quickest way back to camp.

And unsuccessful we were, since for three days we found no trail. But Alaric was not in the least discouraged.

"You can never tell about moose," he said; "they travel so. There were moose in this country before the snow, and there are moose within a day's walk of us now. It's just as I told you; we may have to spend five days in finding where they are."

It was on the second day that we found that, while after moose, we had been tracked by a catamount. The print of its paw was generously large.

"I've seen bigger," said Alaric, "but this feller's big enough. He's just waiting round, I guess, so as to get some of the meat we kill. We'll remember him," he said, looking up at me as he knelt on the snow, "so's to see that he doesn't spoil the hide or the head."

I accepted the theory, and thought little more of the matter for twenty-four hours.

At the end of the third day we found that the catamount had for a second time been following our trail—not only *our* trail, but also *mine*. He had followed me all day as I walked along the hillside, looking ahead and on both sides, but seldom behind. Alaric examined his tracks carefully for half a mile.

"He was in sight of you all the way," he said. "See here, where he stood for some time, just shifting about in one place, watching?" I saw—and thought.

After a while, it seemed to me, a catamount might get tired of waiting for us to kill his meat, and would start in to kill it for himself. Unquestionably the easiest game for him to get would be human.

For there were no deer in the region, and the caribou were all herded on Katahdin and Traveler. The previous severe winter had decimated the partridges, and big is the catamount that will tackle a moose. I mentioned the theory to Alaric.

"Um—yes, perhaps," he said, and eyed me dubiously.

Then I wished that I had not said anything. It is not well to let your guide think that you are afraid.

In the morning, when we had attained our valley's mouth, Alaric was about to keep with me, instead of leaving me as before; but that made our hunting much slower, for we could cover much less ground, and I sent him around the other way.

"All right," said he. "But keep a good lookout behind you now."

He disappeared in a cedar swamp, and I made my way along the slope of a hill. I watched indeed behind as well as in front, and in every fox's track I crossed I saw a catamount's, until finally I got used to the situation, and believed that the "Indian devil" had concluded to let me alone.

The day was fine. The sun shone bright, and the softening snow, dropping from the upper branches of the trees, kept up a constant movement in the woods. I took and held a good pace, and with my eyes searching the snow ahead and on all sides of me for signs of moose, walked for a full hour, seeing nothing living but the woodpeckers and the chickadees, hearing nothing but the rustle of the branches, as released of their loads they sprang back into place. Then, quite needlessly, I found insecure footing under the snow, and plunged suddenly at full length. My rifle whirled from my hand with force, and I heard it strike against the uncovered top of a sugar-loaf stone. I jumped up in fear and hastily examined it. The breech was shattered—my rifle was as useless as any stick.

Now I thought of the catamount, as, with the broken rifle in my hands, I looked about me in the woods, bright with sun and snow. I was not entirely helpless, for my revolver and knife were in my belt.

Yet a thirty-eight caliber revolver, even with a long cartridge and a long barrel, is not a sure defense against an animal as heavy as myself, which in facing me would present for a mark only a round head and a chest with muscles so thick and knotty that they would probably stop any revolver bullet. I doubted my ability to hit the eye.

Very likely I was no longer followed; and in any case, I might call Alaric. And yet he was too far away for a shout to reach him, and I dared not fire signal shots, for in order to travel light, I had left at camp all revolver cartridges but those in the chambers.

So I started at once for the bottom of the valley, hoping to strike Alaric's trail on the opposite slope, and intending to follow it until I caught him. My rifle I left where it was; it was useless and heavy. I cast many a glance behind me as, almost at a trot, I made my way down the long hillside.

I strode on rapidly, for I had certainly a mile to cover before I could strike Alaric's trail, much more before I could catch my nimble guide. I was cheerful and unalarmed until, pausing to look behind, I saw, a hundred yards away, a tawny animal, quickly slip behind a tree.

I hastily drew my revolver and knife; but no movement came from its hidden breast, and rather than stand and wait, I pursued my retreat. I moved more slowly, yet as fast as I could and still guard myself against another fall and watch for a rush from behind. I scanned the ground in front of me, and glanced back every second. For some time I saw no more of the catamount.

But when I did see him, I was startled at his nearness; he was within fifty yards. I hurried on as he slipped aside again; but looking again in a moment, I saw him now following boldly upon my trail. I stopped, but he stopped, too, and stood regarding me. He was too far away for me to fire yet, and as he made no movement to approach, I cautiously continued my retreat, always after a few steps stopping to face him.

He stopped as I stopped, yet each time I turned away he came quickly closer. I was already thinking of awaiting him without further movement, when the way was blocked by a ravine.

It was cut by the stream that drained the valley, and its steep sides were nearly fifteen feet in height. They even overhung in places, but this I did not then know. I was in no mind to trust myself in the deep gully, where the catamount might drop upon me before I could scramble out upon the other side.

I walked into an open space, and took my stand close to a birch that grew on the very edge of the bank. For thirty feet there was no good cover for the catamount; so, armed and determined, I waited.

The animal skirted the bushes about me, as if examining the ground, and to my disappointment, began to come upon me along the edge of the ravine. This gave him the best cover before his charge, and at the same time assured him that the momentum of his rush would not carry him tumbling into the gully. Always keeping too well concealed for a good mark, he crept up behind a fallen tree, on the near side of which a little bush grew, and flattened himself there, watching me, I felt sure, and waiting, in the hope that he might catch me off my guard.

I cannot describe how stealthy and noiseless and altogether perfect his maneuvering was. Although the trees that grew about were all small and the bushes bare, and although the white snow gave no background for concealment, he covered himself so perfectly at one time, and slipped in and out of sight so quickly at another, that although I stood with revolver pointed and cocked, I could find no opportunity for a shot.

As he circled for position he came ever nearer, and I could see at one time the round head, with its short, pointed ears; at another the long, sinuous muscular body; but they moved so rapidly that before I could shoot they were gone from sight.

All the time he made no sound but a little rustle. In his final concealment I saw nothing of him but his tail, that twitched and twitched and twitched.

Illustration by Frank Shields

I could not save myself.

At last I caught the glint of his pale green eye and fired. There came a snarl from behind the bush, and it was dashed to one side and the other, while round head and bared teeth and tawny body came crashing through. I pulled trigger again, and the report sounded muffled, and the smoke for an instant obscured the beast. All was white, when, like a breath, it passed, and I saw the rushing catamount not ten feet from me.

I had not time to fire or crouch, but with ready legs hurled myself to one side, and threw my left arm around the tree at the edge of the bank. With awful dread I felt the ground giving away beneath me.

I dropped my knife and caught the tree closer, when it, too, leaned to fall. It hung for a moment over the steep slope, and I could not save myself. The frost had not clamped the overhang to the solid ground. The last fall rains had cut under; the first spring thaw would have brought it down, had not my weight been thrown upon it.

With a twist the tree and I fell together. I clutched my revolver desperately, despite the sickening fear of the fall, and in my grasp it exploded in mid-air. Then I fell, and although my body struck easily in the snow-covered ravine, my right hand had been beaten against a sharp rock, and the birch was on me so I could not move.

My legs were on the bank, and underneath the snow beneath my shoulders I soon felt the ice, from which stones protruded. One snow-covered rock received and supported my head. I lay upon my right side, and my right hand, swinging in a curve, had struck with force upon another stone, and lay upon the ice, the only part of my body, except my head, which was free. My left arm was pressed close to my side by the birch, which lay across my body and legs.

The weight was not so great but that I could have lifted it, could I but have gained purchase. But I must at the same time lift my own body, for my hips were lower than my feet, my shoulders lower than my hips; and I could not gather ten pounds of force in that position.

My fall confused me somewhat, and I could not at first feel anything, either the pain in my hand or the danger I was in. I noticed only the fine, powdery snow which, cast up by the fall, settled upon me as I lay. Then I saw my arm, stretched out in front of me, with a bloody hand at the end of it, and I came fully to myself.

A pain shot from finger tip to shoulder as I closed my hand tighter upon the butt of the revolver. But I clenched my teeth and tried to rise—tried twice more before I gave it up as hopeless. Then I raised my hand and put it in a better position, propped upon a stone.

The movements hurt me terribly, but I thought of the catamount, which would surely not be satisfied with two bullets for its breakfast. I was scarcely ready when the head of the beast was thrust over the edge of the bank to look for me.

He saw, and gloated as a human enemy might have done. His savage snarl was full of intelligence, and his slow approach was deliberate torture. He stood for a moment in full view—then slipped and slid down to the surface of the ice, where, ten yards away, he stood and looked at me. I saw his magnificent build, his superb muscular development, as with his body in profile, his head turned toward me, he waited before approaching, playing with my helplessness; but I was not entirely helpless! With shaking hand I took aim; I could not use my thumb to cock the revolver, but drew hard at the trigger and the hammer rose and fell.

My turn for gloating had come now, for the catamount was crying with rage and pain. He fell writhing, striking with his forepaws at the snow, and raising his head to snap at nothing; but this did not last long. Slowly he dragged himself to a sitting posture, and I could understand his plight and estimate my own danger.

My first two bullets had but torn his flesh. My last had broken his back. He was paralyzed in his hind legs, as I have seen a deer, yet he had many minutes to live, perhaps hours, and was strong and angry enough to finish me. Painfully he started on that short journey to me. With his forepaws, his claws digging the snow, he began to drag himself toward me.

I could only wait. I had but one more shot, and wished to hold it till he should be close; but my torn hand was weak, and the bruised tendons had already begun to stiffen. Into that deep place, where bank and trees overhung, the sun did not come, and I felt the cold striking into my raw flesh. My weight upon my shoulder began to cut off the blood from my arm. I felt pricking in my flesh, my arm began to be numb, and I feared that I might not be able to shoot.

If he could but hurry! He dragged himself at a snail's pace. It would be so long before he came close that my hand would be useless. Yet as he crawled directly at me, the mark was a poor one. I saw with satisfaction that he would have to turn aside for one of the rocks in his path. When at last he reached it, and began to drag himself around it, he gave me my last chance.

I saw the space behind his shoulder, prayed my bullet might miss his ribs, summoned the last force to my almost dead hand, and fired.

A little drift of air blew the smoke aside so quickly that I could see the fire fly. He bit savagely at his side, but he crawled on without stopping. From my numb hand the revolver fell without noise in the snow—my fight was finished. He came on; he was only fifteen feet away from me, when he stopped and coughed. Would he sink, unable to move farther?

No; he started again! Although his legs dragged behind him, impeding, although he left a red trail on the snow, and each step forced a snarl from him, he came on. With glittering eyes and hoarse breath, he forced himself to cross the last space. Minutes passed before he was close enough to touch me.

Ah! Even as he turned toward my hand to seize it, even as I waited to see, rather than feel, the crunching of my senseless arm, his head drooped. He raised it once more, but his power was gone. He laid his head, once so powerful, upon my hand, rested his body against the stone, that stood high enough to support him and glared at me with his fierce, malignant eyes.

Then the fire changed in his eyes, clouded, flickered, glowed— went out. The last breath was expelled with a wheeze. He was dead.

Then my own powers sank, and I thought that I was dying, too. Somewhere in the midst of my faintness I had a sense as if I felt, rather than heard, hasty, heavy footsteps on the bank above me. As soon as I knew anything clearly, I knew that the tree had been pulled away, and that Alaric was bending over me. He had, with ears alert for any sound, and with footsteps kept as near to me as they might be with obedience to my order, come rushing to my aid at the sound of my first revolver shot. But the distance was so great that he did not arrive until my fight was over.

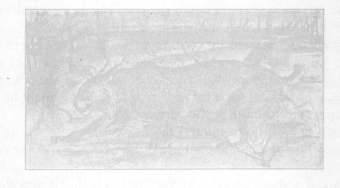

STICKEEN

By *JOHN MUIR*

Illustration by Frank Shields

I N the summer of 1880, I set out from Fort Wrangel in a canoe to continue the exploration of the icy region of southeastern Alaska, begun in the fall of 1879. After the necessary provisions, blankets, etc., had been collected and stowed away, and my Indian crew were in their places ready to start, while a crowd of their relatives and friends on the wharf were bidding them good-bye and good luck, my companion, the Rev. S. H. Young, for whom we were waiting, at last came aboard, followed by a little black dog, that immediately made himself at home by curling up in a hollow among the baggage. I like dogs, but this one seemed so small and worthless that I objected to his going, and asked the missionary why he was taking him.

"Such a little helpless creature will only be in the way," I said; "you had better pass him up to the Indian boys on the wharf, to be taken home to play with the children. This trip is not likely to be good for toy dogs. The poor silly thing will be in rain and snow for weeks or months, and will require care like a baby."

But his master assured me that he would be no trouble at all; that he was a perfect wonder of a dog, could endure cold and hunger like a bear, swim like a seal, and was wondrous wise and cunning, etc.; making out a list of virtues to show he might be the most interesting member of the party.

Nobody could hope to unravel the lines of his ancestry. In all the wonderfully mixed and varied dog tribe, I never saw any creature very much like him, though in some of his sly, soft, gliding motions and gestures he brought the fox to mind. He was short-legged and bunchy-bodied, and his hair, though smooth, was long and silky and slightly waved, so that when the wind was at his back it ruffled, making him look shaggy. At first sight his only noticeable feature was his fine tail, which was about as airy and shady as a squirrel's, and was carried curling forward almost to his nose. On closer inspection you might notice his thin sensitive ears, and sharp eyes with cunning tan spots above them. Mr. Young told me that when the little fellow was a pup about the size of a wood rat he was presented to his wife by an Irish prospector at Sitka, and that on his arrival at Fort Wrangel he was adopted with enthusiasm by the Stickeen Indians as a sort of a new good-luck totem, was named "Stickeen" for the tribe, and became a universal favorite; petted, protected, and admired wherever he went, and regarded as a mysterious fountain of wisdom.

On our trip he soon proved himself a queer character—odd, concealed, independent, keeping invincibly quiet, and doing many little puzzling things that piqued my curiosity. As we sailed week after week through the long intricate channels and inlets among the innumerable islands and mountains of the coast, he spent most of the dull days in sluggish ease, motionless, and apparently as unobserving as if in deep sleep. But I discovered that somehow he always knew what was going on. When the Indians were about to shoot at ducks or seals, or when anything along the shore was exciting our attention, he would rest his chin on the edge of the canoe and calmly look out like a dreamy-eyed tourist. And when he heard us talking about making a landing, he immediately roused himself to see what sort of a place we were coming to, and made ready to jump overboard and swim ashore as soon as the canoe neared the beach. Then, with a vigorous shake to get rid of the brine in his hair, he ran into the woods to hunt small game. But though always the first out of the canoe, he was always the last to get into it. When we were ready to start he could never be found, and refused to come to our call. We soon found out, however, that though we could not see him at such times, he saw us, and from the cover of the briers and huckleberry bushes in the fringe of the woods was watching the canoe with wary eye. For as soon as we were fairly off he came trotting down the beach, plunged into the surf, and swam after us, knowing well that we would cease rowing and take him in. When the contrary little vagabond came alongside, he was lifted by the neck, held at arm's length a moment to drip, and dropped aboard. We tried to cure him of this trick by compelling him to swim a long way, as if we had a mind to abandon him; but this did no good: the longer the swim the better he seemed to like it.

Though capable of great idleness, he never failed to be ready for all sorts of adventures and excursions. One pitch-dark, rainy night we landed about ten o'clock at the mouth of a salmon stream when the water was phosphorescent. The salmon were running, and the myriad fins of the onrushing multitude were churning all the stream into a silvery glow, wonderfully beautiful and impressive in the ebon darkness. To get a good view of the show I set out with one of the Indians and sailed up through the midst of it to the foot of a rapid about half a mile from camp, where the swift current dashing over rocks made the luminous glow most glorious. Happening to look back down the stream, while the Indian was catching a few of the struggling fish, I saw a long spreading fan of light like the tail of a comet, which we thought must be made by some big, strange animal that was pursuing us. On it came with its magnificent train, until we imagined we could see the the monster's head and eyes; but it was only Stickeen, who, finding I had left the camp, came swimming after me to see what was up.

When we camped early, the best hunter of the crew usually went to the woods for a deer, and Stickeen was sure to be at his heels, provided I had not gone out. For, strange to say, though I never carried a gun, he always followed me, forsaking the hunter and even his master to share my wanderings. The days that were too stormy for sailing I spent in the woods, or on the adjacent mountains, wherever my studies called me; and Stickeen always insisted on going with me, however wild the weather, gliding like a fox through dripping huckleberry bushes and thorny tangles of panax and rubus, scarce stirring their rain-laden leaves; wading and wallowing through snow, swimming icy streams, skipping over logs and rocks and the crevasses of glaciers with the patience and endurance of a determined mountaineer, never tiring or getting discouraged. Once he followed me over a glacier the surface of which was so crusty and rough that it cut his feet until every step was marked with blood; but he trotted on with Indian fortitude until I noticed his red track, and, taking pity on him, made him a set of moccasins out of a handkerchief. However great his troubles he never asked help or made any complaint, as if, like a philosopher, he had learned that without hard work and suffering there could be no pleasure worth having.

Yet none of us was able to make out what Stickeen was really good for. He seemed to meet danger and hardships without anything like reason, insisted on having his own way, never obeyed an order, and the hunter could never set him on anything, or make him fetch the birds he shot. His equanimity was so steady it seemed due to want of feeling; ordinary storms were pleasures to him, and as for mere rain, he flourished in it like a vegetable. No matter what advances you might make, scarce a glance or a tail wag would you get for your pains. But though he was apparently as cold as a glacier and about as impervious to fun, I tried hard to make his acquaintance, guessing there must be something worth-while hidden beneath so much courage, endurance, and love of wild-weathery adventure. No superannuated mastiff or bulldog grown old in office surpassed this fluffy midget in stoic dignity. He sometimes reminded me of a small, squat, unshakable, desert cactus. For he never displayed a single trace of the merry, tricksy, elfish fun of the terriers and collies that we all know, nor of their touching affection and devotion. Like children, most small dogs beg to be loved and allowed to love; but Stickeen seemed a very Diogenes, asking only to be let alone: a true child of the wilderness, holding the even tenor of his hidden life with the silence and serenity of nature. His strength of character lay in his eyes. They looked as old as the hills, and as young, and as wild. I never tired of looking into them: it was like looking into a landscape; but they were small and rather deep-set, and had no explaining lines around them to give out particulars. I was accustomed to look into the faces of plants and animals, and I watched the little sphinx more and more keenly as an interesting study. But there is no estimating the wit and wisdom concealed and latent in our lower fellow mortals until made manifest by profound experiences; for it is through suffering that dogs as well as saints are developed and made perfect.

After exploring the Sumdum and Tahkoo fiords and their glaciers, we sailed through Stephen's Passage into Lynn Canal and thence through Icy Strait into Cross Sound, searching for unexplored inlets leading toward the great fountain ice fields of the Fairweather Range. Here, while the tide was in our favor, we were accompanied by a fleet of icebergs drifting out to the ocean from Glacier Bay. Slowly we paddled around Vancouver's Point, Wimbledon, our frail canoe tossed like a feather on the massive heaving swells coming in past Cape Spenser. For miles the Sound is bounded by precipitous mural cliffs, which, lashed with wave spray and their heads hidden in clouds, looked terrribly threatening and stern. Had our canoe been crushed or upset we could have made no landing here, for the cliffs, as high as those of Yosemite, sink sheer into deep water. Eagerly we scanned the wall on the north side for the first sign of an opening fiord or harbor, all of us anxious except Stickeen, who dozed in peace or gazed dreamily at the tremendous precipices when he heard us talking about them. At length we made the joyful discovery of the mouth of the inlet now called "Taylor Bay," and about five o'clock reached the head of it and encamped in a spruce grove near the front of a large glacier.

While camp was being made, Joe the hunter climbed the mountain wall on the east side of the fiord in pursuit of wild goats, while Mr. Young and I went to the glacier. We found that it is separated from the waters of the inlet by a tide-washed moraine, and extends, an abrupt barrier, all the way across from wall to wall of the inlet, a distance of about three miles. But our most interesting discovery was that it had recently advanced, though again slightly receding. A portion of the terminal moraine had been plowed up and shoved forward, uprooting and overwhelming the woods on the east side. Many of the trees were down and buried, or nearly so, others were leaning away from the ice cliffs, ready to fall, and some stood erect, with the bottom of the ice plow still beneath their roots and its lofty crystal spires towering high above their tops. The spectacle presented by these century-old trees standing close beside a spiry wall of ice, with their branches almost touching it, was most novel and striking. And when I climbed around the front, and a little way up the west side of the glacier, I found that it had swelled and increased in height and width in accordance with its advance, and carried away the outer ranks of trees on its bank.

On our way back to camp after these first observations, I planned a far-and-wide excursion for the morrow. I awoke early, called not only by the glacier, which had been on my mind all night, but by a grand floodstorm. The wind was blowing a gale from the north and the rain was flying with the clouds in a wide, passionate horizontal flood, as if it were all passing over the country instead of falling on it. The main perennial streams were booming high above their banks, and hundreds of new ones, roaring like the sea, almost covered the lofty gray walls of the inlet with white cascades and falls. I had intended making a cup of coffee and getting something like a breakfast before starting, but when I heard the storm and looked out I made haste to join it; for many of Nature's finest lessons are to be found in her storms, and if careful to keep in right relations with them, we may safely go abroad with them, rejoicing in the grandeur and beauty of their works and ways, and chanting with the old Norsemen, "The blast of the tempest aids our oars, the hurricane is our servant and drives us whither we wish to go." So omitting breakfast, I put a piece of bread in my pocket and hurried away.

Mr. Young and the Indians were asleep, and so, I hoped, was Stickeen; but I had not gone a dozen rods before he left his bed in the tent and came boring through the blast after me. That a man should welcome storms for their exhilarating music and motion, and go forth to see God making landscapes, is reasonable enough; but what fascination could there be in such tremendous weather for a dog? Surely nothing akin to human enthusiasm for scenery or geology. Anyhow, on he came, breakfastless, through the choking blast. I stopped and did my best to turn him back. "Now don't," I said, shouting to make myself heard in the storm, "now don't, Stickeen. What has got into your queer noodle now? You must be daft. This wild day has nothing for you. There is no game abroad, nothing but weather. Go back to camp and keep warm, get a good breakfast with your master, and be sensible for once. I can't carry you all day or feed you, and this storm will kill you."

But Nature, it seems, was at the bottom of the affair, and she gains her ends with dogs as well as with men, making us do as she likes, shoving and pulling us along her ways, however rough, all but killing us at times in getting her lessons driven hard home. After I had stopped again and again, shouting good warning advice, I saw that he was not to be shaken off; as well might the earth try to shake off the moon. I had once led his master into trouble, when he fell on one of the topmost jags of a mountain and dislocated his arm; now the turn of his humble companion was coming. The pitiful little wanderer just stood there in the wind, drenched and blinking, saying doggedly, "Where thou goest, I will go." So at last I told him to come on if he must, and gave him a piece of the bread I had in my pocket; then we struggled on together, and thus began the most memorable of all my wild days.

The level flood, driving in our faces, thrashed and washed us wildly until we got into the shelter of a grove on the east side of the glacier near the front, where we stopped awhile for breath and to listen and look out. The exploration of the glacier was my main object, but the wind was too high to allow excursions over its open surface, where one might be dangerously shoved while balancing for a jump on the brink of a crevasse. In the meantime the storm was a fine study. Here the end of the glacier, descending an abrupt swell of resisting rock about five hundred feet high, leans forward and falls in ice cascades. And as the storm came down the glacier from the north, Stickeen and I were beneath the main current of the blast, while favorably located to see and hear it. What a psalm the storm was singing, and how fresh the smell of the washed earth and leaves, and how sweet the still small voices of the storm! Detached wafts and swirls were coming through the woods, with music from the leaves and branches and furrowed boles, and even from the splintered rocks and ice crags overhead, many of the tones soft and low and flutelike, as if each leaf and tree, crag and spire were a tuned reed. A broad torrent, draining the side of the glacier, now swollen by scores of new streams from the mountains, was rolling boulders along its rocky channel, with thudding, bumping, muffled sounds, rushing toward the bay with tremendous energy, as if in haste to get out of the mountains; the waters above and beneath calling to each other, and all to the ocean, their home.

Looking southward from our shelter, we had this great torrent and the forested mountain wall above it on our left, the spiry ice crags on our right, and smooth gray gloom ahead. I tried to draw the marvelous scene in my notebook, but the rain blurred the page in spite of all my pains to shelter it, and the sketch was almost worthless. When the wind began to abate, I traced the east side of the glacier. All the trees standing on the edge of the woods were barked and bruised, showing high-ice mark in a very telling way, while tens of thousands of those that had stood for centuries on the bank of the glacier farther out lay crushed and being crushed. In many places, I could see down fifty feet or so beneath the margin of the glacier mill, where trunks from one to two feet in diameter were being ground to pulp against outstanding rock ribs and bosses of the bank.

About three miles above the front of the glacier I climbed to the surface of it by means of ax steps made easy for Stickeen. As far as eye could reach, the level, or nearly level, glacier stretched away indefinitely beneath the gray sky, a seemingly boundless prairie of ice. The rain continued, and grew colder, which I did not mind, but a dim snowy look in the drooping clouds made me hesitate about venturing far from land. No trace of the west shore was visible, and in case the clouds should settle and give snow, or the wind again become violent, I feared getting caught in a tangle of crevasses. Snow crystals, the flowers of the mountain clouds, are frail, beautiful things, but terrible when flying on stormwinds in darkening, benumbing swarms or when welded together into glaciers full of deadly crevasses. Watching the weather, I sauntered about on the crystal sea. For a mile or two out I found the ice remarkably safe. The marginal crevasses were mostly narrow, while the few wider ones were easily avoided by passing around them; and the clouds began to open here and there.

Thus encouraged, I at last pushed out for the other side; for Nature can make us do anything she likes. At first we made rapid progress, and the sky was not very threatening, while I took bearings occasionally with a pocket compass to enable me to find my way back more surely in case the storm should become blinding; but the structure lines of the glacier were my main guide. Toward the west side we came to a closely crevassed section in which we had to make long, narrow tacks and doublings, tracing the edges of tremendous transverse and longitudinal crevasses, many of which were from twenty to thirty feet wide, and perhaps a thousand feet deep— beautiful and awful. In working a way through them I was severely cautious, but Stickeen came on as unhesitatingly as the flying clouds. The widest crevasse that I could jump he would leap without so much as halting to take a look at it. The weather was now making quick changes, scattering bits of dazzling brightness through the wintry gloom; at rare intervals, when the sun broke forth wholly free, the glacier was seen from shore to shore with a bright array of encompassing mountains partly revealed, wearing the clouds as garments, while the prairie bloomed and sparkled with irised light from myriads of washed crystals. Then suddenly all the glorious show would be darkened and blotted out.

Stickeen seemed to care for none of these things, bright or dark, nor for the crevasses, wells, moulins, or swift flashing streams into which he might fall. The little adventurer was only about two years old, yet nothing seemed novel to him, nothing daunted him. He showed neither caution nor curiosity, wonder nor fear, but bravely trotted on as if glaciers were playgrounds. His stout, muffled body seemed all one skipping muscle, and it was truly wonderful to see how swiftly and, to all appearance, heedlessly he flashed across nerve-trying chasms six or eight feet wide. His courage was so unwavering that it seemed to be due to dullness of perception, as if he were only blindly bold; and I kept warning him to be careful. For we had been close companions on so many wilderness trips that I had formed the habit of talking to him as if he were a boy and understood every word.

We gained the west shore in about three hours; the width of the glacier here being about seven miles. Then I pushed northward in order to see as far as possible into the fountains of the Fairweather Mountains, in case the clouds should rise. The walking was easy along the margin of the forest, which, of course, like that on the other side, had been invaded and crushed by the swollen, overflowing glacier. In an hour or so, after passing a massive headland, we came suddenly on a branch of the glacier, which, in the form of a magnificent ice cascade two miles wide, was pouring over the rim of the main basin in a westerly direction, its surface broken into wave-shaped blades and shattered blocks, suggesting the wildest updashing, heaving, plunging motion of a great river cataract. Tracing it down three or four miles, I found that it discharged into a lake, filling it with icebergs.

I would gladly have followed the lake outlet to tidewater, but the day was already far spent, and the threatening sky called for haste on the return trip to get off the ice before dark. I decided therefore to go no farther and, after taking a general view of the wonderful region, turned back, hoping to see it again under more favorable auspices. We made good speed up the cañon of the great ice torrent, and out on the main glacier until we had left the west shore about two miles behind us. Here we got into a difficult network of crevasses, the gathering clouds began to drop misty fringes, and soon the dreaded snow came flying thick and fast. I now began to feel anxious about finding a way in the blurring storm. Stickeen showed no trace of fear. He was still the same silent, able little hero. I noticed, however, that after the storm darkness came on he kept close up behind me. The snow urged us to make still greater haste, but at the same time hid our way. I pushed on as best I could, jumping innumerable crevasses, and, for every hundred rods or so of direct advance, traveling a mile in doubling up and down in the turmoil of chasms and dislocated ice-blocks. After an hour or two of this work we came to a series of longitudinal crevasses of appalling width, and almost straight and regular in trend, like immense furrows. These I traced with firm nerve, excited and strengthened by the danger, making wide jumps, poising cautiously on their dizzy edges, after cutting hollows for my feet, before making the spring, to avoid possible slipping or any uncertainty on the farther sides, where only one trial is granted—exercise at once frightful and inspiring. Stickeen followed seemingly without effort.

Many a mile we thus traveled, mostly up and down, making but little real headway in crossing, running instead of walking most of the time as the danger of being compelled to spend the night on the glacier became threatening. Stickeen seemed able for anything. Doubtless we could have weathered the storm for one night, dancing on a flat spot to keep from freezing, and I faced the threat without feeling anything like despair; but we were hungry and wet, and the wind from the mountains was still thick with snow and bitterly cold, so of course that night would have seemed a very long one. I could not see far enough through the blurring snow to judge in which general direction the least dangerous route lay, while the few dim, momentary glimpses I caught of mountains through rifts in the flying clouds were far from encouraging either as weather signs or as guides. I had simply to grope my way from crevasse to crevasse, holding a general direction by the ice structure, which was not to be seen everywhere, and partly by the wind. Again and again I was put to my mettle, but Stickeen followed easily, his nerve apparently growing more unflinching as the danger increased. So it always is with mountaineers when hard beset. Running hard and jumping, holding every minute of the remaining daylight, poor as it was, precious, we doggedly persevered and tried to hope that every difficult crevasse we overcame would prove to be the last of its kind. But on the contrary, as we advanced they became more deadly trying.

At length our way was barred by a very wide and straight crevasse, which I traced rapidly northward a mile or so without finding a crossing or hope of one; then down the glacier about as far, to where it united with another uncrossable crevasse. In all this distance of perhaps two miles there was only one place where I could possibly jump it, but the width of this jump was the utmost I dared attempt, while the danger of slipping on the farther side was so great that I was loath to try it. Furthermore, the side I was on was about a foot higher than the other, and even with this advantage the crevasse seemed dangerously wide. One is liable to underestimate the width of crevasses where the magnitudes in general are great. I therefore stared at this one mighty keenly, estimating its width and the shape of the edge on the farther side, until I thought that I could jump it if necessary, but that in case I should be compelled to jump back from the lower side I might fail. Now, a cautious mountaineer seldom takes a step on unknown ground, which seems at all dangerous, that he cannot retrace in case he should be stopped by unseen obstacles ahead. This is the rule of mountaineers who live long, and, though in haste, I compelled myself to sit down and calmly deliberate before I broke it.

Retracing my devious path in imagination as if it were drawn on a chart, I saw that I was recrossing the glacier a mile or two farther upstream than the course pursued in the morning, and that I was now entangled in a section I had not before seen. Should I risk this dangerous jump, or try to regain the woods on the west shore, make a fire, and have only hunger to endure while waiting for a new day? I had already crossed so broad a stretch of dangerous ice that I saw it would be difficult to get back to the woods through the storm before dark, and the attempt would most likely result in a dismal night-dance on the glacier; while just beyond the present barrier the surface seemed more promising, and the east shore was now perhaps about as near as the west. I was therefore eager to go on. But this wide jump was a dreadful obstacle.

At length, because of the dangers already behind me, I determined to venture against those that might be ahead, jumped and landed well, but with so little to spare that I more than ever dreaded being compelled to take that jump back from the lower side. Stickeen followed, making nothing of it, and we ran eagerly forward, hoping we were leaving all our troubles behind. But within the distance of a few hundred yards we were stopped by the widest crevasse yet encountered. Of course I made haste to explore it; hoping all might yet be remedied by finding a bridge or a way around either end. About three-fourths of a mile upstream I found that it united with the one we had just crossed, as I feared it would. Then, tracing it down, I found it joined the same crevasse at the lower end also, maintaining throughout its whole course a width of forty or fifty feet. Thus to my dismay I discovered that we were on a narrow island about two miles long, with two barely possible ways of escape; one back by the way we came, the other ahead by an almost inaccessible sliver bridge that crossed the great crevasse from near the middle of it!

After this nerve-trying discovery I ran back to the sliver bridge and cautiously examined it. Crevasses, caused by strains from variations in the rates of motion of different parts of the glacier and convexities in the channel, are mere cracks when they first open, so narrow as hardly to admit the blade of a pocket knife, and gradually widen according to the extent of the strain and the depth of the glacier. Now some of these cracks are interrupted, like the cracks in wood; and in opening, the strip of ice between overlapping ends is dragged out, and may maintain a continuous connection between the sides, just as the two sides of a slivered crack in wood that is being split are connected. Some crevasses remain open for months or even years, and by the melting of their sides continue to increase in width long after the opening strain has ceased; while the sliver bridges, level on top at first and perfectly safe, are at length melted to thin, vertical, knife-edged blades, the upper portion being most exposed to the weather; and since the exposure is greatest in the middle, they at length curve downward like the cables of suspension bridges. This one was evidently very old, for it had been weathered and wasted until it was the most dangerous and inaccessible that ever lay in my way. The width of the crevasse here was about fifty feet, and the sliver crossing diagonally was about seventy feet long; its thin knife-edge near the middle was depressed twenty-five or thirty feet below the level of the glacier, and the upcurving ends were attached to the sides eight or ten feet below the brink. Getting down the nearly vertical wall to the end of the sliver and up the other side were the main difficulties, and they seemed all but insurmountable. Of the many perils encountered in my years of wandering on mountains and glaciers, none seemed so plain and stern and merciless as this. And it was presented when we were wet to the skin and hungry, the sky dark with pick driving snow, and the night near. But we were forced to face it. It was a tremendous necessity.

Beginning, not immediately above the sunken end of the bridge, but a little to one side, I cut a deep hollow on the brink for my knees to rest in. Then, leaning over, with my short-handled ax I cut a step sixteen or eighteen inches below, which on account of the sheerness of the wall was necessarily shallow. That step, however, was well made; its floor sloped slightly inward and formed a good hold for my heels. Then, slipping cautiously upon it, and crouching as low as possible, with my left side toward the wall, I steadied myself against the wind with my left hand in a slight notch, while with the right I cut other similar steps and notches in succession, guarding against losing balance by glinting of the ax, or by wind gusts, for life and death were in every stroke and in the niceness of finish of every foothold.

After the end of the bridge was reached I chipped it down until I had made a level platform six or eight inches wide, and it was a trying thing to poise on this little slippery platform while bending over to get safely astride of the sliver. Crossing was then comparatively easy, by chipping off the sharp edge with short, careful strokes, and hitching forward an inch or two at a time, keeping my balance with my knees pressed against the sides. The tremendous abyss on either hand I studiously ignored. To me the edge of that blue sliver was then all the world. But the most trying part of the adventure, after working my way across inch by inch and chipping another small platform, was to rise from the safe position astride and to cut a stepladder in the nearly vertical face of the wall—chipping, climbing, holding on with feet and fingers in mere notches. At such times one's whole body is eye, and common skill and fortitude are replaced by power beyond our call or knowledge. Never before had I been so long under deadly strain. How I got up that cliff I never could tell. The thing seemed to have been done by somebody else. I never have held death in contempt, though in the course of my explorations I have oftentimes felt that to meet one's fate on a noble mountain, or in the heart of a glacier, would be blessed as compared with death from disease, or from some shabby lowland accident. But the best death, quick and crystal-pure, set so glaringly open before us, is hard enough to face, even though we feel gratefully sure that we have already had happiness enough for a dozen lives.

But poor Stickeen, the wee, hairy, sleekit beastie, think of him! When I had decided to dare the bridge, and while I was on my

knees chipping a hollow on the rounded brow above it, he came behind me, pushed his head past my shoulder, looked down and
across, scanned the sliver and its approaches with his mysterious
eyes, then looked me in the face with a startled air of surprise and
concern, and began to mutter and whine; saying as plainly as if
speaking with words, "Surely, you are not going into that awful
place." This was the first time I had seen him gaze deliberately into
a crevasse, or into my face with an eager, speaking, troubled look.
That he should have recognized and appreciated the danger at the
first glance showed wonderful sagacity. Never before had the daring
midget seemed to know that ice was slippery or that there was any
such thing as danger anywhere. His looks and tones of voice when
he began to complain and speak his fears were so human that I unconsciously talked to him in sympathy as I would to a frightened
boy, and in trying to calm his fears perhaps in some measure moder-
ated my own. "Hush your fears, my boy," I said, "we will get across
safe, though it is not going to be easy. No right way is easy in this
rough world. We must risk our lives to save them. At the worst
we can only slip, and then how grand a grave we will have, and by
and by our nice bones will do good in the terminal moraine."

But my sermon was far from reassuring him: he began to cry,
and after taking another piercing look at the tremendous gulf, ran
away in desperate excitement, seeking some other crossing. By the
time he got back, baffled of course, I had made a step or two. I dared
not look back, but he made himself heard; and when he saw that I
was certainly bent on crossing, he cried aloud in despair. The danger
was enough to daunt anybody, but it seems wonderful that he
should have been able to weigh and appreciate it so justly. No mountaineer could have seen it more quickly or judged it more wisely,
discriminating between real and apparent peril.

When I gained the other side, he screamed louder than ever, and
after running back and forth in vain search for a way of escape, he
would return to the brink of the crevasse above the bridge, moaning
and wailing as if in the bitterness of death. Could this be the silent,
philosophic Stickeen? I shouted encouragement, telling him the
bridge was not so bad as it looked, that I had left it flat and safe for

his feet, and he could walk it easily. But he was afraid to try. Strange so small an animal should be capable of such big, wise fears. I called again and again in a reassuring tone to come on and fear nothing; that he could come if he would only try. He would hush for a moment, look down again at the bridge, and shout his unshakable conviction that he could never, never come that way; then lie back in despair, as if howling, "O-o-oh! what a place! No-o-o, I can never go-o-o down there!" His natural composure and courage had vanished utterly in a tumultuous storm of fear. Had the danger been less, his distress would have seemed ridiculous. But in this dismal, merciless abyss lay the shadow of death, and his heartrending cries might well have called Heaven to his help. Perhaps they did. So hidden before, he was now transparent, and one could see the workings of his heart and mind like the movements of a clock out of its case. His voice and gestures, hopes and fears, were so perfectly human that none could mistake them; while he seemed to understand every word of mine. I was troubled at the thought of having to leave him out all night, and of the danger of not finding him in the morning. It seemed impossible to get him to venture. To compel him to try through fear of being abandoned, I started off as if leaving him to his fate, and disappeared back of a hummock; but this did no good; he only lay down and moaned in utter hopeless misery. So, after hiding a few minutes, I went back to the brink of the crevasse and in a severe tone of voice shouted across to him that now I must certainly leave him, I could wait no longer, and that, if he would not come, all I could promise was that I would return to seek him next day. I warned him that if he went back to the woods the wolves would kill him, and finished by urging him once more by words and gestures to come on, come on.

He knew very well what I meant, and at last, with the courage of despair, hushed and breathless, he crouched down on the brink in the hollow I had made for my knees, pressed his body against the ice as if trying to get the advantage of the friction of every hair, gazed into the first step, put his little feet together and slid them slowly, slowly over the edge and down into it, bunching all four in it and almost standing on his head. Then, without lifting his feet, as well as I could see through the snow, he slowly worked them over the edge of the step and down into the next and the next in succession in the same way, and gained the end of the bridge. Then, lifting his feet with the regularity and slowness of the vibrations of a seconds pendulum, as if counting and measuring *one-two-three,* holding himself steady against the gusty wind, and giving separate attention to each little step, he gained the foot of the cliff, while I was on my knees leaning over to give him a lift should he succeed in getting within reach of my arm. Here he halted in dead silence, and it was here I feared he might fail, for dogs are poor climbers. I had no cord. If I had had one, I would have dropped a noose over his head and hauled him up. But while I was thinking whether an available cord might be made out of clothing, he was looking keenly into the series of notched steps and fingerholds I had made, as if counting them, and fixing the position of each one of them in his mind. Then suddenly up he came in a springy rush, hooking his paws into the steps and notches so quickly that I could not see how it was done, and whizzed past my head, safe at last!

And now came a scene! "Well done, well done, little boy! Brave boy!" I cried, trying to catch and caress him; but he would not be caught. Never before or since have I seen anything like so passionate a revulsion from the depths of despair to exultant, triumphant, uncontrollable joy. He flashed and darted hither and thither as if fairly demented, screaming and shouting, swirling round and round in giddy loops and circles like a leaf in a whirlwind, lying down, and rolling over and over, sidewise and heels over head, and pouring forth a tumultuous flood of hysterical cries and sobs and gasping mutterings. When I ran up to him to shake him, fearing he might die of joy, he flashed off two or three hundred yards, his feet in a mist of motion; then, turning suddenly, came back in a wild rush and launched himself at my face, almost knocking me down, all the time screeching and screaming and shouting as if saying, "Saved! saved! saved!" Then away again, dropping suddenly at times with his feet in the air, trembling and fairly sobbing. Such passionate emotion was enough to kill him. Moses' stately song of triumph after escaping the Egyptians and the Red Sea was nothing to it. Who could have guessed the capacity of the dull, enduring little fellow for all that most stirs this mortal frame? Nobody could have helped crying with him!

But there is nothing like work for toning down excessive fear or joy. So I ran ahead, calling him in as gruff a voice as I could command to come on and stop his nonsense, for we had far to go and it would soon be dark. Neither of us feared another trial like this. Heaven would surely count one enough for a lifetime. The ice ahead was gashed by thousands of crevasses, but they were common ones. The joy of deliverance burned in us like fire, and we ran without fatigue, every muscle with immense rebound glorying in its strength. Stickeen flew across everything in his way, and not till dark did he settle into his normal foxlike trot. At last the cloudy mountains came in sight, and we soon felt the solid rock beneath our feet, and were safe. Then came weakness. Danger had vanished, and so had our strength. We tottered down the lateral moraine in the dark, over boulders and tree trunks, through the bushes and devil-club thickets of the grove where we had sheltered ourselves in the morning, and across the level mud slope of the terminal moraine. We reached camp about ten o'clock, and found a big fire and a big supper. A party of Hoona Indians had visited Mr. Young, bringing a gift of porpoise meat and wild strawberries, and Hunter Joe had brought in a wild goat. But we lay down, too tired to eat much, and soon fell into a troubled sleep. The man who said, "The harder the toil, the sweeter the rest," never was profoundly tired. Stickeen kept springing up and muttering in his sleep, no doubt dreaming that he was still on the brink of the crevasse; and so did I, that night and many others long afterwards, when I was overtired.

Thereafter Stickeen was a changed dog. During the rest of the trip, instead of holding aloof, he always lay by my side, tried to keep me constantly in sight, and would hardly accept a morsel of food, however tempting, from any hand but mine. At night, when all was quiet about the campfire, he would come to me and rest his head on my knee with a look of devotion as if I were his god. And often as he caught my eye he seemed to be trying to say, "Wasn't that an awful time we had together on the glacier?"

Nothing in after years has dimmed that Alaska storm day. As I write, it all comes rushing and roaring to mind as if I were again in the heart of it. Again I see the gray flying clouds with their rain floods and snow, the ice cliffs towering above the shrinking forest, the majestic ice cascade, the vast glacier outspread before its white mountain fountains, and in the heart of it the tremendous crevasse—emblem of the valley of the shadow of death—low clouds trailing over it, the snow falling into it; and on its brink I see little Stickeen, and I hear his cries for help and his shouts of joy. I have known many dogs, and many a story I could tell of their wisdom and devotion; but to none do I owe so much as to Stickeen. At first the least promising and least known of my dog friends, he suddenly became the best known of them all. Our storm battle for life brought him to light, and through him as through a window I have ever since been looking with deeper sympathy into all my fellow mortals.

None of Stickeen's friends knows what finally became of him. After my work for the season was done I departed for California, and I never saw the dear little fellow again. In reply to anxious inquiries, his master wrote me that in the summer of 1883 he was stolen by a tourist at Fort Wrangel and taken away on a steamer. His fate is wrapped in mystery. Doubtless he has left this world—crossed the last crevasse—and gone to another. But he will not be forgotten. To me Stickeen is immortal.

Illustration by Frank Shields

Stories About Animals

THE CAT AND THE CAPTAIN

By ELIZABETH COATSWORTH

I

THE CAT WAS FURIOUS

THE Cat was furious. Not a door or window of the house was open. He went to the front door and mewed. He went to the side door (which was almost never used) and mewed. Then he went to the back door and there he mewed loudest and longest.

He could hear Susannah walking around the kitchen, singing to herself. She was always humming to herself like a bumblebee. When something happened to make her excited, she made up songs, mostly complaining ones telling how she felt. The Cat knew that Susannah heard him there at her door with his feet in the damp and was glad to keep him out.

If only the Captain were home, he would call, "Susannah! Ship ahoy! Lower the gangway to take on passengers!" But the Captain had taken his cane and gone to see his married daughter. Goodness knows when he'd be back.

The Cat picked his way across the grass, shaking the wet off his feet, for it had been raining. Poor Cat, he hated it! He was thinking of the cushioned chair indoors by the fire, where he loved to sit watching the flames with sleepy eyes and purring to himself. But he didn't feel like purring now. He climbed up the lilac bush. He knew just where to put each small paw, just how much spring to give, and how deep to stick his claws in the bark. He did everything beautifully. But the leaves shook raindrops down his neck and made him bristle his whiskers.

He climbed a low branch and looked in at the kitchen window. There was Susannah rolling dough for the biscuits the Captain liked. She was little and old and black, and she wore on her head

179

a big red bandanna. When she saw the Cat, she began to laugh
and point her finger at him. He could hear her singing:

> "Ole Mister Cat, he clumb up a tree.
> What yo' want, Cat, starin' at me?
> Yo' won't git hurted by a li'l' nice rain,
> So when yo' gets tired, jus' yo' climb down again!"

The Cat saw it was no use. Susannah did not like him, and he
knew very well she had several good reasons for it. He mewed one
last mew, just in case she should change her mind. Then he gave
her a look, went down the lilac, head first. He knew now he'd
have to wait until the Captain came back, but he wouldn't forget
Susannah's meanness—not he! He picked his way through the
grass, lifting his feet high and walking around the puddles, and
went in under the veranda by the little opening that only he knew
about. There he sat, out of anyone's sight, switching his big black
tail.

II

A GOOD CAT AT HEART

About five o'clock the Captain came home. He was not a big
man, but he carried a very big umbrella. He had wrinkles around
his eyes from looking long distances, and he walked as though the
street were going up and down under him, because he had spent so
much of his time on the decks of boats. Everybody loved the Captain
the moment they saw him, because he was so kind and so jolly.

The Cat loved him, too, but took a naughty pride in not showing
it, except sometimes when they were alone together. Then he would
jump on the Captain's knee and rub his head against the Captain's
chin, and go to sleep curled in the hollow of his arm. And how
careful the Captain would be not to move! They understood each
other very well, and the Captain used to say that he had never
shipped with a better shipmate than his black cat. But today the Cat
was in a bad humor, as he walked out from under the veranda.

"Well, well, there you are, hey?" said the Captain, and he opened the door and waited for the Cat to come in. But the Cat only looked at him. He was being provoking.

"Don't you want to come in?" asked the Captain.

The cat still looked at him.

"All right," said the Captain, "if you won't, you won't, my lad," and he started to shut the door.

But before he could get it shut the Cat came in.

It was a curious room, though neither the Cat nor the Captain thought so. It was both living room and dining room. There was a big fireplace of red brick with a Dutch oven at one side, and there were hooked rugs on the floor, some of them with designs of harbors or lighthouses on them. On the walls hung compasses and sea charts; and round glass balls (used to float fishing nets) shone in the windows like big blue and white bubbles. A model of the Captain's first ship, the *Foam Flower,* spread its sails high on the mantelpiece beyond reach of the Cat. There was a little boat in a bottle—it was a mystery how the masts and rigging ever got through the neck; and there were two pink conch shells from the West Indies.

In the window hung Jericho, the parrot. Poor Jericho had died a long time ago, before the Cat was so much as born. The Captain had been fond of Jericho, and couldn't bear to think of looking up and not seeing him in his place. So Jericho was stuffed and there he still hung in his cage. Once a week Susannah opened the door of the cage and took Jericho out and carefully dusted him.

And Susannah kept all the brass in the room shining brightly— the Captain was very particular about that. But neither the Captain nor Susannah noticed that sometimes a few crumbs were left under the table. Only the Cat knew it. When the Captain sat down and lit his pipe, the Cat sat down, too, but instead of jumping into his chair opposite the Captain, he sat on the floor and watched the crumbs. It was very still except for the tick-tock-ticking of the cuckoo clock, and the steps of Susannah getting supper ready in the kitchen. The Cat never stirred. After a long while, something moved along the edge of the floor; something ran out on the carpet; something began to nibble a crumb.

Before you could have said, "Jack Robinson!" the Cat had that mouse by the neck.

The door into the kitchen was open a little, so in walked the Cat and dropped the mouse at Susannah's feet. Some cats think that a mouse makes a nice present for the person they love, but this cat *knew* how Susannah felt about mice.

"Help! Fire! Murder! Police! yelled Susannah, climbing onto a kitchen chair as fast as she could scramble.

"Why, what's the trouble?" asked the Captain, stumping into the kitchen in a great hurry.

"He's a-clamberin' up de chair!" yelled Susannah. "He's a-clamberin' up de chair!"

The mouse was far wiser than that. He had run back to his hole like lightning. But the Captain had to look under the chair, and up the chair legs, and then take a candle and hunt in all the corners of the kitchen before Susannah would come down. Even then she was very much upset. Said she to the Captain, "Boss, if I had a cat like this yere one, I wouldn't have him long!" and she began singing:

> "I'se known a heap ob bad cats,
>   But he's the worstest I'se known.
> If he was mine, I'd take him to the gyarden
>   And bury him like a bone——
>   Like a bone, like a bone, jus' like a wicked ol' bone!"

"He's really a good cat at heart," said the Captain sadly, for he always wanted the Cat and Susannah to be friends. He couldn't understand why they didn't get on better, and he scolded the Cat a little when they sat in their chairs by the fire. But the Cat treated the whole thing as an accident, and stretched his paws and looked at the Captain with big sleepy eyes and purred to himself as he listened to Susannah singing crossly in the kitchen.

III

THE FACE AT THE WINDOW

After supper, the Captain got out his spectacles, lit his pipe, and began reading the newspaper. "Humph!" he would say sometimes; or "Well, well!" or, perhaps, "They need some honest sailors in the Senate." But this evening he found something to read to the Cat. He always acted as though the Cat understood him, for it kept him from being lonely.

"Here's a poem," he said, looking up, "called *The Bad Kittens.*" Then he read aloud slowly:

"You may call, you may call,
But the little black cats won't hear you,
The little black cats are maddened
By the bright green light of the moon.
    They are running and whirling and hiding,
    They are wild who were once so confiding,
    They are mad when the moon is riding——
You will not catch the kittens soon!
    They care not for saucers of milk,
    They care not for pillows of silk,
Your softest, crooningest call
Means less than the buzzing of flies.
    They are seeing more than you see,
    They are hearing more than you hear,
And out of the darkness they peer
    With a goblin light in their eyes!"

But the Cat was not interested. He yawned. His mouth opened very wide, showing his sharp, curly tongue, and his whiskers stood out till they nearly touched in front of his nose. The Captain quite understood, and after that read to himself.

Tick-tock-tick went the cuckoo clock. The Cat's big eyes watched it. He knew that foolish bobbing bird would soon pop out of his little door and call, "Cuckoo! cuckoo! cuckoo!" at the top of his lungs, and pop inside his little door again, slamming it behind him. He hated that cuckoo, but it had always been beyond his reach.

Tonight he noticed that the big wing chair was nearer the clock than usual. Perhaps he could reach it, if he ran across the rug, up the seat of the chair to the back, and so straight at the cuckoo. Well, it was worth trying. He waited. He was very patient. The Captain went on reading. At eight o'clock promptly the little door of the clock opened and out popped the wooden cuckoo.

"Cuckoo!" he began, bowing. "Cuckoo! cu—" He didn't finish. There was a black rush across the rug, up the seat of the chair to the back, and so straight at the cuckoo. Then an awful crash! Down came the clock, the Cat, and the cuckoo, onto the floor all together.

"Bless my soul!" cried the Captain, jumping up. "Bless my soul!"

"Cuckoo! cuckoo!" squawked the cuckoo.

The Cat said nothing, but hurried under the sofa when he saw the Captain coming. The Captain was a patient man, but he loved that clock.

"I'll teach you, you pirate!" he shouted, trying to reach him under the sofa. But whichever side of the sofa the Captain tried, the Cat always managed to be on the other. Finally the Captain, very red in the face, got down on his stomach to reach better. Susannah heard him breathing hard, and stuck her turbaned head in through the door.

"What's the trouble, boss?" (She never *could* learn to say "skipper.")

But the Captain even now didn't want to admit how bad the Cat had been, especially to Susannah.

"I'm looking for my handkerchief," he said, getting up, still very red in the face.

Susannah began to giggle. "I bet dat han'kerchief, boss, is a mighty good dodger!"

The Captain didn't say anything, but sighed again, and put the clock gently on the table, and went back to his chair. He looked at the clock sadly, and thought he would mend it in the morning when the light was better. When the Cat was sure that the Captain was quite settled again with his pipe and his paper, he came out from under the sofa, stretching and yawning as though he'd been having a nap. Somehow he wasn't very proud of himself, with the Captain feeling sad about the clock. But the Cat wasn't ready to admit how he felt yet.

Down on the hearthrug he sat to wash his paws. Suddenly he had a feeling that he was being looked at. It couldn't be Susannah. He had heard her go upstairs to bed. And it couldn't be the Captain, for he was puffing his pipe behind the newspaper. Quickly the Cat turned his head and looked at the window nearest the door. There was a face flattened against the pane, with eyes staring into the room. But before the Cat could see who or what it was, the face had disappeared, and nothing could be seen but the dark leaves of the white lilac bush still moving a little.

IV

ONE DAY ON THE "LIVELY ANN"

The first thing that the Cat did the next morning was to walk all around the outside of the house. The grass seemed more crushed than usual, as though someone else, heavier than the Cat, had also been there. The air was filled with the smell of honeysuckle and crimson rambler roses and wet grass and soft earth, and beyond all that the salt fragrance of the sea. All these the Cat was used to. The moment they opened the door both the Cat and the Captain could tell by the smell whether the breeze came over the harbor, or across the hills. They didn't need even a glance at the schooner weather vane which spread its sails, no bigger than a handkerchief, above the roof of the tool shed. But this morning the Cat seemed to smell something strange. Perhaps it was a different tobacco. Perhaps it was boots. He couldn't be sure, but suddenly the odor brought back the memory of the most awful day in his life.

The year before, he had been with the Captain on the *Lively Ann* taking lumber to Havana. The weather was terribly rough for five days. The *Ann* was leaking, the waves were enormous, the wind howled all the time. The Mate of the ship was not an agreeable man at the best, and he was less agreeable after five days of storm.

He hadn't had any real sleep and he'd been too busy to eat much. He hadn't shaved, or even washed himself. His eyes were red with sleepiness, his lips were blue with cold, and he was in a terrible temper, when he happened to come on the ship's cat sitting comfortably washing his paws in the cabin as though there were no storm at all. The sight infuriated him.

"You're the cause of all this tempest," he cried. "Everyone knows that black cats bring bad luck on the sea. Overboard you go and we'll see if the wind won't shift!" With that he grabbed the Cat by the scruff of the neck and started for the deck.

"Mew!" cried the Cat. "Mew! mew! mew!"

Outside, the waves were like the jaws of monsters waiting to swallow him up. They opened and shut their green mouths. They shot out their long, hungry, white tongues.

"Mew! mew! mew!" cried the Cat again. He was usually a brave cat, but now he was limp with helplessness and terror. But who was to hear him in all the noise and hurry? Who was to think of a cat in the midst of such a storm? Right to the rail went the Mate, and the Cat saw the waves reaching for him. But suddenly there were hurrying steps. Someone's fist shot out and hit the Mate on the chin. Down he fell, letting go the Cat as he went, and in a moment more the Cat was trembling but safe in the Captain's arms.

The Mate never forgave either of them for that blow, and when he left the ship at the next port he was scowling and muttering.

V

EVERY FINE MORNING

Every fine morning at about ten, the Captain went to the docks to see his vessel, the *Lively Ann*. On the last voyage he had suffered a good deal from rheumatism, and his married daughter had persuaded him to stay ashore for a year or two. It was no distance from the house to the wharves, and the Cat often watched the sparrows fly from the hedge to the rigging of the schooners. When the Captain went to see the *Ann,* the Cat went, too, walking ahead with his tail proudly in the air. If he saw a dog, he stood on his toes, ruffled up his hair, made his back into an arch, and spit like a firecracker. The result was always the same. The dog would suddenly remember something he had left on the other side of the street, well out of reach. At that the Cat would give one last look and spit once more, daring him to come on, and then trot off again ahead of the Captain with his tail in the air.

When they got to the wharves, they both went aboard the *Lively Ann*. While the Captain walked around the deck seeing that everything was in place, the Cat tried to help by going down into the cabin and the hold to make sure that there were no rats. He was a silent cat. His little feet moved without a sound and his eyes were like two lanterns. He looked into every corner and smelled at every hole. It would take a brave rat to bring his family on board the *Lively Ann!*

When the Cat had made quite sure about rats, he went on deck again and sat by the door of the ship's galley. Many a good dinner had he eaten there in past years. The last cook had been a Chinaman with slanting eyes like the Cat's. He, too, liked to be by himself and do things at his own time in his own way. But he, too, knew how to be fond of his friends. He sometimes gave the Cat the nicest things to eat. The Cat liked Chinamen. Susannah gave him only what was left after she and the Captain had eaten the best of everything. He often had to sit and watch her putting into her mouth things he was sure he'd like for himself. He didn't think much of Susannah anyway.

While the Cat sat thinking about Chinamen, the Captain took a piece of newspaper out of his pocket (he always carried a great many things with him in case he might want them) and unlocked his locker in the cabin, and took out a can of white paint and put it on the paper. It seemed to him that the rail looked a little shabby and he loved to see the *Lively Ann* shipshape. He began painting the rail with a big brush. He was very careful not to get any paint on the deck. The Cat was curious. Pretty soon he *had* to jump on the rail to see what was going on.

"Scoot!" cried the Captain, and the Cat scooted. But every time he hit the deck, there were four little white pawmarks of fresh paint. The Captain was cross, but the Cat was crosser. The paint stuck between his toes. He had to sit down and spread each paw like a fan and lick and bite all the paint off. And what faces he made at the taste of it!

When he was all clean again, he lay on a pile of rope and watched the sea gulls. They had long wings, and big sliding shadows. They floated over his head, and mewed almost like kittens. When a shadow passed very near him, he always got ready to spring at it. But he knew in his heart that no sea gull would ever come within reach. And he knew that he couldn't hold a shadow for all his twenty claws. So after a while he grew tired of the sea gulls, and climbed out on the wharf to look through the cracks at the fish swimming around in the water below. When he saw one move, his eyes grew greedy and he licked his lips. He didn't even hear Susannah ringing the dinner bell from the house.

But the Captain did. He straightened his back with the aid of his hands, for bending over made him feel his rheumatism. Then he put away the paint and the brush and looked for the Cat.

"I wonder," he said when he saw him watching the fish so hard, "why cats love fish and hate water?"

The Captain often asked himself questions he couldn't answer.

VI

"DERE'S TROUBLE COMIN'"

"Boss, dere's trouble comin'," said Susannah, as she was clearing away the dinner dishes.

"What makes you think so, Susannah?" asked the Captain politely.

"I done dream a black dream las' night," said Susannah, putting down her tray, "and dis very mornin' I done los' my lucky rabbit foot. My hair stands all on end an' my knuckles crack. Yo' take my word for it, boss, dere's a heap ob trouble comin' dis way."

"Maybe it's a storm," said the Captain and went to the window to look at the sky. The sky was very blue.

The Cat, too, was looking for trouble, and he was a cat who usually found it. What did he see, walking right across his own lawn but a big long-haired yellow cat with a bell on his neck that went *ting-ting-ting* with every step he took. He was a very large cat, a very soft-looking cat, and a very foolish-looking cat, thought the Captain's Cat, getting between him and the gate.

"Grr," said the Captain's Cat, taking one step toward him on his tiptoes.

"Grr," said the other cat.

"Grrrr," said the Captain's Cat, taking another step.

"Grrrr," said the other cat.

"Grrrrrr," said the Captain's Cat, taking still another step and looking him in the eye.

"Grrrrrr," said the yellow cat.

"Mrow," said the Captain's Cat, standing still and swelling larger and larger, and waving his right front paw.

"Mrow," said the strange cat, swelling to twice his size and waving his left front paw.

"Mrow—meerow—meerowrow," said the Captain's Cat, with his ears flat to his neck and a nasty look in his eye.

"Mrow—meerow—meerowrow," said the other cat just as loudly.

Then they both made a sound together, louder than any of all the loud sounds they had made before. There were spits in it, and growls, and snarls, and howls, and fireworks, and pin wheels, and screams and screeches. Yet it was all one sound. There was even a ringing of the bell on the yellow cat's collar. The noise was very loud. At the same instant the two cats jumped at each other and rolled over and over. They looked like one animal, all legs, and tails, and teeth. They bit and they scratched and they kicked. The Captain's Cat got his mouth full of yellow fur. He had to spit it out before he could get another bite. He tore the pretty little bell off the yellow cat's ribbon. He got his teeth in his ear. And all the time he was making terrible scary noises, even with his mouth full of fur. The yellow cat wasn't doing as well. He was so beautiful that he spent most of the day on a silk cushion, and had cream for breakfast from a yellow bowl. He wasn't used to fighting.

"Meow," he cried, and suddenly leaped free from the Captain's Cat, and ran away with his ear bleeding and his little bell gone from the ribbon around his neck.

The Captain's Cat watched him go and licked a scratch on his nose. Then he looked at the house to see if anyone had seen the fight. He was not a good cat. He was proud of his rough ways. Sure enough, there was Susannah's red bandanna bobbing in one window like a big red poppy, and the Captain's gray head in another. The Cat was glad they had seen him.

"Yo' ought to be ashamed of yo'self," said Susannah, opening the door.

In walked the Cat pleasantly. He had been looking for trouble and he had found it. He was satisfied. He was satisfied even with Susannah. Perhaps this was the trouble she thought was coming. Perhaps not. He didn't care. He would take care of any trouble that dared come along! He went to his saucer. There was no milk in it. Then he was not so well satisfied. But Susannah was busy and paid no attention to him. She was baking little cakes for tea and making up a song.

> "This yere black cat is a hard cat to beat,"
> (hummed Susannah)
> "Yas-sir, yas-sir, jiggamoree——"

The cakes smelled delicious. She put them on the table and began to stir the frosting in a yellow bowl.

> "He's the fightingest cat what lives on our street,
> Yas-sir, yas-sir, jiggamoree!"

The Cat mewed for milk, but Susannah went on stirring and singing:

> "But a one-eyed cat down Alabamy way,
> Yas-sir, yas-sir, jiggamoree,
> Could make him look like a li'l' wisp ob hay——
> Yas-sir, yas-sir, jiggamoree!"

The cat didn't like the song at all. But then he never *did* like Susannah's songs. He was glad when the doorbell rang. Out of the kitchen went Susannah, tying on a clean apron as she went. Up on a chair leaped the Cat, and up on his hind legs he stood, and scooped one paw into the bowl of frosting. He licked it. In went the paw again. But at that moment the front door slammed and made him jump. Down came the bowl, frosting and all, on top of him, and before he got over the scare of that, in came Susannah running. She gave one look and reached for the broom. Away went the Cat with Susannah and the broom after him. Across the living room, and up the stairs, into the Captain's room (upsetting a chair), across the little hall. To his surprise, the door was open into the spare chamber, so in the Cat tore with Susannah close behind. There was frosting in his eyes, but he could see an open window (usually the spare chamber was kept tight as a drum, unless Susannah was cleaning it) and through that open window he sailed, just in the nick of time. Down came the broom with a thud, but it only hit the very least and littlest tip of his tail.

VII

SH! WHAT'S THAT?

The Cat sat on the roof of the veranda, licking frosting off his coat. He always liked things to be neat, so he had a good deal of washing to do on his busy days. But the frosting was delicious—not at all like the paint. The sun was shining. Two or three birds sang, "Cheer-up, cheer-up," in a tree near by. It was on just such days that the Cat enjoyed sitting all alone by himself on the roof, quietly watching everything.

Yet somehow this afternoon he was worried. He remembered the face at the window last night, and the smell in the morning which made him think of the Mate, and the door and window of the spare chamber which he had found so unexpectedly open. He felt responsible, for he alone had noticed these things, and he could tell no one of his anxiety, not even the Captain. If only Susannah had not shut the window, he would have visited all the rooms to see if any-thing were wrong with them. He was worried. He kept washing his whiskers long after the last bit of frosting was off them. He got a whisker down his throat and nearly coughed his head off. He got a whisker up his nose and nearly sneezed his head off. Then he stopped washing his whiskers, and went to look in the windows of the spare chamber. Everything seemed in place. There was nothing more that he could do for the time being but forget about it.

From where he lay, he could see out over the harbor and watch the sails moving, and hear the put-put-put of the motor launches. Once a sea gull flew over him with a fish hanging out of his bill. Several times he heard steps on the street, and people went by. He watched everything they did, but they never saw him lying on the roof, with his toes sedately tucked in under his white shirt front.

About four o'clock the Captain's married daughter and her little boy turned in at the gate. They were coming for tea. They, too, passed right under the Cat but never thought to look up. He was looking down at them, though. He saw the flowers on the hat of the Captain's daughter, and the paper pinwheel Ted-Ted was carrying. He heard them knocking at the door and Susannah opening it sud-denly, just the way the cuckoo used to open his little door.

The Cat stayed where he was. He hadn't been invited.

But suddenly he heard another sound. It was like a step in the spare chamber. Sh! what's that? The Cat ran to the windows, but he could see nothing unusual. Everything seemed in its place. Perhaps the Captain had come upstairs to get a handkerchief.

VIII

THE CAT'S FIRST PARTY

Susannah brought in the tea on a big red tray from China. The teapot was shaped like an elephant with steam coming from his trunk. Ted-Ted loved it. The cream came in a pitcher like a bright brown cow with her tail curled for a handle. Ted-Ted was so little he sat on a stool near the fire and held his cup in both hands. The grown-up people drank real tea, but Ted-Ted had only a spoonful of tea mixed with a great deal of milk.

Susannah smiled from ear to ear. She loved tea parties. She had made little cookies shaped like fish with caraway seeds for eyes, and big cookies filled with raisins, and cup cakes. But the cup cakes didn't have any frosting on them because most of the frosting was on the kitchen floor, and the rest was inside the Cat. Susannah told the Captain's daughter just how bad that cat was.

"We must call him for Ted-Ted to play with," said the Captain's daughter, who always laughed at Susannah's stories of the Cat.

"Yo'd bes' leave him whar he is, mum," said Susannah.

"Oh, cats are always good with little children," said the Captain's daughter, who knew a great deal about cats.

"Kitty, kitty," said Ted-Ted, who had been listening.

"Well, well, where is he?" asked the Captain, pleased that they wanted to see his cat.

"He was walkin' right on air, boss, the las' I see ob him," said Susannah with a sniff.

The Captain opened the door and called:

"Here, kitty, kitty, kitty! Here, kitty, kitty, kitty! Come, puss, puss, puss!"

The Cat's head appeared over the edge of the veranda roof. He was delighted at being called, but he tried to appear unconcerned. He looked at the Captain, then slid down the veranda pillar, walked into the house, passed Susannah as though he didn't see her, and went right up to the Captain's daughter. She knew what cats like. She tickled him under the chin and rubbed his back and sang nonsense to him under her breath:

> "Cat, Cat, it's perfectly evident
>   You are a calico cat,
> And your eyes are a pair of underclothes' buttons
>   Sewed on with a black thread, at that.

"Cat, Cat, it's perfectly evident
    Your whiskers are made out of string.
Someone's tangled up those on the left of your nose
    Which I think is a rather good thing.

"And, Cat, that magnificent pout of your chest
    Just shows all the sawdust that's in it!
I must teach you your place as a little doorstop——
    At least for the half of a minute!"

At first when Ted-Ted came near, the Cat ran away. He had never seen him before, and he thought Ted-Ted must be a man who was very little. He wasn't used to children, anyway, and seeing such a *very* little man reaching out such a *very* little hand somehow scared him.

But pretty soon he got used to it. Ted-Ted poured cream from the brown cow's mouth into a saucer. Then the Cat settled down and tucked his paws under the saucer neatly, and very carefully lapped up the cream, keeping his whiskers dry. The last drop was on his chin. He licked it off, wet the back of his right paw to smooth his shining fur, and then lightly jumped up on the Captain's lap and poked his head under the Captain's hand to be petted, which was very unusual for him to do in company. Ted-Ted leaned against the Captain's knee to listen to the Cat purring. It was better than the ticking of a watch.

"How happy they all look," thought the Captain's daughter. "It would make a pretty picture."

"His engine's going," said Ted-Ted, whose father had an automobile, and they all laughed.

But the grown-ups began talking about other things, and the Cat grew sleepy and forgot to purr. "His engine's stopped," said Ted-Ted in his little voice. But the Captain didn't hear exactly what he said and only patted him on the back and said, "Yes, yes," kindly.

The Cat's big black tail, with a little curl at the tip of it, hung near Ted-Ted's hand.

"I'll crank him," said Ted-Ted, helpfully. If only the Captain had heard that time! But again he just said, "Yes, yes," and went on talking with his daughter.

Ted-Ted gave one crank and then everything happened at once.
The Cat yowled.
The Captain said, "Bless my soul!" in a loud voice.
The Captain's daughter cried, "What did you do, Ted-Ted?"
Ted-Ted began dropping tears on five pink scratches on his hand.
Susannah popped her head into the door, and then, without any
questions, ran for the broom. It was really unfair of Susannah, for
the Cat had meant to be as good as gold at his very first tea party.

IX

THIS CAT SAVED US

Before going to bed at night the Captain always wrote in his log
book. A log book is a diary of a ship at sea and the Captain pretended to himself that his house was a ship. He was more used to
ships than to houses.

"This day comes in fair with light westerly breeze," he
wrote carefully.
"At four bells, morning watch (which is the sea way of
saying ten o'clock in the morning) boarded the *Lively Ann*.
Found all shipshape. Painted rail.
"During the afternoon watch, some trouble in the galley
(that referred to Susannah's chasing the Cat with a broom).
"At eight bells received on board the mate and cabin
boy of the brig *Garfield* (that was his daughter's married
name). Tea for all hands.
"At eight bells evening watch wind freshened, backed to
N. E. Saw all serene for the night. So ends this day."

The Captain wished he could say how far the house had sailed,
but he knew it had stayed in its own yard behind its white paling
fence. The log book of a house is not half so exciting as a ship's. He
sighed as he closed the book. Then he locked the door, looked at all
the windows, wound the grandfather's clock, and put the screen

around the fire. The Cat still lay in his chair and made no move to go upstairs. He often waited until the embers were cool before he curled up on his rug in the Captain's room.

It didn't take the Captain long to get into bed. For that matter he didn't have a bed, because a bed never stirs during the night. He slept in a hammock that swung a little when he turned over, and reminded him of the sea. He was so sleepy that he paid no attention when he saw the Cat come to his door, hesitate, and then turn toward the spare chamber instead of coming in as usual. He blew out the candle, tumbled into his hammock, and was almost asleep when he heard a mewing. Still he paid no attention.

"Mew, mew!" went the Cat.

"Do let me go to sleep," muttered the Captain, from his pillow.

"Mew, mew, mew!" went the Cat and jumped on the hammock.

The Captain pulled the blankets over his ears. He couldn't bear to be disturbed just now.

"Mew, mew!" went the Cat.

"Mew, mew!" went the Cat, scratching at the blankets.

"Well, well!" said the Captain, wide awake at last. "Whatever is the matter with you this evening?"

At that, down jumped the Cat, ran to the door, ran back to the Captain again, and then to the door. His hair was ruffled. His whiskers were bristling. His eyes were green. The Captain, who had lighted his candle, saw that something was wrong. He put on his dressing gown and picked up his cane. Across the little hall went the Cat, and into the spare chamber and up to the door of the closet.

"Mrow," went the Cat, looking very frightened, but brave.

The Captain opened the door carefully.

And there hidden in the closet was the Mate.

The Captain had quite a hard time before he finally got the Mate tied up with the clothesline Susannah brought. The Cat jumped up on the bureau to keep out of harm's way. Susannah, in a yellow woolen nightdress, stood in the doorway humming and singing and rolling her eyes until the Captain sent her for the police.

"He evidently had a grudge against you, Captain," said the policeman later, "and was waiting for you to go to sleep. He must have gotten in through an upper window during the day. When the house was quiet and you were asleep he'd have come out and robbed you and maybe worse, too."

"I *was* almost asleep," said the Captain. "It was this cat here who saved us. He came into my room and woke me up, and led me to this door. He must have heard or seen something after I went to bed."

Then everyone turned and looked at the Cat, who was still sitting on the bureau and couldn't help feeling proud. Even Susannah knew at last that the Captain was right. This *was* a good cat, a very good cat. After what had happened, she could never be angry with him again. When Susannah begged anyone's pardon she did it thoroughly.

"I wants to 'pologize to yo' right here and now 'fo' all de people fo' de mean things I evah done said about yo', honey," she said, shaking the Cat by the paw, and then she began rocking herself backward and forward in the way she had when she was excited. And pretty soon she was singing:

"Ev'ry li'l' ol' cat's got his own li'l' ways——
    Praise be!
But who wouldn't put up with a li'l' cat's plays?
    Praise be!
He's de finest best cat yo' ever did see,
He done save de Captain an' he done save me!
    Praise be!
        Hallelujah!"

"I always knew he was a good cat," said the Captain happily. The Cat jumped down and rubbed against Susannah's ankles to show that he, too, could forget any little misunderstandings. Then he looked at his friend, the Captain, as though asking for something, and ran to the top of the stairs. . . .

Susannah didn't say anything, but before the Captain was half-way down she hurried to the ice box. And the beautiful long slice of white chicken meat she had put away as a special treat for herself went into the Cat's saucer.

THE MONKEY THAT WOULD NOT KILL

By HENRY DRUMMOND

Illustration by Lois Lenski

I

THERE is no such thing as an immortal monkey, but this monkey was as near it as possible. Talk of a cat's nine lives— this monkey had ninety! A monkey's business in the world is usually to make everybody merry, but the special mission of this one, I fear, was to make everybody as angry as ever they could be. In wrath-producing power, in fact, this monkey positively shone.

How many escapes the monkey had before the runaway slave presented it to the missionary—from whom I first heard of it—no one knows. It certainly had not much hair on when it arrived, and there was an ominous scar on its head, and its ears were not wholly symmetrical. But the children were vastly delighted with it, and after much kind treatment the creature was restored to rude health, and, I must confess, to quite too rude spirits. The children wanted him baptized by the time-honored title of "Jocko"; but by a series of exploits in which the monkey distinguished himself at the expense of every member of the household in turn, it became evident that only one name would fit a quadruped of his peculiar disposition; and that was "Tricky." Tricky, therefore, he was called, and as Tricky he lived and—did *not* die.

There was no peace in the home after Tricky came. He ate everything, upset everything, broke everything, stole everything, did everything that the average monkey ought not to do. If they shut him in a room, Tricky got out by the chimney. If they put him out of the room, Tricky came in by the chimney. What could you do with such a creature? He could not be kept in, and he could not be kept out; so a court-martial was held, and Tricky was sentenced to be given away.

But by this time the whole place knew Tricky, and no one would have him. Such an unusual refusal of a present was never known before. Even the runaway slave smiled sweetly when his old friend

Lois Lenski

There was no peace in the home after Tricky came. He did everything a monkey ought not to do.

was offered to him, and protested that, to his deep regret, he was unable to buy nuts enough to keep him.

The idea of "wandering" Tricky in the woods, of course, occurred to the genius of the village, and a detachment of boys set off one Saturday to carry it into effect. But you might as well have tried to wander a carrier pigeon. Like Mary's little lamb, everywhere these boys went, that monkey went. When they ran, it ran, when they doubled back, it doubled back; and when they got home, dead tired, it was only to find Tricky laughing at them from the church roof.

That night the worst happened. When the people assembled for the weekly meeting, there was not found in that church one whole hymnbook. Someone, apparently, had been pelting the pulpit with them. The cushions were torn, the blinds were a wreck; two stops in the harmonium were pulled out bodily. After the service the missionary was solemnly waited on by a deputation. They were closeted for an hour and a half, but no one, except themselves, ever knew what was said or done. The only circumstances that one could in any way connect with this mysterious council was that about midnight a small boat was seen stealthily putting out to sea. It contained two figures—one, who rowed, was the senior elder; the other, who sat in the stern, looked like a very small boy.

II

The day was not yet broken when the "watch" of the ship *Vulcan*, lying becalmed off the ———— coast, was roused by a peculiar noise aft. Going to the spot, he was surprised to find a much-bedraggled monkey rubbing itself on a pile of sailcloth. The creature had evidently swum or drifted a long distance, and was now endeavoring to restore circulation. Jerry, being a humane man, got it some biscuit, and a saucer of grog, and waited developments. These were not slow to show themselves; within twenty-four hours the commander of the ship *Vulcan*, 740 tons register, was a monkey named Tricky.

Time would fail me to tell of the life that monkey led them all on board the *Vulcan*. After the first week only two things lay between him and death at any moment. One was his inventiveness. Tricky's wickedness was nothing, if not original. Every day he was at some new villainy; and anything *new* on board ship is sacred. There is no *Punch* published on board ship; but Tricky was all the comic papers rolled into one. But that was not the main reason. There is a good deal of quiet quarreling on board ship. The mate spared Tricky because he thought he would some day give the Captain a "turn;

the Captain let him live, hoping he would do something dreadful to the mate. Everybody waited to see Tricky do something to somebody else. So he rose to the highest rank in the merchant-marine, and was respected almost to idolatry by all on board the *Vulcan*.

One day Tricky was hanged—formally, deliberately, and judicially hanged. What had he done? He had killed the ship cat. It was a deliberate murder, with no extenuating circumstances, and a rope, with a noose, was swung over the yardarm, and Tricky run up in the presence of all the crew. This happened about eight bells, and at dusk Tricky was still hanging there, very quiet and motionless. Next morning Tricky was still there—as live as you are. Tricky was not hanged, he was only hanging; and, as everybody knows, monkeys rather like hanging. In fact, though Tricky was still up there, he had got his hands well round the rope, and was, on the whole, fairly at home. The rope round a neck like Tricky's was a mere boa.

The executioners were rather ashamed of themselves when they saw how matters stood; but instead of softening them, this dangling mockery of a dead monkey still further roused their wrath, and the boatswain was told off to end the drama by tossing Tricky into the sea. The boatswain was up the shrouds in a moment, and loosening the rope with one hand, and catching the monkey by the tail with the other, he swung poor Tricky a good yard over the ship's side into the Atlantic.

When the boatswain descended upon the deck he was greeted with a sudden deluge of rain. It was only Tricky shaking the salt water off. The monkey had climbed up the stern rope, and reached the deck before him. What would have happened next is hard to predict, but at this point the Captain, attracted by the scream of laughter which greeted the drenching of the boatswain, came up and was told the sequel to the hanging. Now the Captain was a blunt, good-natured man, and he avowed that neither man nor monkey who had ever been hanged on board his ship should ever be put to death again. This was the law on shore, he said, and he would see fair play. So Tricky received another lease of life, and thus the ship *Vulcan* was kept in hot water for two months more.

About the end of that period there came a crisis. The ship was nearing port, and a heavy cleaning was in progress. Among other things, the ship's boats had to be painted. In an evil hour one of the men went below to dinner, and left his paintpot standing on the deck. If Tricky had lost such a chance he would not have been a monkey at all. Needless to say he rose to the occasion. That his supreme hour was come was quite evident from the way he set to work at once. He began with the parrot, which he painted vermilion; then he passed the brush gayly along the newly varnished woodwork—daubed the masts and shrouds all over, obliterated the name on the life buoys, and wound up a somewhat successful performance by emptying the pot over the Captain's best coat, which was laid in the sun to get the creases out.

I draw a veil over what happened on the *Vulcan* during the next quarter of an hour. There was never such a muster of the crew since they left port. Everybody seemed to have business on deck. When the Captain came up you could have heard a pin drop. I shall not repeat his language, nor try to compare with anything earthly the voice with which he ordered every man below. All I will record is— and it is to his everlasting honor—that in that awful hour the Captain was true to his vow. "Do you see land?" he roared to the steersman. "Aye, aye, sir," said the man, "land on the larboard bow." "Then," said the Captain, "put her head to it."

That night, late, the ship stood close in to a small island on the north coast of Scotland, and a boat was solemnly sent ashore, and after that Tricky was no more seen by any of the crew of the *Vulcan*.

III

The island on which the Captain of the *Vulcan* exiled Tricky was marked on the chart "uninhabited." But the chart was wrong. Ten years before, a shepherd had come there, and now lived with his wife and family near the top of the great sea cliff. You may judge of the sensation when a real live monkey appeared in the early morning in this remote and lonely spot. The shepherd was watching his sheep when the apparition rose, as it were, from the ground. He had never seen a monkey before, any more than the sheep; and sheep and shepherd bolted like wildfire. Tricky, of course, followed the biped, for he had always been accustomed to human society; and, as the shepherd fled toward the hut, he saw the monkey close at his heels. So he made a rush at the open door, and pulled it after him with a bang which almost brought down the house.

The fugitive had just got inside when, in a moment, he felt himself seized from behind. It seemed as if a powerful hand was dragging him backward, and he threw himself down on the ground, and roared with fear. What had happened was that the flying end of his plaid had got jammed in the door, but he felt sure the evil spirit was holding him in its clutches, and it was some time before his startled wife could convince him that there was nothing there. The good woman gathered him up, and soothed him; and as soon as he could speak he told her in a shivering voice about the awful monster which had come to slay them all. He had scarcely got out the word "monster," when there was a scurrying in the chimney, and the monster presented himself before them, and calmly sat down on the meal barrel. "It's just a puggy!" cried the shepherd's wife (she had been to Inverness), and began to stroke Tricky on the back. As she did so, she noticed that the creature had a strand of an old ship's rope round its neck, and to this was attached a small piece of paper. She opened it and read four words, scrawled in a hasty hand:

"Won't Hang.
Won't Drown."

The shepherd seemed more frightened than ever at this revelation. "Won't hang, won't drown," he muttered. "Then, we'll see if it won't *shoot*," and he reached over the fireplace for the gun which he killed the rabbits with. As he loaded it, it seemed to the shepherd's wife as if all the powder and shot in the house was being poured into the barrel. She pleaded with her husband to spare Tricky's life, and it almost looked as if she had succeeded, for the shepherd lowered the gun from his shoulder and stood for a moment as if in doubt. But it was not because of his wife he stopped. It was partly because he was quite too shaky to aim straight; and partly because he was too much of a sportsman to shoot offhand a thing which was sitting quiet and still on his own meal barrel; but the main reason was that he was afraid to shoot the baby, whose crib was just beside it. So he gave the meal barrel a kick with his foot to dislodge the monkey. He thought it would make for the door, and there, in the open air, he would shoot it fair and square.

But the monkey had other views. What it wanted was something to eat; and the children's porridge being handy, it put its paw in and began breakfast. The shepherd was too much petrified to interfere, and it was only when Tricky next spilt the milk jug over the baby that he roused himself to do his duty to his family. He raised the gun once more, and, watching his chance, when Tricky was exactly opposite the door aimed straight at its heart, and pulled the trigger. Now, the next moment that monkey ought to have been scattered all over the hillside in multitudinous fragments. On the contrary, it was up on the table, imitating the click of the gun with a spoon. Not that the shepherd missed. For the first time in its life the rusty lock had "struck," and the dazed shepherd was more than ever confirmed in his belief that the monkey was a witch.

"Won't shoot," he muttered to himself, "won't hang, won't drown. I have tried the first; I'll prove the next." So, as he was too superstitious to try to shoot it again, he went out to hang the monkey.

But there was no tree on the island. All day the shepherd searched for a place to hang Tricky, but in vain. That night he lay thinking, hour after hour, where he would hang it, and in the early morning an inspiration came to him—he would try the pump! So he rose softly and fixed the handle of the pump high in the air, so that it stuck out like a gallows, and tied a rope with a noose to the end of it. Then he got Tricky to perch on the top of the pump, tied the rope round his neck, and all was ready. The shepherd had heard that the object of hanging was to break the neck of the criminal by a sudden "drop," but as he could not give Tricky a long enough drop he determined to make up for it in another way. So he gathered all his strength, and with a tremendous sweep of his arms sent Tricky flying into space. Of course you know what happened. The rope—it was quite rotten—broke, and Tricky landed on his four paws, and stood grinning at his executioner, as if he would like it all over again.

That whole day the sheep and lambs on the Island of —— were neglected. All day long you might have seen the shepherd sitting by the marsh side plaiting something with his fingers. Round him, the ground was strewn with rushes, some loose, and some in bundles; but for every one the workman chose, he threw away a hundred, because it was not tough and strong. And as he plaited, and twisted, and knotted, and tested, there was fire in the shepherd's eye, and thunder all over his face.

At daybreak next morning the shepherd and the monkey once more formed in procession and wended their way to the old pump. The new rope could hang an elephant. It was thick as a boa constrictor, and the shepherd took a full hour to adjust the noose and get the gallows into working order. Then the fatal moment came. With a mightier shove than before the monkey was launched into the air, and the rope stiffened and held like a ship's hawser. But the executioner had not calculated everything. The rope and the "drop" were all right, but when the gallows felt the shock, the pump handle cracked off like a match, and the old moss-covered tube gave two rocks and reeled from its moorings, and lay split in pieces on the ground. Jagged and needlelike splinters at the same moment scraped and pierced and gouged at the shepherd's shins, and tore his nether garments, and made him dance with pain and rage. If anything could have added more agony to the next few minutes it was the sight of Tricky. That ever gay animal was careening down the hill straight toward the feeding sheep. The pump handle was still tied to its neck, and it clattered over the stones with a noise weird enough to drive the whole flock into the sea. The shepherd knew there must be a catastrophe, but he was powerless to avert it. He was too sore to follow, so he slowly limped toward the hut, to nurse his wrath and his wounds.

IV

For three days after the monkey had been "hanged," it did not come near the shepherd or his house. A monkey has feelings. To be nearly hanged is bad enough, but to have a boa constrictor and a pump handle tied to your neck is more than any self-respecting animal would stand. So Tricky devoted himself exclusively to the sheep. For the space of three days, with the invaluable aid of the pump handle, Tricky shepherded that flock. Not a blade of grass was nibbled during this period; one prolonged stampede was kept up night and day. The lambs dropped with hunger. The old sheep tottered with fatigue. The whole flock was demoralized. In fact, when the "Reign of Terror" closed there was not a pound of sound mutton left on the island.

Why did not the shepherd interfere? Because, as we shall see, for these three days he had more urgent work to do. When the shepherd's wife went out to the pump that morning for water to make the porridge with, she found it a heap of ruins. She came back and broke the tidings to the shepherd, and said she believed it had been struck with lightning. The shepherd discreetly said nothing, but presently stole sullenly out to inspect the damage once more. It was worse than he thought. A pump must hold in both air and water; this pump was rent and split in a dozen places. There was no water either to drink or make the porridge with, till the tube was mended. So all that day the shepherd was splicing, and hammering, and gluing, and bandaging. All the next day he was doing the same. He got nothing to eat or drink; nobody got anything to eat or drink. The poor children were kept alive on a single bowlful which happened to be in the house, but this was now finished, and they were crying out from want. Positively, if this drought and famine had been kept up for a few days more the island would certainly have been restored to the condition described on the chart—"uninhabited."

On the morning of the fourth day the pump stood erect, and wind and water tight once more. Only one thing was wanting—there was no handle. The only thing left was to try to catch Tricky, for there was nothing else on the island which would make a handle. But just then Tricky required no catching. At that moment he was sitting on the doorstep contemplating the group round the pump. Everybody being out, he had seized the opportunity to have a good breakfast—consisting of every particle of meal in the barrel—and was now enjoying a period of repose before recommencing hostilities. The shepherd made a rush at him, but, alas, what he wanted was no longer there. A piece of frayed rope dangled on its neck, but the pump handle was gone.

It took two days more to find it. Every inch of the island was patiently examined. Even the child next the baby had to join in the search. Night and day they were all at it; and at last it was found by the shepherd's wife—stuck in a rabbit hole. All this time no one had leisure to kill Tricky. But on the seventh day the shepherd rose with murder written on his brow. The monkey would not shoot, and he would not hang; it remained to try what drowning would do. So he tied a large stone round the monkey's neck, and led him forth to the edge of the great sea cliff.

A hundred feet below, the sea lay like a mirror; and the shepherd, as he looked over for a deep place, saw the great fronds of the seaweeds and the jellyfish and the anemones lying motionless in the crystal waters. Then he took the monkey and the stone in his great hands, examined the knots hastily, and, with one sudden swing, heaved them over the cliff.

The shepherd would much rather at this point have retired from the scene. But he dared not. He could not trust that monkey. An actual certificate of death was due to himself and to his family. So he peered over the cliff and saw the splash in the sea, and watched the ripples clearing off till sea bottom stood out again with every shell distinct. And there, sure enough, was Tricky, down among the starfish, safely moored to his gravestone, and the yard of good rope holding like a chain cable. The shepherd rose for the first time since that monkey set foot upon the island and breathed freely. Then he slowly went back to the house and told the tale of the end of Tricky.

It was not till midnight that Tricky came back. Of course you knew Tricky would come back. You knew the rope would slip over the stone, or break, or be eaten through by a great fish, or something, and, though none of these things happened, it is certainly true that that night at midnight Tricky did turn up. Perhaps I should say turn down, for he came in, as usual, by the chimney. But the exact way in which this singular creature escaped from its watery grave must be reserved for another chapter.

V

If the shepherd had stood looking over the cliff for one moment longer he would have witnessed a curious scene. Every schoolboy knows that a stone is lighter in water than in air. How the monkey knew this, or whether he did or did not, it is impossible to say, but his actions were certainly those of a philosopher. For, instead of resigning himself to his fate, he bent down and grasped the stone which held him to his watery grave, picked it up in his arms, and walked calmly along the bottom toward the shore. With a supreme effort he next got the stone edged on to a half-submerged ledge; but now that it was half out of the water it was once more too heavy to lift, and Tricky lay in great perplexity in the shallow water, wondering how ever he was to get out of this fresh dilemma. There appeared nothing for it but to attack the rope with his teeth and for an hour Tricky worked at the tough strands, but without almost any success. After another hour's work the monkey made an appalling discovery. When he began work, the water was only up to his knees; and to his consternation, it now covered him up to his middle. In a short time more it came up to his neck, and it was clear to Tricky that if the ledge went on sinking at this rate he was a dead monkey. Tricky thought he knew all about the sea, but in the foreign sea, where he had lived with the missionary, there were no tides, and this creeping in of the water greatly disturbed his peace of mind. To his great joy, however, he found that the stone, now wholly covered with water, was once more light enough to lift, and he trundled it along the ledge till the water became too shallow to move it farther. Just above this point was another ledge, high and dry above tide-mark, and the yard of rope was just long enough to allow the monkey to take up his position there, and shake himself dry in the sun.

Now, this shaking process suggested an idea to Tricky—a very obvious one to you or me, but a real inspiration to a monkey. Tricky noticed that the very part of the rope where he had been gnawing rested against the sharp edge of the rocky ledge, and that one frayed strand had suddenly parted while he was shaking himself. The rock edge, in fact, was a regular knife, and after much and hard rubbing, and many rests, Tricky found himself within three or four strands of freedom. It was all but midnight when the last strand parted and in a few minutes more the gallant monkey crawled up the cliff and stood once more at the door of his executioner's house.

I am afraid you will be as much surprised as Tricky was at the startling discovery he made when he got there. The cottage was on fire! For days, you will remember, there had been no food in the shepherd's home. But that day the family had celebrated the mending of the pump by a great banquet and a washing. Such a fire was lit as had not blazed on the hearth for years, and when it grew dark the red sparks flew into the air and fell in dangerous showers upon the dry thatched roof. The wind, too, rose about nightfall, and fanned one smouldering square of turf into life; and when Tricky reached the spot, at least half the roof was already in a blaze. But Tricky was hungry after his day's adventures, and the chimney end of the roof being still untouched by the fire, he jumped on to the roof and down into the kitchen with a bound. The baby's cradle lay, as usual, close to the side of the fire, and the monkey, in passing, must have swished it with his tail, for the infant broke into a sudden yell, which rang through the room, and woke the shepherd with a start. The good man was awake not a moment too soon. Had the monkey arrived five minutes later, the whole family must have perished; the smoke had already filled the other room, and was pouring in, in rolling clouds, below the kitchen door. With one thunderstruck glare at the night-watchman who had awakened him so opportunely—and who now occupied his usual throne on the meal barrel, violently sneezing out smoke, and wondering whether it was not better to be drowned—the shepherd rushed toward the door to save the two elder children who lay locked in slumber in the burning room beyond. Seizing them in his arms, he bore them safely to the open air, and then returned for his wife and the other children. Tricky followed at their heels; and the next moment the rescued family stood in a shivering group, helplessly watching the flames. The roof soon fell in, and in the morning all that remained of the shepherd's house was a few charred rafters.

. . . . .

On the spot where the shepherd's cottage was burned now stands a noble lighthouse. It was put up a few months after the fire, and one of the three lighthouse keepers is the shepherd. The second is a man who is fond of telling tales of the sea, and how he was once mate of a ship called the *Vulcan*. The third keeper of the lighthouse is a quadruped called Tricky. The affection between him and the ex-shepherd is peculiar. Other people think there is some history connected with it, but the shepherd never says much. When asked if it is really true that the monkey cannot be killed, he always replies, "Yes; but that is not why it is alive." Only on one occasion was the shepherd known to add anything to that remark. It was one night when Tricky had held back the baby—it had just learned to creep— from tumbling over the cliff. Then the shepherd smiled as he threw Tricky a whole bagful of nuts, and said, "That monkey won't kill— nor let anybody else kill."

BLACK BEAUTY

By *ANNA SEWELL*

Illustrations by Katharine Pyle

I

MY EARLY HOME

THE first place that I can well remember, was a large, pleasant meadow with a pond of clear water in it. Some shady trees leaned over it, and rushes and water lilies grew at the deep end. Over the hedge on one side we looked into a plowed field, and on the other we looked over a gate at our master's house, which stood by the roadside; at the top of the meadow was a plantation of fir trees, and at the bottom a running brook overhung by a steep bank.

While I was young I lived upon my mother's milk, as I could not eat grass. In the daytime I ran by her side, and at night I lay down close by her. When it was hot, we used to stand by the pond in the shade of the trees, and when it was cold, we had a nice, warm shed near the plantation.

As soon as I was old enough to eat grass, my mother used to go out to work in the daytime, and come back in the evening.

There were six young colts in the meadow besides me; they were older than I was; some were nearly as large as grown-up horses. I used to run with them, and had great fun; we used to gallop all together round and round the field, as hard as we could go. Sometimes we had rather rough play, for they would frequently bite and kick as well as gallop.

One day, when there was a good deal of kicking, my mother whinnied to me to come to her, and then she said:

"I wish you to pay attention to what I am going to say to you. The colts who live here are very good colts, but they are cart-horse colts, and, of course, they have not learned manners. You have been well bred and well born; your father has a great name in these parts, and your grandfather won the cup two years at the Newmarket races; your grandmother had the sweetest temper of any horse I ever knew, and I think you have never seen me kick or bite. I hope you will grow up gentle and good, and never learn bad ways; do your work with a good will, lift your feet up well when you trot, and never bite or kick even in play."

I have never forgotten my mother's advice! I knew she was a wise old horse, and our master thought a great deal of her. Her name was Duchess, but he often called her Pet.

Our master was a good, kind man. He gave us good food, good lodging, and kind words; he spoke as kindly to us as he did to his little children. We were all fond of him, and my mother loved him very much. When she saw him at the gate, she would neigh with joy, and trot up to him. He would pat and stroke her and say, "Well, old Pet, and how is your little Darkie?" I was a dull black, so he called me Darkie; then he would give me a piece of bread, which was very good, and sometimes he brought a carrot for my mother. All the horses would come to him, but I think we were his favorites. My mother always took him to the town on a market day in a light gig.

There was a plowboy, Dick, who sometimes came into our field to pluck blackberries from the hedge. When he had eaten all he wanted, he would have what he called fun with the colts, throwing stones and sticks at them to make them gallop. We did not much mind him, for we could gallop off; but sometimes a stone would hit and hurt us.

One day he was at this game, and did not know that the master was in the next field; but he was there, watching what was going on; over the hedge he jumped in a snap, and catching Dick by the arm, he gave him such a box on the ear as made him roar with the pain and surprise. As soon as we saw the master, we trotted up nearer to see what went on.

"Bad boy!" he said, "Bad boy! to chase the colts. This is not the first time, nor the second, but it shall be the last—there—take your money and go home, I shall not want you on my farm again." So we never saw Dick any more. Old Daniel, the man who looked after the horses, was just as gentle as our master, so we were well off.

II

THE HUNT

Before I was two years old, a circumstance happened which I have never forgotten. It was early in the spring; there had been a little frost in the night, and a light mist still hung over the plantations and meadows. I and the other colts were feeding at the lower part of the field when we heard, quite in the distance, what sounded like the cry of dogs. The oldest of the colts raised his head, pricked his ears, and said, "There are the hounds!" and immediately cantered off, followed by the rest of us to the upper part of the field, where we could look over the hedge and see several fields beyond. My mother, and an old riding horse of our master's were also standing near, and seemed to know all about it.

"They have found a hare," said my mother, "and if they come this way, we shall see the hunt."

And soon the dogs were all tearing down the field of young wheat next to ours. I never heard such a noise as they made. They did not bark, nor howl, nor whine, but kept on a "yo! yo, o, o! yo! yo, o, o!" at the top of their voices. After them came a number of men on horseback, some of them in green coats, all galloping as fast as they could. The old horse snorted and looked eagerly after them, and we young colts wanted to be galloping with them, but they were soon away into the fields lower down; here it seemed as if they had come to a stand; the dogs left off barking, and ran about every way with their noses to the ground.

"They have lost the scent," said the old horse; "perhaps the hare will get off."

"What hare?" I said.

"Oh! I don't know *what* hare; likely enough it may be one of our own hares out of the plantation; any hare they can find will do for the dogs and men to run after." And before long the dogs began their "yo! yo, o, o!" again, and back they came all together at full speed, making straight for our meadow at the part where the high bank and hedge overhang the brook.

"Now we shall see the hare," said my mother; and just then a hare wild with fright rushed by, and made for the plantation. On came the dogs; they burst over the bank, leaped the stream, and came dashing across the field, followed by the huntsmen. Six or eight men leaped their horses clean over, close upon the dogs. The hare tried to get through the fence; it was too thick, and she turned sharp round to make for the road, but it was too late; the dogs were upon her with their wild cries; we heard one shriek, and that was the end of her. One of the huntsmen rode up and whipped off the dogs, who would soon have torn her to pieces. He held her up by the leg, torn and bleeding, and all the gentlemen seemed well pleased.

As for me, I was so astonished that I did not at first see what was going on by the brook; but when I did look, there was a sad sight; two fine horses were down, one was struggling in the stream, and the other was groaning on the grass. One of the riders was getting out of the water covered with mud, the other lay quite still.

"His neck is broken," said my mother.

"And serves him right, too," said one of the colts.

I thought the same, but my mother did not join with us.

"Well, no," she said, "you must not say that; but though I am an old horse, and have seen and heard a great deal, I never yet could make out why men are so fond of this sport. They often hurt themselves, often spoil good horses, and tear up the fields, and all for a hare or a fox, or a stag, that they could get more easily some other way; but we are only horses, and don't know."

While my mother was saying this, we stood and looked on. Many of the riders had gone to the young man; but my master, who had been watching what was going on, was the first to raise him. His head fell back and his arms hung down, and everyone looked very serious. There was no noise now; even the dogs were quiet, and seemed to know that something was wrong. They carried him to

our master's house. I heard afterwards that it was young George
Gordon, the squire's only son, a fine, tall young man, and the pride
of his family.

There was now riding off in all directions to the doctor's, to the
farrier's, and no doubt to Squire Gordon's, to let him know about his
son. When Mr. Bond, the farrier, came to look at the black horse
that lay groaning on the grass, he felt him all over, and shook his
head; one of his legs was broken. Then someone ran to our master's
house and came back with a gun; presently there was a loud bang
and a dreadful shriek, and then all was still; the black horse moved
no more.

My mother seemed much troubled; she said she had known that
horse for years, and that his name was "Rob Roy"; he was a good
bold horse, and there was no vice in him. She never would go to
that part of the field afterwards.

Not many days after, we heard the church bell tolling for a long
time; and looking over the gate we saw a long, strange black coach
that was covered with black cloth and was drawn by black horses;
after that came another and another and another, and all were black;
while the bell kept tolling, tolling. They were carrying young Gordon to the churchyard to bury him. He would never ride again.
What they did with Rob Roy I never knew; but 'twas all for one
little hare.

III

MY BREAKING IN

I was now beginning to grow handsome; my coat had grown fine
and soft, and was bright black. I had one white foot, and a pretty
white star on my forehead. I was thought very handsome; my
master would not sell me till I was four years old; he said lads ought
not to work like men, and colts ought not to work like horses till
they were quite grown-up.

When I was four years old, Squire Gordon came to look at me.
He examined my eyes, my mouth, and my legs; he felt them all

down; and then I had to walk and trot and gallop before him; he seemed to like me, and said, "When he has been well broken in, he will do very well." My master said he would break me in himself, as he should not like me to be frightened or hurt, and he lost no time about it, for the next day he began.

Everyone may not know what breaking in is, therefore I will describe it. It means to teach a horse to wear a saddle and bridle and to carry on his back a man, woman, or child; to go just the way they wish, and to go quietly. Besides this, he has to learn to wear a collar, a crupper, and a breeching, and to stand still while they are put on; then to have a cart or a chaise fixed behind him, so that he cannot walk or trot without dragging it after him; and he must go fast or slow, just as his driver wishes. He must never start at what he sees, nor speak to other horses, nor bite, nor kick, nor have any will of his own; but always do his master's will, even though he may be very tired or hungry; but the worst of all is, when his harness is once on, he may neither jump for joy nor lie down for weariness. So you see this breaking in is a great thing.

I had of course long been used to a halter and a headstall, and to be led about in the field and lanes quietly, but now I was to have a bit and a bridle; my master gave me some oats as usual, and after a good deal of coaxing, he got the bit into my mouth, and the bridle fixed, but it was a nasty thing! Those who have never had a bit in their mouths cannot think how bad it feels; a great piece of cold hard steel as thick as a man's finger to be pushed into one's mouth, between one's teeth and over one's tongue, with the ends coming out at the corner of your mouth, and held fast there by straps over your head, under your throat, round your nose, and under your chin; so that no way in the world can you get rid of the nasty hard thing; it is very bad! yes, very bad! at least I thought so; but I knew my mother always wore one when she went out, and all horses did when they were grown up; and so, what with the nice oats, and what with my master's pats, kind words, and gentle ways, I got to wear my bit and bridle.

Next came the saddle, but that was not half so bad; my master put it on my back very gently, whilst old Daniel held my head; he then made the girths fast under my body, patting and talking to me all the time; then I had a few oats, then a little leading about, and this he did every day until I began to look for the oats and the saddle. At length, one morning my master got on my back and rode me round the meadow on the soft grass. It certainly did feel queer; but I must say I felt rather proud to carry my master, and as he continued to ride me a little every day, I soon became accustomed to it.

The next unpleasant business was putting on the iron shoes; that too was very hard at first. My master went with me to the smith's forge, to see that I was not hurt or got any fright. The blacksmith took my feet in his hand one after the other, and cut away some of the hoof. It did not pain me, so I stood still on three legs till he had done them all. Then he took a piece of iron the shape of my foot, and clapped it on, and drove some nails through the shoe quite into my hoof, so that the shoe was firmly on. My feet felt very stiff and heavy, but in time I got used to it.

And now having got so far, my master went on to break me to harness; there were more new things to wear. First, a stiff heavy collar just on my neck, and a bridle with great sidepieces against my eyes called blinkers, and blinkers indeed they were, for I could not see on either side, but only straight in front of me; next there was a small saddle with a nasty stiff strap that went right under my tail; that was the crupper. I hated the crupper—to have my long tail doubled up and poked through that strap was almost as bad as the bit. I never felt more like kicking, but of course I could not kick such a good master, and so in time I got used to everything, and could work as well as my mother.

I must not forget to mention one part of my training, which I have always considered a very great advantage. My master sent me for a fortnight to a neighboring farmer's, who had a meadow which was skirted on one side by the railway. Here were some sheep and cows, and I was turned in among them.

I shall never forget the first train that ran by. I was feeding quietly near the pales which separated the meadow from the railway, when I heard a strange sound at a distance, and before I knew whence it came—with a rush and a clatter, and a puffing out of smoke—a long black train of something flew by, and was gone almost before I could draw my breath. I turned, and galloped to the farther side of the meadow as fast as I could go, and there I stood snorting with astonishment and fear. In the course of the day many other trains went by, some more slowly; these drew up at the station close by, and sometimes made an awful shriek and groan before they stopped. I thought it very dreadful, but the cows went on eating very quietly, and hardly raised their heads as the black, frightful thing came puffing and grinding past.

For the first few days I could not feed in peace; but as I found that this terrible creature never came into the field, or did me any harm, I began to disregard it, and very soon I cared as little about the passing of the train as the cows and sheep did.

Since then I have seen many horses much alarmed and restive at the sight or sound of a steam engine; but thanks to my good master's care, I am as fearless at railway stations as in my own stable.

Now if anyone wants to break in a young horse well, that is the way.

My master often drove me in double harness with my mother, because she was steady, and could teach me how to go better than a strange horse. She told me the better I behaved, the better I should be treated, and that it was wisest always to do my best to please my master; "But," said she, "there are a great many kinds of men; there are good, thoughtful men like our master, that any horse may be proud to serve; but there are bad, cruel men, who never ought to have a horse or dog to call their own. Besides, there are a great many foolish men, vain, ignorant, and careless, who never trouble themselves to think; these spoil more horses than all, just for want of sense; they don't mean it, but they do it for all that. I hope you will fall into good hands; but a horse never knows who may buy him, or who may drive him; it is all a chance for us, but still I say, do your best whatever it is, and keep up your good name."

IV

BIRTWICK PARK

At this time I used to stand in the stable, and my coat was brushed every day until it shone like a rook's wing. It was early in May, when there came a man from Squire Gordon's, who took me away to the Hall. My master said, "Good-bye, Darkie; be a good horse, and always do your best." I could not say "good-bye," so I put my nose into his hand; he patted me kindly, and I left my first home. As I lived some years with Squire Gordon, I may as well tell something about the place.

Squire Gordon's Park skirted the village of Birtwick. It was entered by a large iron gate, at which stood the first lodge, and then you trotted along a smooth road between clumps of large old trees; then another lodge and another gate, which brought you to the house and the gardens. Beyond this lay the home paddock, the old orchard, and the stables. There was accommodation for many horses and carriages; but I need only describe the stable into which I was taken; this was very roomy, with four good stalls; a large swinging window opened into the yard, which made it pleasant and airy.

The first stall was a large square one, shut in behind with a wooden gate; the others were common stalls, good stalls, but not nearly so large; it had a low rack for hay and a low manger for corn; it was called a loose box, because the horse that was put into it was not tied up, but left loose, to do as he liked. It is a great thing to have a loose box.

Into this fine box the groom put me; it was clean, sweet, and airy. I never was in a better box than that, and the sides were not so high but that I could see all that went on through the iron rails that were at the top. He gave me some very nice oats, he patted me, spoke kindly, and then went away.

When I had eaten my corn, I looked around. In the stall next to mine stood a little gray pony, with a thick mane and tail, a very pretty head, and a pert little nose.

I put my head up to the iron rails at the top of my box and said,

"How do you do? What is your name?"

He turned round as far as his halter would allow, held up his head, and said, "My name is Merrylegs; I am very handsome, I carry the young ladies on my back, and sometimes I take our mistress out in the low chair. They think a great deal of me, and so does James. Are you going to live next door to me in the box?"

I said, "Yes."

"Well, then," he said, "I hope you are good-tempered; I do not like anyone next door who bites."

Just then a horse's head looked over from the stall beyond; the ears were laid back, and the eye looked rather ill-tempered. This was a tall chestnut mare, with a long handsome neck; she looked across to me and said:

"So it is you who have turned me out of my box; it is a very strange thing for a colt like you to come and turn a lady out of her own home."

"I beg your pardon," I said, "I have turned no one out; the man who brought me put me here, and I had nothing to do with it; and as to my being a colt, I am turned four years old, and am a grown-up horse; I never had words yet with horse or mare, and it is my wish to live at peace."

"Well," she said, "we shall see; of course I do not want to have words with a young thing like you." I said no more.

In the afternoon when she went out, Merrylegs told me all about it.

"The thing is this," said Merrylegs; "Ginger has a bad habit of biting and snapping; that is why they call her Ginger, and when she was in the loose box, she used to snap very much. One day she bit James in the arm and made it bleed, and so Miss Flora and Miss Jessie, who are very fond of me, were afraid to come into the stable. They used to bring me nice things to eat, an apple or a carrot, or a piece of bread, but after Ginger stood in that box they dare not come, and I missed them very much. I hope they will now come again, if you do not bite."

I told them I never bit anything but grass, hay, and corn, and could not think what pleasure Ginger found it.

"Well, I don't think she does find pleasure," said Merrylegs; "it is just a bad habit; she says no one was ever kind to her, and why should she not bite? Of course it is a very bad habit; but I am sure, if all she says be true, she must have been very ill-used before she came here. John does all he can to please her, and James does all he can, and our master never uses a whip if a horse acts right; so I think she might be good-tempered here. You see," he said with a wise look, "I am twelve years old; I know a great deal, and I can tell you there is not a better place for a horse all round the country than this. John is the best groom that ever was, he has been here fourteen years; and you never saw such a kind boy as James is, so that it is all Ginger's own fault that she did not stay in that box."

V

A FAIR START

The name of the coachman was John Manly; he had a wife and one little child, and they lived in the coachman's cottage, very near the stables.

The next morning, he took me into the yard and gave me a good grooming, and just as I was going into my box with my coat soft and bright, the Squire came in to look at me, and seemed pleased. "John," he said, "I meant to have tried the new horse this morning, but I have other business. You may as well take him around after breakfast; go by the common and the Highwood, and back by the watermill and the river; that will show his paces."

"I will, sir," said John. After breakfast he came and fitted me with a bridle. He was very particular in letting out and taking in the straps, to fit my head comfortably; then he brought the saddle; that was not broad enough for my back; he saw it in a minute and went for another, which fitted nicely. He rode me first slowly, then a trot, then a canter, and when we were on the common he gave me a light touch with his whip, and we had a splendid gallop.

"Ho-ho, my boy," he said, as he pulled me up, "you would like to follow the hounds, I think, wouldn't you?"

As we came back through the Park we met the Squire and Mrs. Gordon walking; they stopped and John jumped off.

"Well, John, how does he go?"

"First-rate, sir," answered John, "he is as fleet as a deer, and has a fine spirit, too; but the lightest touch of the rein will guide him. Down at the end of the common we met one of those traveling carts hung all over with baskets, rugs, and such like; you know, sir, many horses will not pass those carts quietly; he just took a good look at it, and then went on as quietly and pleasant as could be. They were shooting rabbits near the Highwood, and a gun went off close by; he pulled up a little and looked, but did not stir a step to right or left. I just held the rein steady and did not hurry him, and it's my opinion he has not been frightened or ill-used while he was young."

"That's well," said the Squire, "I will try him myself tomorrow."

The next day I was brought up for my master. I remembered my mother's counsel and my good old master's, and I tried to do exactly what he wanted me to do. I found he was a very good rider, and thoughtful for his horse, too. When we came home, the lady was at the hall door as he rode up.

"Well, my dear," she said, "how do you like him?"

"He is exactly what John said," he replied; "a pleasanter creature I never wish to mount. What shall we call him?"

"Would you like Ebony?" said she. "He is as black as ebony."

"No, not Ebony."

"Will you call him Blackbird, like your uncle's old horse?"

"No, he is far handsomer than old Blackbird ever was."

"Yes," she said, "he is really quite a beauty, and he has such a sweet, good-tempered face and such a fine, intelligent eye—what do you say to calling him Black Beauty?"

"Black Beauty—why, yes, I think that is a very good name. If you like, it shall be his name," and so it was.

When John went into the stable, he told James that the master and mistress had chosen a good sensible English name for me, that meant something, not like Marengo, or Pegasus, or Abdallah. They both laughed, and James said. "If it was not for bringing back the past, I should have named him Rob Roy, for I never saw two horses more alike."

"That's no wonder," said John; "didn't you know that Farmer Grey's old Duchess was the mother of them both?"

I had never heard that before, and so poor Rob Roy who was killed at that hunt was my brother! I did not wonder that my mother was so troubled: It seems that horses have no relations; at least, they never know each other after they are sold.

John seemed very proud of me; he used to make my mane and tail almost as smooth as a lady's hair, and he would talk to me a great deal; of course I did not understand all he said, but I learned more and more to know what he *meant,* and what he wanted me to do. I grew very fond of him, he was so gentle and kind, he seemed to know just how a horse feels, and when he cleaned me, he knew the tender places, and the ticklish places; when he brushed my head, he went as carefully over my eyes as if they were his own, and never stirred up any ill temper.

James Howard, the stable boy, was just as gentle and pleasant in his way, so I thought myself well off. There was another man who helped in the ward, but he had very little to do with Ginger and me.

A few days after this, I had to go out with Ginger in the carriage. I wondered how we should get on together; but except laying her ears back when I was led up to her, she behaved very well. She did her work honestly, and did her full share, and I never wish to have a better partner in double harness. When we came to a hill, instead of slackening her pace, she would throw her weight right into the collar, and pull away straight up. We had both the same sort of courage at work, and John had oftener to hold us in than to urge us forward; he never had to use the whip with either of us; then our paces were much the same, and I found it very easy to keep step with her when trotting, which made it pleasant, and master always liked it when we kept step well, and so did John. After we had been out two or three times together we grew quite friendly and sociable, which made me feel very much at home.

As for Merrylegs, he and I soon became great friends; he was such a cheerful, plucky, good-tempered little fellow, that he was a favorite with everyone, and especially with Miss Jessie and Flora, who used to ride him about in the orchard, and have fine games with him and their little dog Frisky.

Our master had two other horses that stood in another stable. One was Justice, a roan cob, used for riding, or for the luggage cart; the other was an old brown hunter, named Sir Oliver; he was past work now, but was a great favorite with the master, who gave him the run of the park; he sometimes did a little light carting on the estate, or carried one of the young ladies when they rode out with their father; for he was very gentle, and could be trusted with a child as well as Merrylegs. The cob was a strong, well-made, good-tempered horse, and we sometimes had a little chat in the paddock, but of course I could not be so intimate with him as with Ginger, who stood in the same stable.

VI

LIBERTY

I was quite happy in my new place, and if there was one thing that I missed, it must not be thought I was discontented; all who had to do with me were good, and I had a light, airy stable and the best of food. What more could I want? Why, liberty! For three years and a half of my life I had had all the liberty I could wish for; but now, week after week, month after month, and no doubt year after year, I must stand up in a stable night and day except when I am wanted, and then I must be just as steady and quiet as any old horse who has worked twenty years. Straps here and straps there, a bit in my mouth, and blinkers over my eyes. Now, I am not complaining, for I know it must be so. I only mean to say that for a young horse full of strength and spirits who has been used to some large field or plain, where he can fling up his head and toss up his tail and gallop away at full speed, then round and back again with a snort to his companions—I say it is hard never to have a bit more liberty to do as you like. Sometimes, when I have had less exercise than usual, I have felt so full of life and spring that when John has taken me out to exercise I really could not keep quiet; do what I would, it seemed as if I must jump, or dance, or prance, and many a good shake I know I must have given him, specially at the first; but he was always good and patient.

"Steady, steady, my boy," he would say; "wait a bit, and we'll have a good swing and soon get the tickle out of your feet." Then as soon as we were out of the village, he would give me a few miles at a spanking trot, and then bring me back as fresh as before, only clear of the fidgets, as he called them. Spirited horses, when not enough exercised, are often called skittish, when it is only play; and some grooms will punish them, but our John did not, he knew it was only high spirits. Still, he had his own ways of making me understand by the tone of his voice or the touch of the rein. If he was very serious and quite determined, I always knew it by his voice, and that had more power with me than anything else, for I was very fond of him.

I ought to say that sometimes we had our liberty for a few hours; this used to be on fine Sundays in the summertime. The carriage never went out on Sundays, because the church was not far off.

It was a great treat to us to be turned out into the home paddock or the old orchard. The grass was so cool and soft to our feet; the air so sweet, and the freedom to do as we liked was so pleasant; to gallop, to lie down, and roll over on our backs, or to nibble the sweet grass. Then it was a very good time for talking, as we stood together under the shade of the large chestnut tree.

VII

GINGER

One day when Ginger and I were standing alone in the shade we had a great deal of talk; she wanted to know all about my bringing up and breaking in, and I told her.

"Well," said she, "if I had had your bringing up I might have had as good a temper as you, but now I don't believe I ever shall."

"Why not?" I said.

"Because it has been all so different with me," she replied; "I never had anyone, horse or man, that was kind to me, or that I cared to please, for in the first place I was taken from my mother as soon as I was weaned, and put with a lot of other young colts; none of them cared for me, and I cared for none of them. There was no kind master like yours to look after me, and talk to me, and bring me nice things to eat. The man that had the care of us never gave me a kind word in my life. I do not mean that he ill-used me, but he did not care for us one bit further than to see that we had plenty to eat and shelter in the winter. A footpath ran through our field, and very often the great boys passing through would fling stones to make us gallop. I was never hit, but one fine colt was badly cut in the face, and I should think it would be a scar for life. We did not care for them, but of course it made us more wild, and we settled it in our minds that boys were our enemies. We had very good fun in the free meadows, galloping up and down and chasing each other round and round the field; then standing still under the shade of the trees. But when it came to breaking in, that was a bad time for me; several men came to catch me, and when at last they closed me in at one corner of the field, one caught me by the forelock, another caught me by the nose, and held it so tight I could hardly draw my breath; then another took my under jaw in his hard hand and wrenched my mouth open, and so by force they got on the halter, and the bar into my mouth; then one dragged me along by the halter, another flogging behind, and this was the first experience I had of men's kindness; it was all force. They did not give me a chance to know what they wanted. I was high bred and had a great deal of spirit, and was very wild, no doubt, and gave them, I daresay, plenty of trouble, but then it was dreadful to be shut up in a stall day after day instead of having my liberty, and I fretted and pined and wanted to get loose. You know yourself, it's bad enough when you have a kind master and plenty of coaxing, but there was nothing of that sort for me.

"There was one—the old master, Mr. Ryder, who I think could soon have brought me round, and could have done anything with me, but he had given up all the hard part of the trade to his son and to another experienced man, and he only came at times to oversee. His son was a strong, tall, bold man; they called him Samson, and he used to boast that he had never found a horse that could throw him. There was no gentleness in him as there was in his father, but only hardness, a hard voice, a hard eye, a hard hand, and I felt from the first that what he wanted was to wear all the spirit out of me, and just make me into a quiet, humble, obedient piece of horseflesh. 'Horseflesh!' Yes, that is all that he thought about," and Ginger stamped her foot as if the very thought of him made her angry. And she went on: "If I did not do exactly what he wanted, he would get put out, and make me run round with that long rein in the training field till he had me tired out. I think he drank a good deal, and I am quite sure that the oftener he drank the worse it was for me. One day he had worked me hard in every way he could, and when I laid down I was tired and miserable, and angry; it all seemed so hard. The next morning he came for me early, and ran me round again for a long time. I had scarcely had an hour's rest, when he came again for me with a saddle and bridle and a new kind of bit. I could never quite tell how it came about; he had only just mounted me on the training ground, when something I did put him out of temper, and he chucked me hard with the rein. The new bit was very painful, and I reared up suddenly, which angered him still more, and he began to flog me. I felt my whole spirit set against him, and I began to kick, and plunge, and rear as I had never done before, and we had a regular fight; for a long time he stuck to the saddle and punished me cruelly with his whip and spurs, but my blood was thoroughly up, and I cared for nothing he could do if only I could get him off. At last, after a terrible struggle, I threw him off backwards. I heard him fall heavily on the turf, and without looking behind me, I galloped off to the other end of the field; there I turned round and saw my persecutor slowly rising from the ground and going into the stable. I stood under an oak tree and watched, but no one came to catch me. The time went on, the sun was very hot, the flies swarmed round me and settled on my bleeding flanks where the spurs had dug in. I felt hungry, for I had not eaten since the early morning, but there was not enough grass in that

Katherine Pyle

After a terrible struggle, I threw him off backwards.

meadow for a goose to live on. I wanted to lie down and rest, but with the saddle strapped tightly on, there was no comfort, and there was not a drop of water to drink. The afternoon wore on, and the sun got low. I saw the other colts led in, and I knew they were having a good feed.

"At last, just as the sun went down, I saw the old master come out with a sieve in his hand. He was a very fine old gentleman with quite white hair, but his voice was what I should know him by among a thousand. It was not high, nor yet low, but full, and clear, and kind; and when he gave orders, it was so steady and decided that everyone knew, both horses and men, that he expected to be obeyed. He came quietly along, now and then shaking the oats about that he had in the sieve, and speaking cheerfully and gently to me, 'Come along, lassie, come along, lassie; come along, come along.' I stood still and let him come up; he held the oats to me and I began to eat without fear; his voice took all my fear away. He stood by, patting and stroking me while I was eating, and seeing the clots of blood on my side he seemed very vexed; 'Poor lassie! it was a bad business, a bad business!' then he quietly took the rein and led me to the stable. Just at the door stood Samson. I laid my ears back and snapped at him. 'Stand back,' said the master, 'and keep out of her way; you've done a bad day's work for this filly.' He growled out something about a vicious brute. 'Hark ye,' said the father, 'a bad-tempered man will never make a good-tempered horse. You've not learned your trade yet, Samson.' Then he led me into my box, took off the saddle and bridle with his own hands, and tied me up; then he called for a pail of warm water and a sponge, took off his coat, and while the stableman held the pail, he sponged my sides a good while so tenderly that I was sure he knew how sore and bruised they were. 'Whoa! my pretty one,' he said, 'stand still, stand still.' His very voice did me good, and the bathing was very comfortable. The skin was so broken at the corners of my mouth that I could not eat the hay, the stalks hurt me. He looked closely at it, shook his head, and told the man to fetch a good bran mash and put some meal into it. How good that mash was! and so soft and healing to my mouth. He stood by all the time I was eating, stroking me and talking to the man. 'If a high-mettled creature like this,' said he, 'can't be broken in by fair means, she will never be good for anything.'

"After that he often came to see me, and when my mouth was healed, the other breaker, Job, they called him, went on training me; he was steady and thoughtful, and I soon learned what he wanted."

VIII

GINGER'S STORY CONTINUED

The next time that Ginger and I were together in the paddock, she told me about her first place.

"After my breaking in," she said, "I was bought by a dealer to match another chestnut horse. For some weeks he drove us together, and then we were sold to a fashionable gentleman, and were sent up to London. I had been driven with a bearing rein by the dealer, and I hated it worse than anything else; but in this place we were reined far tighter; the coachman and his master thinking we looked more stylish so. We were often driven about in the park and other fashionable places. You who never had a bearing rein on don't know what it is, but I can tell you it is dreadful.

"I like to toss my head about, and hold it as high as any horse; but fancy, now, yourself, if you tossed your head up high and were obliged to hold it there, and that for hours together, not able to move it at all, except with a jerk still higher, your neck aching till you did not know how to bear it. Besides that, to have two bits instead of one; and mine was a sharp one, it hurt my tongue and my jaw, and the blood from my tongue colored the froth that kept flying from my lips, as I chafed and fretted at the bits and rein; it was worst when we had to stand by the hour waiting for our mistress at some grand party or entertainment; and if I fretted or stamped with impatience the whip was laid on. It was enough to drive one mad."

"Did not your master take any thought for you?" I said.

"No," she said, "he only cared to have a stylish turnout, as they call it; I think he knew very little about horses, he left that to his coachman, who told him I was an irritable temper; that I had not been well broken to the bearing rein, but I should soon get used to it; but *he* was not the man to do it, for when I was in the stable, miserable and angry, instead of being soothed and quieted by kindness, I got only a surly word or a blow. If he had been civil, I would have tried to bear it. I was willing to work, and ready to work hard, too; but to be tormented for nothing but their fancies angered me. What right had they to make me suffer like that? Besides the soreness in my mouth and the pain in my neck, it always made my windpipe feel bad, and if I had stopped there long, I know it would have spoiled my breathing; but I grew more and more restless and irritable, I could not help it; and I began to snap and kick when anyone came to harness me; for this, the groom beat me, and one day, as they had just buckled us into the carriage, and were straining my head up with that rein, I began to plunge and kick with all my might. I soon broke a lot of harness, and kicked myself clear; so that was an end of that place.

"After this, I was sent to Tattersall's to be sold; of course I could not be warranted free from vice, so nothing was said about that. My handsome appearance and good paces soon brought a gentleman to bid for me, and I was bought by another dealer; he tried me in all kinds of ways and with different bits, and soon found out what I could bear. At last he drove me quite without a bearing rein, and then sold me as a perfectly quiet horse to a gentleman in the country; he was a good master, and I was getting along very well, but his old groom left him and a new one came. This man was as hard-tempered and hard-handed as Samson; he always spoke in a rough, impatient voice, and if I did not move in the stall the moment he wanted me, he would hit me above the hocks with his stable broom or the fork, whichever he might have in his hand. Everything he did was rough, and I began to hate him; he wanted to make me afraid of him, but I was too high-mettled for that; and one day when he had aggravated me more than usual, I bit him, which of course put him in a great rage, and he began to hit me about the head with a riding whip. After that, he never dared to come into my stall again, either my heels or my teeth were ready for him, and he knew it. I was quite quiet with my master, but of course he listened to what the man said, and so I was sold again.

"The same dealer heard of me, and said he thought he knew one place where I should do well. ' 'Twas a pity,' he said, 'that such a fine horse should go to the bad, for want of a real good chance,' and the end of it was that I came here not long before you did; but I had then made up my mind that men were my natural enemies, and that I must defend myself. Of course it is very different here, but who knows how long it will last? I wish I could think about things as you do; but I can't, after all I have gone through."

"Well," I said, "I think it would be a real shame if you were to bite or kick John or James."

"I don't mean to," he said, "while they are good to me, I did bite James once pretty sharp; but John said, 'Try her with kindness,' and instead of punishing me as I expected, James came to me with his arm bound up, and brought me a bran mash and stroked me; and I have never snapped at him since, and I won't either."

I was sorry for Ginger, but of course I knew very little then, and I thought most likely she made the worst of it; however, I found that as the weeks went on, she grew much more gentle and cheerful, and had lost the watchful, defiant look that she used to turn on any strange person who came near her; and one day James said, "I do believe that mare is getting fond of me, she quite whinnied after me this morning when I had been rubbing her forehead."

"Ay, ay, Jim, 'tis the Birtwick balls," said John, "she'll be as good as Black Beauty by and by; kindness is all the physic she wants, poor thing!" Master noticed the change too, and one day when he got out of the carriage and came to speak to us as he often did, he stroked her beautiful neck, "Well, my pretty one, well, how do things go with you now? You are a good bit happier than when you came to us, I think."

She put her nose up to him in a friendly, trustful way, while he rubbed it gently.

"We shall make a cure of her, John," he said.

"Yes, sir, she's wonderfully improved, she's not the same creature that she was; it's the Birtwick balls, sir," said John, laughing.

This was a little joke of John's; he used to say that a regular course of the Birtwick horse balls would cure almost any vicious horse; these balls, he said, were made up of patience and gentleness, firmness and petting, one pound of each to be mixed up with half a pint of common sense, and given to the horse every day.

IX

MERRYLEGS

Mr. Blomefield, the Vicar, had a large family of boys and girls; sometimes they used to come and play with Miss Jessie and Flora. One of the girls was as old as Miss Jessie; two of the boys were older, and there were several little ones. When they came, there was plenty of work for Merrylegs, for nothing pleased them so much as getting on him by turns and riding him all about the orchard and the home paddock, and this they would do by the hour together.

One afternoon he had been out with them a long time, and when James brought him in and put on his halter, he said:

"There, you rogue, mind how you behave yourself, or we shall get into trouble."

"What have you been doing, Merrylegs," I asked.

"Oh!" said he, tossing his little head, "I have only been giving those young people a lesson. They did not know when they had had enough, nor when I had had enough, so I just pitched them off backward; that was the only thing they could understand."

"What?" said I, "You threw the children off? I thought you did know better than that! Did you throw Miss Jessie or Miss Flora?"

He looked very much offended, and said:

"Of course not, I would not do such a thing for the best oats that ever came into the stable; why, I am as careful of our young ladies as the master could be, and as for the little ones, it is I who teach them to ride. When they seem frightened, or a little unsteady on my back, I go as smooth and as quiet as old pussy when she is after a bird; and when they are all right, I go on again faster, you see, just to use them to it; so don't trouble yourself preaching to me; I am the best friend, and the best riding master those children have. It is not them, it is the boys; "boys," said he, shaking his mane, "are quite different; they must be broken in, as we were broken in when we were colts, and just be taught what's what. The other children had ridden me about for nearly two hours, and then the boys thought it was their turn, and so it was, and I was quite agreeable. They rode me by turns, and I galloped them about up and down the fields and all about the orchard for a good hour. They had each cut a great hazel stick for a riding whip, and laid it on a little too hard; but I took it in good part, till at last I thought we had had enough so I stopped two or three times by way of a hint. Boys, you see, think a horse or pony is like a steam engine or a thrashing machine, and can go on as long and as fast as they please; they never think that a pony can get tired, or have any feelings; so as the one who was whipping me could not understand, I just rose up on my hind legs and let him slip off behind—that was all; he mounted me again, and I did the same. Then the other boy got up, and as soon as he began to use his stick I laid him on the grass, and so on, till they were able to understand that was all. They are not bad boys; they don't wish to be cruel. I like them very well; but you see I had to give them a lesson. When they brought me to James and told him, I think he was very angry to see such big sticks. He said they were only fit for drovers or gypsies, and not for young gentlemen."

"If I had been you," said Ginger, "I would have given those boys a good kick, and that would have given them a lesson."

"No doubt you would," said Merrylegs, "but then I am not quite such a fool (begging your pardon) as to anger our master or make James ashamed of me; besides, those children are under my charge when they are riding; I tell you they are entrusted to me. Why, only the other day I heard our master say to Mrs. Blomefield, 'My dear madam, you need not be anxious about the children, my old Merrylegs will take as much care of them as you or I could; I assure you I would not sell that pony for any money, he is so perfectly good-tempered and trustworthy'; and do you think I am such an ungrateful brute as to forget all the kind treatment I have had here for five years, and all the trust they place in me, and turn vicious because a couple of ignorant boys used me badly? No! no! You never had a good place where they were kind to you; and so you don't know, and I'm sorry for you, but I can tell you good places make good horses. I wouldn't vex our people for anything; I love them, I do," said Merrylegs, and he gave a low "ho, ho, ho," through his nose as he used to do in the morning when he heard James's footstep at the door.

"Besides," he went on, "if I took to kicking where should I be? Why, sold off in a jiffy, and no character, and I might find myself slaved about under a butcher's boy, or worked to death at some seaside place where no one cared for me, except to find out how fast I could go, or be flogged along in some cart with three or four great men in it going out for a Sunday spree, as I have often seen in the place I lived in before I came here; no," said he, shaking his head, "I hope I shall never come to that."

X

A TALK IN THE ORCHARD

Ginger and I were not of the regular tall carriage horse breed, we had more of the racing blood in us. We stood about fifteen and a half hands high; we were therefore just as good for riding as we were for driving, and our master used to say that he disliked either horse or man that could do but one thing; and as he did not want to show off in London parks he preferred a more active and useful kind of horse. As for us, our greatest pleasure was when we were saddled for a riding party, the master on Ginger, the mistress on me, and the young ladies on Sir Oliver and Merrylegs. It was so cheerful to be trotting and cantering all together that it always put us in high spirits. I had the best of it, for I always carried the mistress; her weight was little, her voice was sweet, and her hand was so light on the rein that I was guided almost without feeling it.

Oh! if people knew what a comfort to horses a light hand is, and how it keeps a good mouth and a good temper, they surely would not chuck, and drag, and pull at the rein as they often do. Our mouths are so tender that where they have not been spoiled or hardened with bad or ignorant treatment they feel the slightest movement of the driver's hand, and we know in an instant what is required of us. My mouth had never been spoiled, and I believe that was why the mistress preferred me to Ginger, although her paces were certainly quite as good. She used often to envy me, and said it was all the fault of breaking in, and the gag bit in London, that her mouth was not so perfect as mine; and then old Sir Oliver would say, "There, there! don't vex yourself; you have the greatest honor; a mare that can carry a tall man of our master's weight, with all your spring and sprightly action, does not need to hold her head down because she does not carry the lady; we horses must take things as they come, and always be contented and willing so long as we are kindly used."

I had often wondered how it was that Sir Oliver had such a very short tail; it really was only six or seven inches long, with a tassel of hair hanging from it; and on one of our holidays in the orchard I ventured to ask him by what accident it was that he had lost his tail. "Accident," he snorted, with a fierce look, "it was no accident! It was a cruel, shameful, cold-blooded act! When I was young I was taken to a place where these cruel things were done. I was tied up and made fast so that I could not stir, and then they came and cut off my long, beautiful tail, through the flesh, and through the bone, and took it away."

"How dreadful!" I exclaimed.

"Dreadful! Ah! It was dreadful; but it was not only the pain, though that was terrible and lasted a long time; it was not only the indignity of having my best ornament taken from me, though that was bad; but it was this, how could I ever brush the flies off my sides and my hind legs any more? You who have tails just whisk the flies off without thinking about it, and you can't tell what a torment it is to have them settle upon you and sting and sting, and have nothing in the world to lash them off with. I tell you, it is a lifelong wrong, and a lifelong loss; but thank Heaven! they don't do it now."

"What did they do it for then?" said Ginger.

"For fashion!" said the old horse with a stamp of his foot; "For fashion! if you know what that means. There was not a well-bred young horse in my time that had not his tail docked in that shameful way, just as if the good God that made us did not know what we wanted and what looked best."

"I suppose it is fashion that makes them strap our heads up with those horrid bits that I was tortured with in London," said Ginger.

"Of course, it is," said he; "to my mind, fashion is one of the wickedest things in the world. Now look, for instance, at the way they serve dogs, cutting off their tails to make them look plucky, and shearing up their pretty little ears to a point to make them look sharp, forsooth! I had a dear friend once, a brown terrier—Skye, they called her; she was so fond of me that she never would sleep out of my stall; she made her bed under the manger, and there she had a litter of five as pretty little puppies as need be; none were drowned, for they were a valuable kind, and how pleased she was with them! And when they got their eyes open and crawled about, it was a real pretty sight. But one day the man came and took them all away. I thought he might be afraid I should tread upon them. But it was not so; in the evening poor Skye brought them back again, one by one, in her mouth; not the happy little things that they were, but bleeding and crying pitifully. They had all had a piece of their tails cut off, and the soft flap of their pretty little ears was cut quite off. How their mother licked them and how troubled she was, poor thing! I never forgot it. They healed in time, and they forgot the pain, but the nice, soft flap that, of course, was intended to protect the delicate part of their ears from dust and injury was gone forever. Why don't they cut their own children's ears into points to make them look sharp? Why don't they cut the end off their noses to make them look plucky? One would be just as sensible as the other. What right have they to torment and disfigure God's creatures?"

Sir Oliver, though he was so gentle, was a fiery old fellow, and what he said was all so new to me and so dreadful that I found a bitter feeling toward men rise up in my mind that I had never had before. Of course, Ginger was much excited; she flung up her head with flashing eyes and distended nostrils, declaring that men were both brutes and blockheads.

"Who talks about blockheads?" said Merrylegs, who just came up from the old apple tree, where he had been rubbing himself against the low branch; "Who talks about blockheads? I believe that is a bad word."

"Bad words were made for bad things," said Ginger, and she told him what Sir Oliver had said. "It is all true," said Merrylegs sadly, "and I've seen that about the dogs over and over again where I lived first; but we won't talk about it here. You know that master, and John, and James are always good to us, and talking against men in such a place as this doesn't seem fair or grateful, and you know there are good masters and good grooms besides ours, though, of course, ours are the best." This wise speech of good little Merrylegs, which we knew was quite true, cooled us all down, specially Sir Oliver, who was dearly fond of his master; and to turn the subject I said, "Can anyone tell me the use of blinkers?"

"No!" said Sir Oliver shortly, "because they are no use."

"They are supposed," said Justice in his calm way, "to prevent horses from shying and starting, and getting so frightened as to cause accidents."

"Then what is the reason they do not put them on riding horses; especially on ladies' horses?" said I.

"There is no reason at all," said he quietly, "except the fashion; they say that a horse would be so frightened to see the wheels of his own cart or carriage coming behind him that he would be sure to run away, although, of course, when he is ridden he sees them all about him if the streets are crowded. I admit they do sometimes come too close to be pleasant, but we don't run away; we are used to it, and understand it, and if we had never blinkers put on, we should never want them; we should see what was there, and know what was what, and be much less frightened than by only seeing bits of things that we can't understand."

Of course, there may be some nervous horses who have been hurt or frightened when they were young, and may be the better for them, but as I never was nervous I can't judge.

"I consider," said Sir Oliver, "that blinkers are dangerous things in the night; we horses can see much better in the dark than man can, and many an accident would never have happened if horses might have had the full use of their eyes. Some years ago, I remember, there was a hearse with two horses returning one dark night, and just by Farmer Sparrow's house, where the pond is close to the road, the wheels went too near the edge, and the hearse was overturned into the water; both the horses were drowned, and the driver hardly escaped. Of course, after this accident a stout white rail was put up that might be easily seen, but if those horses had not been partly blinded they would of themselves have kept farther from the edge, and no accident would have happened. When our master's carriage was overturned, before you came here, it was said that if the lamp on the left side had not gone out John would have seen the great hole that the road makers had left; and so he might, but if old Colin had not had blinkers on he would have seen it, lamp or no lamp, for he was far too knowing an old horse to run into danger. As it was, he was very much hurt, the carriage was broken, and how John escaped nobody knew."

"I should say," said Ginger, curling her nostril, "that these men, who are so wise, had better give orders that in future all foals should be born with their eyes set just in the middle of their foreheads, instead of on the side; they always think they can improve upon Nature and mend what God has made."

Things were getting rather sore again, when Merrylegs held up his knowing little face and said. "I'll tell you a secret; I believe John does not approve of blinkers; I heard him talking with master about it one day. The master said that if horses had been used to them it might be dangerous in some cases to leave them off, and John said he thought it would be a good thing if all colts were broken in without blinkers, as was the case in some foreign countries; so let us cheer up, and have a run to the other end of the orchard; I believe the wind has blown down some apples, and we might just as well eat them as the slugs."

Merrylegs could not be resisted, so we broke off our long conversation, and got up our spirits by munching some very sweet apples which lay scattered on the grass.

XI

PLAIN SPEAKING

The longer I lived at Birtwick, the more proud and happy I felt at having such a place. Our master and mistress were respected and beloved by all who knew them; they were good and kind to everybody and everything; not only men and women, but horses and donkeys, dogs and cats, cattle and birds. There was no oppressed or ill-used creature that had not a friend in them, and their servants took the same tone. If any of the village children were known to treat any creature cruelly, they soon heard about it from the Hall.

The Squire and Farmer Grey had worked together, as they said, for more than twenty years to get bearing reins on the cart horses done away with, and in our parts you seldom saw them; but sometimes if mistress met a heavily laden horse, with his head strained up, she would stop the carriage and get out, and reason with the driver in her sweet serious voice, and try to show him how foolish and cruel it was. I don't think any man could withstand our mistress. I wish all ladies were like her.

Our master, too, used to come down very heavy sometimes. I remember he was riding me toward home one morning when we saw a powerful man driving toward us in a little pony chaise, with a beautiful little bay pony, with slender legs and a high-bred, sensitive head and face. Just as he came to the Park gates the little thing turned toward them; the man, without word or warning, wrenched the creature's head round with such force and suddenness that he nearly threw it on its haunches; recovering itself, it was going on when he began to lash it furiously; the pony plunged forward, but the strong, heavy hand held the pretty creature back with force almost enough to break its jaw, while the whip still cut into him. It was a dreadful sight to me, for I knew what fearful pain it gave that delicate little mouth; but master gave me the word, and we were up with him in a second.

"Sawyer," he cried in a stern voice, "is that pony made of flesh and blood?"

"Flesh and blood and temper," he said; "he's too fond of his own will, and that won't suit me." He spoke as if he was in a strong passion; he was a builder who had often been to the Park on business. "And do you think," said master sternly, "that treatment like this will make him fond of your will?"

"He had no business to make that turn; his road was straight on!" said the man roughly.

"You have often driven that pony up to my place," said the master; "it only shows the creature's memory and intelligence; how did he know that you were not going there again? But that has little to do with it. I must say, Mr. Sawyer, that more unmanly, brutal treatment of a little pony it was never my painful lot to witness; and by giving way to such passion you injure your own character as much, nay, more, than you injure your horse, and remember, we shall all have to be judged according to our works, whether they be toward man or toward beast."

Master rode me home slowly, and I could tell by his voice how the thing had grieved him. He was just as free to speak to gentlemen of his own rank as to those below him; for another day, when we were out, we met a Captain Langley, a friend of our master's; he was driving a splendid pair of grays in a kind of break. After a little conversation the Captain said:

"What do you think of my new team, Mr. Douglas? You know, you are the judge of horses in these parts, and I should like your opinion."

The master backed me a little, so as to get a good view of them. "They are an uncommonly handsome pair," he said, "and if they are as good as they look I am sure you need not wish for anything better; but I see you still hold that pet scheme of yours for worrying your horses and lessening their power."

"What do you mean," said the other, "the bearing reins? Oh, ah! I know that's a hobby of yours; well, the fact is, I like to see my horses hold their heads up."

"So do I," said master, "as well as any man, but I don't like to see them *held up;* that takes all the shine out of it. Now, you are a military man, Langley, and no doubt like to see your regiment look well on parade, 'Heads up,' and all that; but you would not take much credit for your drill if all your men had their heads tied to a backboard! It might not be much harm on parade except to worry and fatigue them, but how would it be in a bayonet charge against the enemy, when they want the free use of every muscle and all their strength thrown forward? I would not give much for their chance of victory, and it is just the same with horses; you fret and worry their tempers and decrease their power; you will not let them throw their weight against their work, and so they have to do too much with their joints and muscles, and, of course, it wears them up faster. You may depend upon it, horses were intended to have their heads free, as free as men's are; and if we could act a little more according to common sense, and a good deal less according to fashion, we should find many things work easier; besides, you know as well as I that if a horse makes a false step he has much less chance of recovering himself if his head and neck are fastened back. And now," said the master, laughing, "I have given my hobby a good trot out, can't you make up your mind to mount him, too, Captain? Your example would go a long way."

"I believe you are right in theory," said the other, "and that's rather a hard hit about the soldiers; but—well—I'll think about it." and so they parted.

XII

A STORMY DAY

One day late in the autumn, my master had a long journey to go on business. I was put into the dogcart, and John went with his master. I always liked to go in the dogcart, it was so light and the high wheels ran along so pleasantly. There had been a great deal of rain, and now the wind was very high and blew the dry leaves across the road in a shower. We went along merrily till we came to the toll bar and the low wooden bridge. The river banks were rather high, and the bridge, instead of rising, went across just level, so that in the middle, if the river was full, the water would be nearly up to the woodwork and planks; but as there were good, substantial rails on each side people did not mind it.

The man at the gate said the river was rising fast, and he feared it would be a bad night. Many of the meadows were under water, and in one low part of the road the water was half-way up to my knees; the bottom was good, and master drove gently, so it was no matter.

When we got to the town, of course, I had a good bait, but as the master's business engaged him a long time we did not start for home till rather late in the afternoon. The wind was then much higher, and I heard the master say to John he had never been out in such a storm; and so I thought, as we went along the skirts of a wood, where the great branches were swaying about like twigs, and the rushing sound was terrible.

"I wish we were well out of this wood," said my master.

"Yes, sir," said John, "it would be rather awkward if one of these branches came down upon us."

The words were scarcely out of his mouth when there was a groan and a crack, and a splitting sound; and tearing, crashing down among the other trees came an oak, torn up by the roots, and it fell right across the road just before us. I will never say I was not frightened, for I was. I stopped still, and I believe I trembled; of course, I did not turn around or run away; I was not brought up to that. John jumped out and was in a moment at my head. "That was a very near touch," said my master. "What's to be done now?"

"Well, sir, we can't drive over that tree nor yet get round it; there will be nothing for it but to go back to the four crossways, and that will be a good six miles before we get round to the wooden bridge again; it will make us late, but the horse is fresh."

So back we went, and round by the crossroads; but by the time we got to the bridge it was very nearly dark. We could just see that the water was over the middle of it; but as that happened sometimes when the floods were out, master did not stop. We were going along at a good pace, but the moment my feet touched the first part of the bridge, I felt sure there was something wrong. I dare not go forward, and I made a dead stop. "Go on, Beauty," said my master, and he gave me a touch of the whip, but I dare not stir; he then gave me a sharp cut; I jumped, but I dare not go forward.

"There's something wrong, sir," said John, and he sprang out of the dogcart and came to my head and looked all about. He tried to lead me forward, "Come on, Beauty, what's the matter?" Of course, I could not tell him, but I knew very well that the bridge was not safe.

Just then the man at the tollgate on the other side ran out of the house, tossing a torch about like one mad.

"Hoy, hoy, hoy, halloo, stop!" he cried.

"What's the matter?" shouted my master.

"The bridge is broken in the middle, and part of it is carried away; if you come on you'll be into the river."

"Thank God!" said my master. "You Beauty!" said John, and took the bridle and gently turned me round to the right-hand road by the river side. The sun had set some time, the wind seemed to have lulled off after that furious blast which tore up the tree. It grew darker and darker, stiller and stiller. I trotted quietly along, the wheels hardly making a sound on the soft road. For a good while neither master nor John spoke, and then master began in a serious voice. I could not understand much of what they said, but I found they thought, if I had gone on as the master wanted me, most likely the bridge would have given way under us, and horse, chaise, master, and man would have fallen into the river; and as the current was flowing very strongly, and there was no light and no help at hand, it was more than likely we should all have been drowned. Master said God had given men reason by which they could find out things for themselves, but He had given animals knowledge which did not depend on reason, and which was much more prompt and perfect in its way, and by which they often saved the lives of men. John had many stories to tell of dogs and horses, and the wonderful things they had done; he thought people did not value their animals half enough, nor make friends of them as they ought to do. I am sure he makes friends of them if ever a man did.

At last we came to the Park gates, and found the gardener looking out for us. He said that mistress had been in a dreadful way ever since dark, fearing some accident had happened, and that she had sent James off on Justice, the roan cob, toward the wooden bridge to make inquiry after us.

We saw a light at the hall door and at the upper windows, and as we came up mistress ran out, saying, "Are you really safe, my dear? Oh! I have been so anxious, fancying all sorts of things. Have you had no accident?"

"No, my dear; but if your Black Beauty had not been wiser than we were, we should all have been carried down the river at the wooden bridge." I heard no more, as they went into the house, and John took me to the stable. Oh! what a good supper he gave me that night, a good bran mash and some crushed beans with my oats, and such a thick bed of straw, and I was glad of it, for I was tired.

XIII

THE DEVIL'S TRADE-MARK

One day when John and I had been out on some business of our master's, and were returning gently on a long, straight road, at some distance we saw a boy trying to leap a pony over a gate; the pony would not take the leap, and the boy cut him with the whip, but he only turned off on one side. He whipped him again, but the pony turned off on the other side. Then the boy got off and gave him a hard thrashing, and knocked him about the head; then he got up again and tried to make him leap the gate, kicking him all the time shamefully, but still the pony refused. When we were nearly at the spot, the pony put down his head and threw up his heels and sent the boy neatly over into a broad, quickset hedge, and with the rein dangling from his head he set off home at a full gallop. John laughed out quite aloud. "Served him right," he said.

"Oh! oh! oh!" cried the boy, as he struggled about among the thorns; "I say, come and help me out."

"Thank ye," said John, "I think you are quite in the right place, and maybe a little scratching will teach you not to leap a pony over a gate that is too high for him," and so with that John rode off. "It may be," said he to himself, "that young fellow is a liar as well as a cruel one; we'll just go home by Farmer Bushby's, Beauty, and then if anybody wants to know you and I can tell 'em, ye see"; so we turned off to the right, and soon came up to the stack yard, and within sight of the house. The farmer was hurrying out into the road, and his wife was standing at the gate, looking very frightened.

"Have you seen my boy?" said Mr. Bushby, as we came up. "He

went out an hour ago on my black pony, and the creature is just come back without a rider."

"I should think, sir," said John, "he had better be without a rider, unless he can be ridden properly."

"What do you mean?" said the farmer.

"Well, sir, I saw your son whipping and kicking and knocking that good little pony about shamefully, because he would not leap a gate that was too high for him. The pony behaved well, sir, and showed no vice; but at last he just threw up his heels and tipped the young gentleman into the thorn hedge; he wanted me to help him out; but I hope you'll excuse me, sir, I did not feel inclined to do so. There's no bones broken, sir, he'll only get a few scratches. I love horses, and it riles me to see them badly used; it is a bad plan to aggravate an animal till he uses his heels; the first time is not always the last."

During this time the mother began to cry, "Oh! my poor Bill, I must go and meet him, he must be hurt."

"You had better go into the house, wife," said the farmer; "Bill wants a lesson about this, and I must see that he gets it; this is not the first time nor the second that he has ill-used that pony, and I shall stop it. I am much obliged to you, Manly. Good evening."

So we went on, John chuckling all the way home. Then he told James about it, who laughed and said, "Serve him right. I knew that boy at school; he took great airs on himself because he was a farmer's son; he used to swagger about and bully the little boys; of course, we elder ones would not have any of that nonsense, and let him know that in the school and the playground farmers' sons and laborers' sons were all alike. I well remember one day, just before afternoon school, I found him at the large window catching flies and pulling off their wings. He did not see me, and I gave him a box on the ears that laid him sprawling on the floor. Well, angry as I was, I was almost frightened, he roared and bellowed in such a style. The boys rushed in from the playground, and the master ran in from the road to see who was being murdered. Of course, I said fair and square at once what I had done, and why; then I showed the master the poor flies, some crushed and some crawling about helpless, and I showed him the wings on the window sill. I never saw him so angry before; but as Bill was still howling and whining, like the coward that he was, he did not give him any more punishment of that kind, but set him up on a stool for the rest of the afternoon, and said that he should not go out to play for that week. Then he talked to all the boys very seriously about cruelty, and said how hardhearted and cowardly it was to hurt the weak and helpless; but what stuck in my mind was this, he said that cruelty was the Devil's own trade-mark, and if we saw anyone who took pleasure in cruelty we might know who he belonged to, for the devil was a murderer from the beginning and a tormentor to the end. On the other hand, where we saw people who loved their neighbors, and were kind to man and beast, we might know that was God's mark, for 'God is Love.'"

"Your master never taught you a truer thing," said John; "there is no religion without love, and people may talk as much as they like about their religion, but if it does not teach them to be good and kind to man and beast, it is all a sham—all a sham, James, and it won't stand when things come to be turned inside out and put down for what they are."

XIV

JAMES HOWARD

One morning, early in December, John had just led me into my box after my daily exercise, and was strapping my cloth on, and James was coming in from the corn chamber with some oats, when the master came into the stable; he looked rather serious, and held an open letter in his hand. John fastened the door of my box, touched his cap, and waited for orders.

"Good morning, John," said the master; "I want to know if you have any complaint to make of James?"

"Complaint, sir? No, sir."

"Is he industrious at his work and respectful to you?"

"Yes, sir, always."

"You never find he slights his work when your back is turned?"

"Never, sir."

"That's well; but I must put another question: Have you any reason to suspect that when he goes out with the horses to exercise them, or to take a message, he stops about talking to his acquaintances, or goes into houses where he has no business, leaving the horses outside?"

"No, certainly not, and if anybody has been saying that about James, I don't believe it, and I don't mean to believe it unless I have it fairly proved before witnesses; it's not for me to say who has been trying to take away James's character, but I will say this, sir, that a steadier, pleasanter, honester, smarter young fellow I never had in this stable. I can trust his word and I can trust his work; he is gentle and clever with the horses, and I would rather have them in his charge than in that of half the young fellows I know in laced hats and liveries; and whoever wants a character of James Howard," said John, with a decided jerk of his head, "let them come to John Manly."

The master stood all this time grave and attentive, but as John finished his speech a broad smile spread over his face, and looking kindly across at James, who all this time had stood still at the door, he said, "James, my lad, set down the oats and come here; I am very glad to find that John's opinion of your character agrees so exactly with my own. John is a cautious man," he said, with a droll smile, "and it is not always easy to get his opinion about people, so I thought if I beat the bush on this side the birds would fly out, and I should learn what I wanted to know quickly; so now we will come to business. I have a letter from my brother-in-law, Sir Clifford Williams of Clifford Hall; he wants me to find him a trustworthy young groom about twenty or twenty-one, who knows his business. His old coachman, who has lived with him twenty years, is getting feeble, and he wants a man to work with him and get into his ways, who would be able, when the old man was pensioned off, to step into his place. He would have eighteen shillings a week at first, a stable suit, a driving suit, a bedroom over the coach house, and a boy under him. Sir Clifford is a good master, and if you could get the place it would be a good start for you. I don't want to part with you, and if you left us I know that John would lose his right hand."

"That I would, sir," said John, "but I would not stand in his light for the world."

"How old are you, James?" said the master.

"Nineteen next May, sir."

"That's young; what do you think, John?"

"Well, sir, it is young; but he is as steady as a man, and is strong, and well grown, and though he has not had much experience in driving, he has a light, firm hand and a quick eye, and he is very careful, and I am quite sure no horse of his will be ruined for want of having his feet and shoes looked after."

"Your word will go the furthest, John," said the master, "for Sir Clifford adds in a postscript, 'If I could find a man trained by your John, I should like him better than any other'; so James, lad, think it over, talk to your mother at dinner time, and then let me know what you wish."

In a few days after this conversation it was fully settled that James should go to Clifford Hall in a month or six weeks, as it suited his master, and in the meantime he was to get all the practice in driving that could be given to him. I never knew the carriage go out so often before; when the mistress did not go out, the master drove himself in the two-wheeled chaise; but now, whether it was master or the young ladies, or only an errand, Ginger and I were put into the carriage and James drove us. At the first John rode with him on the box, telling him this and that, and after that James drove alone.

Then it was wonderful what a number of places the master would go to in the city on Saturday, and what queer streets we were driven through. He was sure to go to the railway station just as the train was coming in, and cabs and carriages, carts and omnibuses were all trying to get over the bridge together; that bridge wanted good horses and good drivers when the railway bell was ringing, for it was narrow, and there was a very sharp turn up to the station, where it would not have been at all difficult for people to run into each other if they did not look sharp and keep their wits about them.

XV

THE OLD OSTLER

After this it was decided by my master and mistress to pay a visit to some friends who lived about forty-six miles from our home, and James was to drive them. The first day we traveled thirty-two miles; there were some long, heavy hills, but James drove so carefully and thoughtfully that we were not at all harassed. He never forgot to put on the drag as we went downhill, nor to take it off at the right place. He kept our feet on the smoothest part of the road, and if the uphill was very long he set the carriage wheels a little across the road, so as not to run back, and he gave us a breathing. All these little things help a horse very much, particularly if he gets kind words in the bargain.

We stopped once or twice on the road, and just as the sun was going down we reached the town where we were to spend the night. We stopped at the principal hotel, which was in the Market Place; it was a very large one; we drove under an archway into a long yard, at the farther end of which were the stables and coach houses. Two ostlers came to take us out. The head ostler was a pleasant, active little man, with a crooked leg and a yellow striped waistcoat, I never saw a man unbuckle harness so quickly as he did, and with a pat and a good word he led me to a long stable, with six or eight stalls in it and two or three horses. The other man brought Ginger; James stood by while we were rubbed down and cleaned.

I never was cleaned so lightly and quickly as by that little old man. When he had done, James stepped up and felt me over, as if he thought I could not be thoroughly done, but he found my coat as clean and smooth as silk.

"Well," he said, "I thought I was pretty quick, and our John quicker still, but you do beat all I ever saw for being quick and thorough at the same time."

"Practice makes perfect," said the crooked little ostler, "and 'twould be a pity if it didn't; forty years' practice and not perfect! ha, ha! that would be a pity; and as to being quick, why, bless you! that is only a matter of habit; if you get into the habit of being quick, it is just as easy as being slow; easier, I should say; in fact, it don't agree with my health to be hulking about over a job twice as long as it need take. Bless you! I couldn't whistle if I crawled over my work as some folks do! You see, I have been about horses ever since I was twelve years old, in hunting stables and racing stables; and being small, ye see, I was jockey for several years; but at the Goodwood, ye see, the turf was very slippery and my poor Larkspur got a fall, and I broke my knee, and so, of course, I was of no more use there; but I could not live without horses, of course I couldn't, so I took to the hotels, and I can tell ye it is a downright pleasure to handle an animal like this, well bred, well mannered, well cared for; bless ye! I can tell how a horse is treated. Give me the handling of a horse for twenty minutes, and I'll tell you what sort of a groom he has had. Look at this one, pleasant, quiet, turns about just as you want him, holds up his feet to be cleaned out, or anything else you please to wish; then you'll find another, fidgety, fretty, won't move the right way, or starts across the stall, tosses up his head as soon as you come near him, lays his ears, and seems afraid of you; or else squares about at you with his heels. Poor things! I know what sort of treatment they have had. If they are timid, it makes them start or shy; if they are high mettled, it makes them vicious or dangerous; their tempers are mostly made when they are young. Bless you! they are like children, train 'em in the way they should go, as the good Book says, and when they are old they will not depart from it, if they've a chance, that is."

"I like to hear you talk," said James. "That's the way we lay it down at home, at our master's.

"Who is your master, young man? if it be a proper question. I should judge he is a good one, from what I see."

"He is Squire Gordon, of Birtwick Park, the other side the Beacon hills," said James.

"Ah! so, so, I have heard tell of him; fine judge of horses, ain't he? The best rider in the county?"

"I believe he is," said James, "but he rides very little now, since the poor young master was killed."

"Ah! poor gentleman; I read all about it in the paper; a fine horse killed, too, wasn't there?"

"Yes," said James, "he was a splendid creature, brother to this one, and just like him."

"Pity! pity!" said the old man. 'Twas a bad place to leap, if I remember; a thin fence at top, a steep bank down to the stream, wasn't it? No chance for a horse to see where he is going. Now, I am for bold riding as much as any man, but still there are some leaps that only a very knowing old huntsman has any right to take; a man's life and a horse's life are worth more than a fox's tail; at least I should say they ought to be."

During this time the other man had finished Ginger, and had brought our corn, and James and the old man left the stable together.

XVI

THE FIRE

Later on in the evening a traveler's horse was brought in by the second ostler, and while he was cleaning him a young man with a pipe in his mouth lounged into the stable to gossip awhile.

"I say, Towler," said the ostler, "just run up the ladder into the loft and put some hay down into this horse's rack, will you? Only lay down your pipe."

"All right," said the other, and went up through the trap door; and I heard him step across the floor overhead and put down the hay. James came in to look at us the last thing, and then the door was locked.

I cannot say how long I had slept, nor what time in the night it was, but I woke up very uncomfortable, though I hardly knew why. I got up, the air seemed all thick and choking. I heard Ginger coughing, and one of the horses moved about restlessly; it was quite dark, and I could see nothing, but the stable was full of smoke and I hardly knew how to breathe.

The trap door had been left open, and I thought that was the

Katharine Pyle

He tied the scarf over my eyes and led me out of the stable.

[See page 253]

place it came through. I listened and heard a soft rushing sort of noise, and a low crackling and snapping. I did not know what it was, but there was something in the sound so strange that it made me tremble all over. The other horses were now all awake; some were pulling at their halters, others were stamping.

At last I heard steps outside, and the ostler who had put up the traveler's horse burst into the stable with a lantern, and began to untie the horses, and try to lead them out; but he seemed in such a hurry and so frightened himself that he frightened me still more. The first horse would not go with him; he tried the second and third; they, too, would not stir. He came to me next and tried to drag me out of the stall by force; of course, that was of no use. He tried us all by turns and then left the stable.

No doubt, we were very foolish, but danger seemed to be all round, and there was nobody we knew to trust in, and all was strange and uncertain. The fresh air that had come in through the open door made it easier to breathe, but the rushing sound overhead grew louder, and as I looked upward through the bars of my empty rack, I saw a red light flickering on the wall. Then I heard a cry of "Fire!" outside, and the old ostler quietly and quickly came in; he got one horse out, and went to another, but the flames were playing round the trap door, and the roaring overhead was dreadful.

The next thing I heard was James' voice, quiet and cheery, as it always was.

"Come, my beauties, it is time for us to be off, so wake up and come along." I stood nearest the door, so he came to me first, patting me as he came in.

"Come, Beauty, on with your bridle, my boy, we'll soon be out of this smother." It was on in no time; then he took the scarf off his neck and tied it lightly over my eyes, and patting and coaxing he led me out of the stable. Safe in the yard, he slipped the scarf off my eyes and shouted, "Here, somebody! take this horse while I go back for the other."

A tall, broad man stepped forward and took me, and James darted back into the stable. I set up a shrill whinny as I saw him go. Ginger told me afterwards that whinny was the best thing I could have done for her, for had she not heard me outside she would never have had courage to come out.

There was much confusion in the yard; the horses being got out of other stables, and the carriages and gigs being pulled out of houses and sheds, lest the flames should spread farther. On the other side the ward windows were thrown up, and people were shouting all sorts of things; but I kept my eye fixed on the stable door, where the smoke poured out thicker than ever, and I could see flashes of red light. Presently I heard above all the stir and din a loud, clear voice, which I knew was master's:

"James Howard! James Howard! are you there?" There was no answer, but I heard a crash of something falling in the stable, and the next moment I gave a loud, joyful neigh, for I saw James coming through the smoke leading Ginger with him; she was coughing violently, and he was not able to speak.

"My brave lad!" said master, laying his hand on his shoulder. "Are you hurt?"

James shook his head, for he could not yet speak.

"Ay," said the big man who held me, "he is a brave lad, and no mistake."

"And now," said master, "when you have got your breath, James, we'll get out of this place as quickly as we can," and we were moving toward the entry, when from the Market Place there came a sound of galloping feet and loud, rumbling wheels.

"'Tis the fire engine! the fire engine!" shouted two or three voices. "Stand back, make way!" and clattering and thundering over the stones two horses dashed into the yard with the heavy engine behind them. The firemen leaped to the ground; no need to ask where the fire was—it was torching up in a great blaze from the roof.

We got out as fast as we could into the broad, quiet Market Place; the stars were shining, and except the noise behind us all was still. Master led the way to a large hotel on the other side, and as soon as the ostler came he said, "James, I must now hasten to your mistress; I trust the horses entirely to you, order whatever you think is needed," and with that he was gone. The master did not run, but I never saw mortal man walk so fast as he did that night.

There was a dreadful sound before we got into our stalls; the shrieks of those poor horses that were left burning to death in the stable—it was very terrible! and made both Ginger and me feel very bad. We were taken in and well done by.

The next morning the master came to see how we were and to speak to James. I did not hear much, for the ostler was rubbing me down, but I could see that James looked very happy, and I thought the master was proud of him. Our mistress had been so much alarmed in the night that the journey was put off till the afternoon, so James had the morning on hand, and went first to the inn to see about our harness and the carriage, and then to hear more about the fire. When he came back, we heard him tell the ostler about it. At first no one could guess how the fire had been caused, but at last a man said he saw Dick Towler go into the stable with a pipe in his mouth, and when he came out he had not one, and went to the tap for another. Then the under ostler said he had asked Dick to go up the ladder to put down some hay, but told him to lay down his pipe first. Dick denied taking the pipe with him, but no one believed him. I remember our John Manly's rule, never to allow a pipe in the stable, and thought it ought to be the rule everywhere.

James said the roof and floor had all fallen in, and that only the black walls were standing; the two poor horses that could not be got out were buried under the burned rafters and tiles.

XVII

JOHN MANLY'S TALK

The rest of our journey was very easy, and a little after sunset we reached the house of my master's friend. We were taken into a clean, snug stable; there was a kind coachman, who made us very comfortable, and who seemed to think a good deal of James when he heard about the fire.

"There is one thing quite clear, young man," he said, "your horses know who they can trust; it is one of the hardest things in the world to get horses out of a stable when there is either fire or flood. I don't know why they won't come out, but they won't—not one in twenty."

We stopped two or three days at this place, and then returned home. All went well on the journey; we were glad to be in our own stable again, and John was equally glad to see us.

Before he and James left us for the night, James said, "I wonder who is coming in my place."

"Little Joe Green at the Lodge," said John.

"Little Joe Green! why, he's a child!"

"He is fourteen and a half," said John.

"But he is such a little chap!"

"Yes, he is small, but he is quick, and willing, and kindhearted, too, and then he wishes very much to come, and his father would like it, and I know the master would like to give him the chance. He said if I thought he would not do he would look out for a bigger boy; but I said I was quite agreeable to try him for six weeks."

"Six weeks!" said James, "why, it will be six months before he can be of much use! It will make you a deal of work, John."

"Well," said John with a laugh, "work and I are very good friends; I never was afraid of work yet."

"You are a very good man," said James, "I wish I may ever be like you."

"I don't often speak of myself," said John, "but as you are going away from us out into the world to shift for yourself I'll tell you just how I look on these things. I was just as old as Joseph when my father and mother died of the fever within ten days of each other, and left me and my crippled sister Nelly alone in the world, without a relation that we could look to for help. I was a farmer's boy, not earning enough to keep myself, much less both of us, and she must have gone to the workhouse but for our mistress (Nelly calls her Angel, and she has good right to do so). She went and hired a room for her with old Widow Mallet, and she gave her knitting and needlework when she was able to do it; and when she was ill, she sent her dinners and many nice, comfortable things, and was like a mother to her. Then the master, he took me into the stable under old

Norman, the coachman that was then. I had my food at the house, and my bed in the loft, and a suit of clothes and three shillings a week, so that I could help Nelly. Then there was Norman; he might have turned round and said that at his age he could not be troubled with a raw boy from the plowtail; but he was like a father to me, and took no end of pains with me. When the old man died some years after, I stepped into his place, and now, of course, I have top wages, and can lay by for a rainy day or a sunny day, as it may happen, and Nelly is as happy as a bird. So, you see, James, I am not the man that should turn up his nose at a little boy and vex a good, kind master. No! no! I shall miss you very much, James, but we shall pull through, and there's nothing like doing a kindness when 'tis put in your way, and I am glad I can do it."

"Then," said James, "you don't hold with that saying, 'Everybody look after himself and take care of number one.'"

"No, indeed," said John, "where should I and Nelly have been if master and mistress and old Norman had only taken care of number one? Why—she in the workhouse and I hoeing turnips! Where would Black Beauty and Ginger have been if you had only thought of number one? Why, roasted to death! No, Jim, no! that is a selfish, heathenish saying, whoever uses it, and any man who thinks he has nothing to do but take care of number one, why, it's a pity but what he had been drowned like a puppy or a kitten, before he got his eyes open, that's what I think," said John, with a very decided jerk of his head.

James laughed at this; but there was a thickness in his voice when he said, "You have been my best friend except my mother. I hope you won't forget me."

"No, lad, no," said John, "and if I ever can do you a good turn I hope you won't forget me."

The next day Joe came to the stable to learn all he could before James left. He learned to sweep the stable, to bring in the straw and hay; he began to clean the harness, and helped to wash the carriage. As he was quite too short to do anything in the way of grooming Ginger and me, James taught him upon Merrylegs, for he was to have full charge of him, under John. He was a nice little bright fellow, and always came whistling to his work.

Merrylegs was a good deal put out at being "mauled about," as he said, "by a boy who knew nothing"; but at the end of the second week he told me confidentially that he thought the boy would turn out well.

At last the day came when James had to leave us; cheerful as he always was, he looked quite downhearted that morning.

"You see," he said to John, "I am leaving a great deal behind; my mother and Betsy, and you, and a good master and mistress, and then the horses, and my old Merrylegs. At the new place there will not be a soul that I shall know. If it were not that I shall get a higher place, and be able to help my mother better, I don't think I should have made up my mind to it; it's a real pinch, John."

"Ay, James, lad, so it is, but I should not think much of you if you could leave your home for the first time and not feel it; cheer up, you'll make friends there, and if you get on well—as I am sure you will—it will be a fine thing for your mother, and she will be proud enough that you have got into such a good place as that."

So John cheered him up, but everyone was sorry to lose James; as for Merrylegs, he pined after him for several days, and went quite off his appetite. So John took him out several mornings with a leading rein, when he exercised me, and trotting and galloping by my side got up the little fellow's spirits again, and he was soon all right.

Joe's father would often come in and give a little help, as he understood the work, and Joe took a great deal of pains to learn, and John was quite encouraged about him.

XVIII

GOING FOR THE DOCTOR

One night, a few days after James had left, I had eaten my hay and was lying down in my straw fast asleep when I was suddenly awakened by the stable bell ringing very loud. I heard the door of John's house open, and his feet running up to the Hall. He was back in no time; he unlocked the stable door and came in, calling out, "Wake up, Beauty, you must go well now, if you ever did"; and almost before I could think he had got the saddle on my back and the bridle on my head; he just ran round for his coat, and then took me at a quick trot up to the Hall door. The Squire stood there with a lamp in his hand.

"Now, John," he said, "ride for your life, that is, for your mistress' life; there is not a moment to lose; give this note to Doctor White; rest your horse at the inn and be back as soon as you can."

John said, "Yes, sir," and was on my back in a minute. The gardener who lived at the lodge had heard the bell ring, and was ready with the gate open, and away we went through the Park and through the village, and down the hill till we came to the tollgate. John called very loudly and thumped upon the door; the man was soon out and flung open the gate.

"Now," said John, "do you keep the gate open for the Doctor; here's the money," and off we went again.

There was before us a long piece of level road by the river side; John said to me, "Now, Beauty, do your best," and so I did; I wanted no whip nor spur, and for two miles I galloped as fast as I could lay my feet to the ground; I don't believe that my old grandfather who won the race at Newmarket could have gone faster. When we came to the bridge, John pulled me up a little and patted my neck. "Well, done, Beauty! good old fellow," he said. He would have let me go slower, but my spirit was up, and I was off again as fast as before. The air was frosty, the moon was bright, it was very pleasant; we came through a village, then through a dark wood, then uphill, then downhill, till after eight miles' run we came to the town, through the streets and into the Market Place. It was all quite still except the clatter of my feet on the stones—everybody was asleep. The church clock struck three as we drew up at Doctor White's door. John rang the bell twice, and then knocked at the door like thunder. A window was thrown up, and Doctor White, in his nightcap, put his head out and said, "What do you want?"

"Mrs. Gordon is very ill, sir; master wants you to go at once, he thinks she will die if you cannot get there—here's a note."

"Wait," he said, "I will come."

He shut the window, and was soon at the door.

"The worst of it is," he said, "that my horse has been out all day and is quite done up; my son has just been sent for, and he has taken the other. What is to be done? Can I have your horse?"

"He has come at a gallop nearly all the way, sir, and I was to give him a rest here; but I think my master would not be against it if you think fit, sir."

"All right," he said, "I will soon be ready."

John stood by me and stroked my neck, I was very hot. The Doctor came out with his riding whip.

"You need not take that, sir," said John. "Black Beauty will go till he drops; take care of him, sir, if you can; I should not like any harm to come to him."

"No! no! John," said the Doctor, "I hope not," and in a minute we had left John far behind.

I will not tell about our way back; the Doctor was a heavier man than John, and not so good a rider; however, I did my very best. The man at the tollgate had it open. When we came to the hill, the Doctor drew me up. "Now, my good fellow," he said, "take some breath." I was glad he did, for I was nearly spent, but that breathing helped me on, and soon we were in the Park, Joe was at the lodge gate, my master was at the Hall door, for he had heard us coming. He spoke not a word; the Doctor went into the house with him, and Joe led me to the stable. I was glad to get home, my legs shook under me, and I could only stand and pant. I had not a dry hair on my body; the water ran down my legs, and I steamed all over—Joe used to say, like a pot on the fire. Poor Joe! he was young and small, and as yet he knew very little, and his father, who would have helped him, had been sent to the next village; but I am sure he did the very best he knew. He rubbed my legs and my chest, but he did not put my warm cloth on me; he thought I was so hot I should not like it. Then he gave me a pail full of water to drink; it was cold and very good, and I drank it all; then he gave me some hay and some corn, and thinking he had done right he went away. Soon I began to shake and tremble, and turned deadly cold, my legs ached, my loins ached, and my chest ached, and I felt sore all over. Oh! how I wished for my warm, thick cloth as I stood and trembled. I wished for John, but he had eight miles to walk, so I lay down in my straw and tried to go to sleep. After a long while I heard John at the door; I gave a low moan, for I was in great pain. He was at my side in a moment, stooping down by me; I could not tell him how I felt; but he seemed to know it all; he covered me up with two or three warm cloths, and then ran to the house for some hot water; he made me some warm gruel, which I drank, and then I think I went to sleep.

John seemed to be very much put out. I heard him say to himself, over and over again, "Stupid boy! stupid boy! no cloth put on, and I dare say the water was cold, too; boys are no good," but Joe was a good boy after all.

I was now very ill; a strong inflammation had attacked my lungs and I could not draw my breath without pain. John nursed me night and day, he would get up two or three times in the night to come to me; my master, too, often came to see me. "My poor Beauty," he said one day, "my good horse, you saved your mistress' life, Beauty! Yes, you saved her life." I was very glad to hear that, for it seems the Doctor had said if we had been a little longer it would have been too late. John told my master he never saw a horse go so fast in his life, it seemed as if the horse knew what was the matter. Of course I did, though John thought not; at least, I knew as much as this, that John and I must go at the top of our speed, and that it was for the sake of the mistress.

XIX

ONLY IGNORANCE

I do not know how long I was ill. Mr. Bond, the horse doctor, came every day. One day he bled me; John held a pail for the blood; I felt very faint after it, and thought I should die, and I believe they all thought so, too.

Ginger and Merrylegs had been moved into the other stable, so that I might be quiet, for the fever made me very quick of hearing; any little noise seemed quite loud, and I could tell everyone's footstep going to and from the house. I knew all that was going on. One night John had to give me a draught; Thomas Green came in to help him. After I had taken it and John had made me as comfortable as he could, he said he should stay half an hour to see how the medicine settled. Thomas said he would stay with him, so they went and sat on a bench that had been brought into Merrylegs' stall, and put the lantern at their feet that I might not be disturbed with the light.

For a while both men sat silent, and then Tom Green said in a low voice: "I wish, John, you'd say a bit of a kind word to Joe; the boy is quite brokenhearted, he can't eat his meals, and he can't smile. He says he knows it was all his fault, though he is sure he did the best he knew, and he says, if Beauty dies, no one will ever speak to him again. It goes to my heart to hear him. I think you might give him just a word; he is not a bad boy."

After a short pause, John said slowly, "You must not be too hard upon me, Tom. I know he meant no harm. I never said he did; I know he is not a bad boy, but you see, I am sore myself. That horse is the pride of my heart, to say nothing of his being such a favorite with the master and mistress; and to think that his life may be flung away in this manner is more than I can bear; but if you think I am hard on the boy I will try to give him a good word tomorrow—that is, I mean, if Beauty is better."

"Well, John! thank you. I knew you did not wish to be too hard, and I am glad you see it was only ignorance."

John's voice almost startled me as he answered, *"Only* ignorance; only *ignorance!* how can you talk about *only* ignorance? Don't you know that's the worst thing in the world, next to wickedness?—and which does the most mischief Heaven only knows. If people can say, 'Oh! I did not know, I did not mean any harm,' they think it is all right. I suppose Martha Mulwash did not mean to kill that baby when she dosed it with Dalby and soothing syrups; but she did kill it, and was tried for manslaughter."

"And serve her right, too," said Tom. "A woman should not undertake to nurse a tender little child without knowing what is good and what is bad for it."

"Bill Starkey," continued John, "did not mean to frighten his brother into fits when he dressed up like a ghost and ran after him in the moonlight; but he did; and that bright, handsome little fellow, that might have been the pride of any mother's heart, is just no better than an idiot, and never will be, if he live to be eighty years old. You were a good deal cut up yourself, Tom, two weeks ago, when those young ladies left your hothouse door open, with a frosty east wind blowing right in; you said it killed a good many of your plants."

"A good many!" said Tom. "There was not one of the tender cuttings that was not nipped off; I shall have to strike all over again, and the worst of it is that I don't know where to go to get fresh ones. I was nearly mad when I came in and saw what was done."

"And yet," said John, "I am sure the young ladies did not mean it; it was only ignorance!"

I heard no more of this conversation, for the medicine did well and sent me to sleep, and in the morning I felt better; but I often thought of John's words when I came to know more of the world.

XX

JOE GREEN

Joe Green went on very well; he learned quickly, and was so attentive and careful that John began to trust him in many things; but, as I have said, he was small of his age, and it was seldom that he was allowed to exercise either Ginger or me; but it so happened one morning that John was out with Justice in the luggage cart, and the master wanted a note to be taken immediately to a gentleman's house, about three miles distant, and sent his orders for Joe to saddle me and take it, adding the caution that he was to ride carefully.

The note was delivered, and we were quietly returning till we came to the brickfield. Here we saw a cart heavily laden with bricks; the wheels had stuck fast in the stiff mud of some deep ruts, and the carter was shouting and flogging the two horses unmercifully. Joe pulled up. It was a sad sight. There were the two horses straining and struggling with all their might to drag the cart out, but they could not move it; the sweat streamed from their legs and flanks, their sides heaved, and every muscle was strained, while the man, fiercely pulling at the head of the forehorse, swore and lashed most brutally.

"Hold hard," said Joe, "don't go on flogging the horses like that; the wheels are so stuck that they cannot move the cart." The man took no heed, but went on lashing.

"Stop! Pray stop," said Joe; "I'll help you to lighten the cart, they can't move it now."

"Mind your own business, you impudent young rascal, and I'll mind mine." The man was in a towering passion, and the worse for drink, and laid on the whip again. Joe turned my head, and the next moment we were going at a round gallop toward the house of the master brickmaker. I cannot say if John would have approved of our pace, but Joe and I were both of one mind, and so angry that we could not have gone slower.

The house stood close by the roadside. Joe knocked at the door and shouted, "Hulloa! is Mr. Clay at home?" The door was opened, and Mr. Clay himself came out.

"Hulloa! young man! you seem in a hurry; any orders from the squire this morning?"

"No, Mr. Clay, but there's a fellow in your brickyard flogging two horses to death. I told him to stop and he wouldn't; I said I'd help him to lighten the cart, and he wouldn't; so I have come to tell you; pray, sir, go." Joe's voice shook with excitement.

"Thank ye, my lad," said the man, running in for his hat; then pausing for a moment—"Will you give evidence of what you saw if I should bring the fellow up before a magistrate?"

"That I will," said Joe, "and glad, too." The man was gone, and we were on our way home at a smart trot.

"Why, what's the matter with you, Joe? You look angry all over," said John, as the boy flung himself from the saddle.

"I am angry all over, I can tell you," said the boy, and then in hurried, excited words he told all that had happened. Joe was usually such a quiet fellow that it was wonderful to see him so roused.

"Right, Joe! You did right, my boy, whether the fellow gets a summons or not. Many folks would have ridden by and said 'twas not their business to interfere. Now, I say that with cruelty and oppression it is everybody's business to interfere when they see it; you did right, my boy."

Joe was quite calm by this time, and proud that John approved of him, and he cleaned out my feet, and rubbed me down with a firmer hand than usual.

They were just going home to dinner when the footman came down to the stable to say that Joe was wanted directly in master's private room; there was a man brought up for ill-using horses, and Joe's evidence was wanted. The boy flushed up to his forehead, and his eyes sparkled. "They shall have it," said he.

"Put yourself a bit straight," said John. Joe gave a pull at his necktie and a twitch at his jacket, and was off in a moment. Our master being one of the county magistrates, cases were often brought to him to settle, or say what should be done. In the stable we heard no more for some time, as it was the men's dinner hour, but when Joe came next into the stable I saw he was in high spirits; he gave me a good-natured slap and said, "We won't see such things done, will we, old fellow?" We heard afterwards that he had given his evidence so clearly, and the horses were in such an exhausted state, bearing marks of such brutal usage, that the carter was committed to trial, and might possibly be sentenced to two or three months in prison. It was wonderful what a change had come over Joe. John laughed and said he had grown an inch taller in that week, and I believe he had. He was just as kind and gentle as before, but there was more purpose and determination in all that he did—as if he had jumped at once from a boy into a man.

XXI

THE PARTING

I had now lived in this happy place three years, but sad changes were about to come over us. We heard from time to time that our mistress was ill. The Doctor was often at the house, and the master looked grave and anxious. Then we heard that she must leave her home at once and go to a warm country for two or three years. The news fell on the household like the tolling of a death bell. Everybody was sorry; but the master began directly to make arrangements for breaking up his establishment and leaving England. We used to hear it talked about in our stable; indeed, nothing else was talked about.

John went about his work silent and sad, and Joe scarcely whistled. There was a deal of coming and going; Ginger and I had full work.

The first of the party who went were Miss Jessie and Flora, with their governess. They came to bid us good-bye. They hugged poor Merrylegs like an old friend, and so, indeed, he was. Then we heard what had been arranged for us. Master had sold Ginger and me to his old friend, the Earl of W——, for he thought we should have a good place there. Merrylegs he had given to the vicar, who was wanting a pony for Mrs. Blomefield, but it was on condition he should never be sold, and when he was past work he should be shot and buried.

Joe was engaged to take care of him and to help in the house, so I thought that Merrylegs was well off. John had the offer of several good places, but he said he should wait a little and look around.

The evening before they left, the master came into the stable to give some directions and to give his horses the last pat. He seemed very low-spirited; I knew that by his voice. I believe we horses can tell more by the voice than many men can.

"Have you decided what to do, John?" he said. "I find you have not accepted any of those offers."

"No, sir. I have made up my mind that if I could get a situation with some first-rate colt breaker and horse trainer that it would be the right thing for me. Many young animals are frightened and spoiled by wrong treatment, which need not be if the right man took them in hand. I always get on well with horses, and if I could help some of them to a fair start I should feel as if I was doing some good. What do you think of it, sir?"

"I don't know a man anywhere," said master, "that I should think so suitable for it. You understand horses, and somehow they understand you, and in time you might set up for yourself; I think you could not do better. If in any way I can help you, write me; I shall speak to my agent in London, and leave your character with him."

Master gave John the name and address, and then he thanked him for his long and faithful service; but that was too much for John. "Pray don't, sir, I can't bear it; you and my dear mistress have done so much for me that I could never repay it; but we shall never forget you sir, and please God we may some day see mistress back again like herself; we must keep up hope, sir." Master gave John his hand, but he did not speak, and they both left the stable.

The last sad day had come; the footman and the heavy luggage had gone off the day before, and there was only master and mistress and her maid. Ginger and I brought the carriage up to the Hall door for the last time. The servants brought out cushions and rugs and many other things, and when all were arranged master came down the steps carrying the mistress in his arms (I was on the side next the house and could see all that went on); he placed her carefully in the carriage, while the house servants stood round crying.

"Good-bye again," he said, "we shall not forget any of you," and he got in—"Drive on, John." Joe jumped up, and we trotted slowly through the Park and through the village where the people were standing at their doors to have a last look and to say, "God bless them."

When we reached the railway station, I think mistress walked from the carriage to the waiting room. I heard her say in her own sweet voice, "Good-bye, John, God bless you." I felt the rein twitch, but John made no answer, perhaps he could not speak. As soon as Joe had taken the things out of the carriage, John called him to stand by the horses, while he went on the platform. Poor Joe! he stood close to our heads to hide his tears. Very soon the train came puffing up into the station; then two or three minutes, and the doors were slammed to; the guard whistled, and the train glided away, leaving behind it only clouds of white smoke, and some heavy hearts.

When it was quite out of sight, John came back. "We shall never see her again," he said—"never." He took the reins, mounted the box, and with Joe drove slowly home; but it was not our home now.

"ONE MINUTE LONGER"

By *ALBERT PAYSON TERHUNE*

Illustration by Marguerite Kirmse

WOLF was a collie, red-gold and white of coat, with a shape more like his long-ago wolf ancestors' than like a domesticated dog's. It was from this ancestral throw back that he was named Wolf.

He looked not at all like his great sire, Sunnybank Lad, nor like his dainty, thoroughbred mother, Lady. Nor was he like them in any other way, except that he inherited old Lad's stanchly gallant spirit and loyalty, and uncanny brain. No, in traits as well as in looks, he was more wolf than dog. He almost never barked, his snarl supplying all vocal needs.

The Mistress, or the Master, or the Boy—any of these three could romp with him, roll him over, tickle him, or subject him to all sorts of playful indignities. And Wolf entered gleefully into the fun of the romp. But let any human, besides these three, lay a hand on his slender body, and a snarling plunge for the offender's throat was Wolf's invariable reply to the caress.

It had been so nice since his puppyhood. He did not fly at accredited guests, nor, indeed, pay any heed to their presence, so long as they kept their hands off him. But to all of these the Boy was forced to say at the very outset of the visit:

"Pat Lad and Bruce all you want to, but please leave Wolf alone. He doesn't care for people. We've taught him to stand for a pat on the head from guests—but don't touch his body."

Then, to prove his own immunity, the Boy would proceed to tumble Wolf about, to the delight of them both.

In romping with humans whom they love, most dogs will bite, more or less gently—or pretend to bite—as a part of the game. Wolf never did this. In his wildest and roughest romps with the Boy or with the Boy's parents, Wolf did not so much as open his mighty

268

jaws. Perhaps because he dared not trust himself to bite gently. Perhaps because he realized that a bite is not a joke, but an effort to kill.

There had been only one exception to Wolf's hatred for mauling at strangers' hands. A man came to The Place on a business call,

Marguerite Kirmse

The baby was seated astride Wolf's back.

bringing along a chubby two-year-old daughter. The Master warned the baby that she must not go near Wolf, although she might pet any of the other collies. Then he became so much interested in the business talk that he and his guest forgot all about the child.

Ten minutes later the Master chanced to shift his gaze to the far end of the room. And he broke off, with a gasp, in the very middle of a sentence.

The baby was seated astride Wolf's back, her tiny heels digging into the dog's sensitive ribs, and each of her chubby fists gripping one of his ears. Wolf was lying there, with an idiotically happy grin on his face and wagging his tail in ecstasy.

No one knew why he had submitted to the baby's tugging hands, except because she *was* a baby, and because the gallant heart of the dog had gone out to her helplessness.

Wolf was the official watchdog of The Place; and his name carried dread to the loafers and tramps of the region. Also, he was the

Boy's own special dog. He had been born on the Boy's tenth birthday, five years before this story of ours begins; and ever since then the two had been inseparable chums.

One sloppy afternoon in late winter, Wolf and the Boy were sprawled, side by side, on the fur rug in front of the library fire. The Mistress and the Master had gone to town for the day. The house was lonely, and the two chums were left to entertain each other.

The Boy was reading a magazine. The dog beside him was blinking in drowsy comfort at the fire. Presently, finishing the story he had been reading, the Boy looked across at the sleepy dog.

"Wolf," he said, "here's a story about a dog. I think he must have been something like you. Maybe he was your great-great-great-great-grandfather. He lived an awfully long time ago—in Pompeii. Ever hear of Pompeii?"

Now, the Boy was fifteen years old, and he had too much sense to imagine that Wolf could possibly understand the story he was about to tell him. But, long since, he had fallen into a way of talking to his dog, sometimes, as if to another human. It was fun for him to note the almost pathetic eagerness wherewith Wolf listened and tried to grasp the meaning of what he was saying. Again and again, at sound of some familiar word or voice inflection, the collie would prick up his ears or wag his tail, as if in the joyous hope that he had at last found a clew to his owner's meaning.

"You see," went on the Boy, "this dog lived in Pompeii, as I told you. You've never been there, Wolf."

Wolf was looking up at the Boy in wistful excitement, seeking vainly to guess what was expected of him.

"And," continued the Boy, "the kid who owned him seems to have had a regular knack for getting into trouble all the time. And his dog was always on hand to get him out of it. It's a true story, the magazine says. The kid's father was so grateful to the dog that he bought him a solid silver collar. Solid silver! Get that, Wolfie?"

Wolf did not "get it." But he wagged his tail hopefully, his eyes alight with bewildered interest.

"And," said the Boy, "what do you suppose was engraved on the collar? Well, I'll tell you: *'This dog has thrice saved his little master from death. Once by fire, once by flood, and once at the hands of robbers!'* How's that for a record, Wolf? For *one* dog, too!"

At the words "Wolf" and "dog," the collie's tail smote the floor in glad comprehension. Then he edged closer to the Boy as the narrator's voice presently took on a sadder note.

"But at last," resumed the Boy, "there came a time when the dog couldn't save the kid. Mount Vesuvius erupted. All the sky was pitch-dark, as black as midnight, and Pompeii was buried under lava and ashes. The dog could easily have got away by himself—dogs can see in the dark, can't they, Wolf?—but he couldn't get the kid away. And he wouldn't go without him. You wouldn't have gone without me, either, would you, Wolf? Pretty nearly two thousand years later, some people dug through the lava that covered Pompeii. What do you suppose they found? Of course they found a whole lot of things. One of them was that dog—silver collar and inscription and all. He was lying at the feet of a child. The child he couldn't save. He was one grand dog—hey, Wolf?"

The continued strain of trying to understand began to get on the collie's high-strung nerves. He rose to his feet, quivering, and sought to lick the Boy's face, thrusting one upraised white forepaw at him in appeal for a handshake. The Boy slammed shut the magazine.

"It's slow in the house, here, with nothing to do," he said to his chum. "I'm going up the lake with my gun to see if any wild ducks have landed in the marshes yet. It's almost time for them. Want to come along?"

The last sentence Wolf understood perfectly. On the instant he was dancing with excitement at the prospect of a walk. Being a collie, he was of no earthly help in a hunting trip; but, on such tramps, as everywhere else, he was the Boy's inseparable companion.

Out over the slushy snow the two started, the Boy with his light single-barreled shotgun slung over one shoulder, the dog trotting close at his heels. The March thaw was changing to a sharp freeze. The deep and soggy snow was crusted over, just thick enough to make walking a genuine difficulty for both dog and Boy.

The Place was a promontory that ran out into the lake, on the opposite bank from the mile-distant village. Behind, across the high-road, lay the winter-choked forest. At the lake's northerly end, two miles beyond The Place, were the reedy marshes where, a month hence, wild duck would congregate. Thither, with Wolf, the Boy plowed his way through the biting cold.

The going was heavy and heavier. A quarter mile below the marshes, the Boy struck out across the upper corner of the lake. Here the ice was rotten at the top, where the thaw had nibbled at it, but beneath it was still a full eight inches thick; easily strong enough to bear the Boy's weight.

Along the gray ice field the two plodded. The skim of water, which the thaw had spread an inch thick over the ice, had frozen in the day's cold spell. It crackled like broken glass as the chums walked over it. The Boy had on big hunting boots. So, apart from the extra effort, the glasslike ice did not bother him. To Wolf it gave acute pain. The sharp particles were forever getting between the callous black pads of his feet, pricking and cutting him acutely.

Little smears of blood began to mark the dog's course; but it never occurred to Wolf to turn back, or to betray by any sign that he was suffering. It was all a part of the day's work—a cheap price to pay for the joy of tramping with his adored young master.

Then, forty yards or so on the hither side of the marshes, Wolf beheld a right amazing phenomenon. The Boy had been walking directly in front of him, gun over shoulder. With no warning at all, the youthful hunter fell, feet foremost, out of sight, through the ice.

The light shell of new-frozen water that covered the lake's thicker ice also masked an air hole nearly three feet wide. Into this, as he strode carelessly along, the Boy had stepped. Straight down he had gone, with all the force of his hundred-and-twenty pounds and with all the impetus of his forward stride.

Instinctively, he threw out his hands to restore his balance. The only effect of this was to send the gun flying ten feet away.

Down went the Boy through less than three feet of water (for the bottom of the lake at this point had started to slope upward toward the marshes) and through nearly two feet more of sticky marsh mud that underlay the lake bed.

His outflung hands struck against the ice on the edges of the air hole, and clung there.

Sputtering and gurgling, the Boy brought his head above the surface and tried to raise himself by his hands, high enough to wriggle out upon the surface of the ice. Ordinarily, this would have been simple enough for so strong a lad. But the gluelike mud had imprisoned his feet and the lower part of his legs; and held them powerless.

Try as he would, the Boy could not wrench himself free of the slough. The water, as he stood upright, was on a level with his mouth. The airhole was too wide for him, at such a depth, to get a good purchase on its edges and lift himself bodily to safety.

Gaining such a fingerhold as he could, he heaved with all his might, throwing every muscle of his body into the struggle. One leg was pulled almost free of the mud, but the other was driven deeper into it. And, as the Boy's fingers slipped from the smoothly wet ice edge, the attempt to restore his balance drove the free leg back, knee-deep into the mire.

Ten minutes of this hopeless fighting left the Boy panting and tired out. The icy water was numbing his nerves and chilling his blood into torpidity. His hands were without sense of feeling, as far up as the wrists. Even if he could have shaken free his legs from the mud now, he had not strength enough left to crawl out of the hole.

He ceased his uselessly frantic battle and stood dazed. Then he came sharply to himself. For, as he stood, the water crept upward from his lips to his nostrils. He knew why the water seemed to be rising. It was not rising. It was he who was sinking. As soon as he stopped moving, the mud began, very slowly, but very steadily, to suck him downward.

This was not a quicksand, but it was a deep mud bed. And only by constant motion could he avoid sinking farther and farther down into it. He had less than two inches to spare, at best, before the water should fill his nostrils; less than two inches of life, even if he could keep the water down to the level of his lips.

There was a moment of utter panic. Then the Boy's brain cleared. His only hope was to keep on fighting—to rest when he must, for a moment or so, and then to renew his numbed grip on the ice edge and try to pull his feet a few inches higher out of the mud. He must do this as long as his chilled body could be scourged into obeying his will.

He struggled again, but with virtually no result in raising himself. A second struggle, however, brought him chin-high above the water. He remembered confusedly that some of these earlier struggles had scarce budged him, while others had gained him two or three inches. Vaguely, he wondered why. Then turning his head, he realized.

Wolf, as he turned, was just losing his hold on the wide collar of the Boy's mackinaw. His cut forepaws were still braced against a flaw of ragged ice on the air-hole's edge, and all his tawny body was tense.

His body was dripping wet, too. The Boy noted that; and he realized that the repeated effort to draw his master to safety must have resulted, at least once, in pulling the dog down into the water with the floundering Boy.

"Once more, Wolfie! *Once more!*" chattered the Boy through teeth that clicked together like castanets.

The dog darted forward, caught his grip afresh on the edge of the Boy's collar, and tugged with all his fierce strength; growling and whining ferociously the while.

The Boy seconded the collie's tuggings by a supreme struggle that lifted him higher than before. He was able to get one arm and shoulder clear. His numb fingers closed about an upthrust tree limb which had been washed downstream in the autumn freshets and had been frozen into the lake ice.

With this new purchase, and aided by the dog, the boy tried to drag himself out of the hole. But the chill of the water had done its work. He had not the strength to move farther. The mud still sucked at his calves and ankles. The big hunting boots were full of water that seemed to weigh a ton.

He lay there, gasping and chattering. Then, through the gathering twilight, his eyes fell on the gun, lying ten feet away.

"Wolf!" he ordered, nodding toward the weapon. "Get it! *Get* it!"

Not in vain had the Boy talked to Wolf, for years, as if the dog were human. At the words and the nod, the collie trotted over to the gun, lifted it by the stock, and hauled it awkwardly along over the bumpy ice to his master, where he laid it down on the edge of the air hole.

The dog's eyes were cloudy with trouble, and he shivered and whined as with ague. The water on his thick coat was freezing to a mass of ice. But it was from anxiety that he shivered, and not from cold.

Still keeping his numb grasp on the tree branch, the Boy balanced himself as best he could, and thrust two fingers of his free hand into his mouth to warm them into sensation again.

When this was done, he reached out to where the gun lay, and pulled its trigger. The shot boomed deafeningly through the twilight winter silences. The recoil sent the weapon sliding sharply back along the ice, spraining the Boy's trigger finger and cutting it to the bone.

"That's all I can do," said the Boy to himself. "If anyone hears it, well and good. I can't get at another cartridge. I couldn't put it into the breech if I had it. My hands are too numb."

For several minutes he clung there, listening. But this was a desolate part of the lake, far from any road; and the season was too early for other hunters to be abroad. The bitter cold, in any case, tended to make sane folk hug the fireside rather than to venture so far into the open. Nor was the single report of a gun uncommon enough to call for investigation in such weather.

All this the Boy told himself, as the minutes dragged by. Then he looked again at Wolf. The dog, head on one side, still stood protectingly above him. The dog was cold and in pain. But, being only a dog, it did not occur to him to trot off home to the comfort of the library fire and leave his master to fend for himself.

Presently, with a little sigh, Wolf lay down on the ice, his nose across the Boy's arm. Even if he lacked strength to save his beloved master, he could stay and share the Boy's sufferings.

But the Boy himself thought otherwise. He was not at all minded to freeze to death, nor was he willing to let Wolf imitate the dog of

Pompeii by dying helplessly at his master's side. Controlling for an instant the chattering of his teeth, he called:

"Wolf!"

The dog was on his feet again at the word; alert, eager.

"Wolf!" repeated the Boy. *"Go! Hear me? Go!"*

He pointed homeward.

Wolf started at him, hesitant. Again the Boy called in vehement command, *"Go!"*

The collie lifted his head to the twilight sky with a wolf howl hideous in its grief and appeal—a howl as wild and discordant as that of any of his savage ancestors. Then, stooping first to lick the numb hand that clung to the branch, Wolf turned and fled.

Across the cruelly sharp rim of ice he tore, at top speed, head down; whirling through the deeping dusk like a flash of tawny light.

Wolf understood what was wanted of him. Wolf always understood. The pain in his feet was nothing. The stiffness of his numbed body was forgotten in the urgency for speed.

The Boy looked drearily after the swift-vanishing figure which the dusk was swallowing. He knew the dog would try to bring help; as has many another and lesser dog in times of need. Whether or not that help could arrive in time, or at all, was a point on which the Boy would not let himself dwell. Into his benumbed brain crept the memory of an old Norse proverb he had read in school:

"Heroism consists in hanging on, one minute longer."

Unconsciously he tightened his feeble hold on the tree branch and braced himself.

From the marshes to The Place was a full two miles. Despite the deep and sticky snow, Wolf covered the distance in less than nine minutes. He paused in front of the gate lodge, at the highway entrance to the drive. But the superintendent and his wife had gone to Paterson, shopping, that afternoon.

Down the drive to the house he dashed. The maids had taken advantage of their employers' day in New York, to walk across the lake to the village, to a motion picture show.

Wise men claim that dogs have not the power to think or to

reason things out in a logical way. So perhaps it was mere chance that next sent Wolf's flying feet across the lake to the village. Perhaps it was chance, and not the knowledge that where there is a village there are people.

Again and again, in the car, he had sat upon the front seat alongside the Mistress when she drove to the station to meet guests. There were always people at the station. And to the station Wolf now raced.

The usual group of platform idlers had been dispersed by the cold. A solitary baggageman was hauling a trunk and some boxes out of the express coop on to the platform; to be put aboard the five o'clock train from New York.

As the baggageman passed under the clump of station lights, he came to a sudden halt. For out of the darkness dashed a dog. Full tilt, the animal rushed up to him and seized him by the skirt of the overcoat.

The man cried out in scared surprise. He dropped the box he was carrying and struck at the dog, to ward off the seemingly murderous attack. He recognized Wolf, and he knew the collie's repute.

But Wolf was not attacking. Holding tight to the coat skirt, he backed away, trying to draw the man with him, and all the while whimpering aloud like a nervous puppy.

A kick from the heavy-shod boot broke the dog's hold on the coat skirt, even as a second yell from the man brought four or five other people running out from the station waiting room.

One of these, the telegraph operator, took in the scene at a single glance. With great presence of mind he bawled loudly: "MAD DOG!"

This, as Wolf, reeling from the kick, sought to gain another grip on the coat skirt. A second kick sent him rolling over and over on the tracks, while other voices took up the panic cry of "Mad dog!"

Now, a mad dog is supposed to be a dog afflicted by rabies. Once in ten thousand times, at the very most, a mad-dog hue and cry is justified. Certainly not oftener. A harmless and friendly dog loses his master on the street. He runs about, confused and frightened, looking for the owner he has lost. A boy throws a stone at him.

Other boys chase him. His tongue hangs out, and his eyes glaze with terror. Then some fool bellows: "Mad dog!"

And the cruel chase is on—a chase that ends in the pitiful victim's death. Yes, in every crowd there is a voice ready to raise that asinine and murderously cruel shout.

So it was with the men who witnessed Wolf's frenzied effort to take aid to the imperiled Boy.

Voice after voice repeated the cry. Men groped along the platform edge for stones to throw. The village policeman ran puffingly upon the scene, drawing his revolver.

Finding it useless to make a further attempt to drag the baggage-man to the rescue, Wolf leaped back, facing the ever larger group. Back went his head again in that hideous wolf howl. Then he galloped away a few yards, trotted back, howled once more, and again galloped lakeward.

All of which only confirmed the panicky crowd in the belief that they were threatened by a mad dog. A shower of stones hurled about Wolf as he came back a third time to lure these dull humans into following him.

One pointed rock smote the collie's shoulder, glancingly, cutting it to the bone. A shot from the policeman's revolver fanned the fur of his ruff, as it whizzed past.

Knowing that he faced death, he nevertheless stood his ground, not troubling to dodge the fusillade of stones, but continuing to run lakeward and then trot back, whining with excitement.

A second pistol shot flew wide. A third grazed the dog's hip. From all directions people were running toward the station. A man darted into a house next door, and emerged carrying a shotgun. This he steadied on the veranda rail not forty feet away from the leaping dog, and made ready to fire.

It was then the train from New York came in. And, momentarily, the sport of "mad-dog" killing was abandoned, while the crowd scattered to each side of the track.

From a front car of the train the Mistress and the Master emerged into a bedlam of noise and confusion.

"Best hide in the station, Ma'am!" shouted the telegraph operator, at sight of the Mistress. "There is a mad dog loose out here! He's chasing folks around, and——"

"Mad dog!" repeated the Mistress in high contempt. "If you knew anything about dogs, you'd know mad ones never 'chase folks around,' any more than diphtheria patients do. Then——"

A flash of tawny light beneath the station lamp, a scurrying of frightened idlers, a final wasted shot from the policeman's pistol—as Wolf dived headlong through the frightened crowd toward the voice he heard and recognized.

Up to the Mistress and the Master galloped Wolf. He was bleeding, his eyes were bloodshot, his fur was rumpled. He seized the astounded Master's gloved hand lightly between his teeth and sought to pull him across the tracks and toward the lake.

The Master knew dogs. Especially he knew Wolf. And without a word he suffered himself to be led. The Mistress and one or two inquisitive men followed.

Presently, Wolf loosed his hold on the Master's hand and ran on ahead, darting back every few moments to make certain he was followed.

"Heroism—consists—in—hanging—on—one—minute—longer," the Boy was whispering deliriously to himself for the hundredth time, as Wolf pattered up to him in triumph, across the ice, with the human rescuers a scant ten yards behind.

BRINGING UP KARI

By DHAN GOPAL MUKERJI

Illustrations by Frank Shields

KARI, the elephant, was five months old when he was given to me to take care of. I was nine years old, and I could reach his back if I stood on tiptoe. He seemed to remain that high for nearly two years. Perhaps we grew together; that is probably why I never found out just how tall he was. He lived in a pavilion, under a thatched roof which rested on thick tree stumps so that it could not fall in when Kari bumped against the poles as he moved about.

One of the first things Kari did was to save the life of a boy. Kari did not eat much but he nevertheless needed forty pounds of twigs a day to chew and play with. Every day I used to take him to the river in the morning for his bath. He would lie down on the sand bank while I rubbed him with the clean sand of the river for an hour. After that he would lie in the water for a long time. On coming out his skin would be shining like ebony, and he would squeal with pleasure as I rubbed water down his back. Then I would take him by the ear, because that is the easiest way to lead an elephant, and leave him on the edge of the jungle while I went into the forest to get some luscious twigs for his dinner. One has to have a very sharp hatchet to cut down these twigs; it takes half an hour to sharpen the hatchet, because if a twig is mutilated an elephant will not touch it.

When one goes into the jungle, one must remember that there are laws one cannot break. Do you know that anyone who is afraid or who hates one of the animals of the jungle gives out an odor which attracts tigers and wolves? Every day that I was afraid to go into the jungle, I did not dare to stay on the ground for fear lest the tigers would smell my presence and attack me. I climbed a tree instead, because when one is in a tree the odor of one's body does not go into the forest, and the animals cannot tell whether one is afraid or not.

It was not an easy job, as you see, to get twigs and saplings for Kari. I had to climb all kinds of trees to get the most delicate and tender twigs. As he was very fond of the young branches of the banian tree which grows like a cathedral of leaves and branches, I was gathering some, one spring day in March, when I suddenly heard Kari calling to me in the distance. As he was still very young, the call was more like that of a baby than an elephant. I thought somebody was hurting him, so I came down from my tree and ran very fast to the edge of the forest where I had left him, but he was not there.

I looked all over, but I could not find him. I went near the edge of the water, and I saw a black something struggling above its surface. Then it rose higher, and it was the trunk of my elephant. I thought he was drowning. I was helpless, because I could not jump into the water and save his four hundred pounds, since he was much higher than I. But I saw his back rise above the water and the moment he caught my eye, he began to trumpet and struggle up to the shore. Then, still trumpeting, he pushed me into the water, and as I fell into the stream I saw a boy lying flat on the bottom of the river. He had not altogether touched bottom, but was somewhat afloat. I came to the surface of the water to take my breath, and there Kari was standing, his feet planted into the sand bank, and his trunk stretched out like a hand waiting for mine. I dove down again and pulled the body of the drowning boy to the surface; but not being a good swimmer, I could not swim ashore, and the slow current was already dragging me down. I clutched at reeds on the shore but they broke, and the weight of the boy was tiring out one hand while the other was already weak from excessive swimming and clutching at the reeds. Seeing us drift by in the current, Kari, who was usually so slow and ponderous, suddenly darted down like a hawk and came halfway into the water where I saw him stretch out his trunk again. I raised up my hand to catch it and it slipped. I found myself going under the water again; but this time I found that the water was not very deep, so I sank to the bottom of the river and doubled my feet under me, and then suddenly kicked the river bed and so shot upward like an arrow, in spite of the fact that I was holding the drowning boy with my hand. As my body rose above the water I felt a lasso around my neck. This frightened me; I thought some water animal was going to swallow me. I heard the squealing of Kari, and I knew it was his trunk about my neck. He pulled us both ashore.

As the boy lay stretched on the ground I recognized the cowherd. He had gone to bathe in the river, had slipped too far out, and not knowing how to swim had almost been drowned. I put him flat on his face on the sand and the elephant put his trunk about his waist and lifted it gently up and down, and then up again. After doing this three or four times, the water began to come out of the boy's mouth and, not knowing what else to do, because his body was cold, I slapped him very hard all over. After that I propped him up against the elephant's leg. Then the boy slowly came to.

In the meantime all his cows had wandered away in different directions. As I thought some had gone into the jungle, where I was afraid they might be eaten up by tigers, I sent Kari to bring them back to the river bank. But Kari got lost himself; so when the cowherd had recovered entirely, I went to look for his cows and my lost elephant. Where do you think I found him? He had gone right into the forest where I had left the saplings and the twigs, and had buried his trunk into the heap and was eating the best of them, without any concern for the cows, the cowherd or myself.

But I could not punish him that day because he had done his duty by saving the life of the boy. Kari was like a baby. He had to be trained to be good and if you did not tell him when he was naughty, he was up to more mischief than ever.

For instance, one day somebody gave him some bananas to eat. Very soon he developed a great love for ripe bananas. We used to keep large plates of fruit on a table near a window in the dining room. One day all the bananas on that table disappeared, and my family blamed the servants for eating all the fruit in the house. A few days later the fruit disappeared again; this time the blame was put on me, and I knew I had not done it. It made me very angry with my parents and the servants, for I was sure they had taken all the fruit. The next time the fruit disappeared, I found a banana all smashed up in Kari's pavilion. This surprised me very much, for I had never seen fruit there, and as you know, he had always lived on twigs.

Next day while I was sitting in the dining room wondering whether I should take some fruit from the table without my parents' permission, a long, black thing, very much like a snake suddenly came through the window and disappeared with all the bananas. I was very much frightened, because I had never seen snakes eat bananas and I thought it must be a terrible snake that would sneak in and take fruit. I crept out of the room and with great fear in my heart ran out of the house, feeling sure that the snake would come back into the house, eat all the fruit and kill all of us.

As I went out, I saw Kari's back disappeared in the direction of the pavilion and I was so frightened that I wanted his company to cheer me up. I ran after him into the pavilion and I found him there eating bananas. I stood still in astonishment; the bananas were lying strewn all around him. He stretched out his trunk and reached for one far away from where he was standing. That instant the trunk looked like a black snake, and I realized that Kari was the thief. I went to him, pulled him out by the ear and joyously showed my parents that it was Kari and not I that had eaten all the fruit these many weeks. Then I scolded him, for elephants understand words as well as children, and I said to him, "Next time I see you stealing fruit, you will be whipped." He knew that we were all angry with him, even the servants. His pride was so injured that he never stole another thing from the dining room. And from then on, if anybody gave him any fruit, he always squealed as if to thank them.

An elephant is willing to be punished for having done wrong, but if you punish him without any reason, he will remember it and pay you back in your own coin.

Once I had taken him to bathe in the river; this was summer vacation and several boys came with me to help. Kari lay on the bank and we rubbed him all over with sand. Then he went into the water and most of us began to play. As Kari came up from the water, one of the boys, named Sudu, was standing on the bank.

For no reason at all he hit the elephant three or four times with his whip. Kari squealed and ran away. I brought him home.

The next summer Kari had grown so big and fat that I could not reach his back even when I stood on tiptoe. We used to take him out wherever we went, sometimes one riding on his back, sometimes all walking alone with him. We gave him luscious twigs if he behaved well and sometimes delicious fruit. Once in a while, as a special treat we would massage his chest with straw and he would squeal with joy and lie on his back as best he could, staring at the sun.

One day Sudu was standing on the river bank, where I had just taken the elephant to give him his bath. That day Kari had been very good, so we prepared a straw massage for him. As it was very hot, however, we plunged into the river ourselves before giving him his bath, leaving Sudu and the elephant on the bank. Without warning, Kari rushed at him like a mad bull, threw his trunk about Sudu's neck, flung him into the water, and held him there for a long, long time. When Sudu was finally pulled out of the water and stretched on the ground, he was nearly senseless.

When Sudu asked me whether I would punish Kari for having disgraced him in public like that, I answered that the elephant was not rude. When Sudu asked me why, I said, "Don't you remember that about a year ago you whipped him for no reason at all, almost on the exact spot where he has just punished you?" Sudu felt so ashamed of himself that he got angry with all of us and went home alone. But by the next day, we had made it all up and the elephant had forgiven him. As a proof of friendship, when we went to the jungle on a picnic, Kari carried Sudu on his back. Since that day Sudu has never hurt a living creature.

An elephant must be taught when to sit down, when to walk, when to go fast, and when to go slow. You teach him these things as you teach a child. If you say "Dhat" and pull him by the ear, he will gradually learn to sit down. Similarly, if you say "Mali" and pull his trunk forward, he will gradually learn that is the signal to walk.

Kari learned "Mali" after three lessons, but it took him three weeks to learn "Dhat." He was no good at sitting down. And do you know why an elephant should be taught to sit down? Because he grows taller and taller than you who take care of him, so that when he is two or three years old, you can only reach his back with a ladder. It is, therefore, better to teach him to sit down by saying "Dhat" so that you can climb upon his back, for who would want to carry a ladder around all the time?

The most difficult thing to teach an elephant is the master call. He generally takes five years to learn it properly. The master call is a strange hissing, howling sound, as if a snake and a tiger were fighting each other, and you have to make that kind of noise in his

Frank Shields
The elephant pulls down the tree.

ear. And do you know what you expect an elephant to do when you give him the master call? If you are lost in the jungle and there is no way out, and everything is black except the stars above, you dare not stay very long anywhere. The only thing to do then is to give the master call and at once the elephant pulls down the tree in front of him with his trunk. This frightens all the animals away. As the tree comes crashing down, monkeys wake from their sleep and run from branch to branch—you can see them in the moonlight—and you can almost see the stags running in all directions below. You can hear the growl of the tiger in the distance. Even he is frightened. Then the elephant pulls down the next tree and the next, and the next. Soon you will find that he has made a road right through the jungle straight to your house.

COALY-BAY, THE OUTLAW HORSE

By ERNEST THOMPSON SETON

FIVE years ago in the Bitterroot mountains of Idaho there was a beautiful little foal. His coat was bright bay; his legs, mane, and tail were glossy black—coal black and bright bay—so they named him Coaly-bay.

"Coaly-bay" sounds like "Koli-bey," which is an Arab title of nobility, and those who saw the handsome colt, and did not know how he came by the name, though he must be of Arab blood. No doubt he was, in a faraway sense; just as all our best horses have Arab blood, and once in a while it seems to come out strong and show in every part of the creature, in his frame, his power, and his wild, free roving spirit.

Coaly-bay loved to race like the wind, he gloried in his speed, his tireless legs; and when, careering with the herd of colts, they met a fence or ditch, it was as natural to Coaly-bay to overleap it, as it was for the others to sheer off.

So he grew up strong of limb, restless of spirit, and rebellious at any thought of restraint. Even the kindly curb of the hay yard or the stable was unwelcome, and he soon showed that he would rather stand out all night in a driving storm than be locked in a comfortable stall where he had no vestige of the liberty he loved so well.

He became very clever at dodging the horse wrangler whose job it was to bring the horse herd to the corral. The very sight of that man set Coaly-bay a-going. He became what is known as a "Quit-the-bunch"—that is a horse of such independent mind that he will go his own way the moment he does not like the way of the herd.

So each month the colt became more set on living free, and more cunning in the means he took to win his way. Far down in his soul, too, there must have been a streak of cruelty, for he stuck at nothing and spared no one that seemed to stand between him and his one desire.

When he was three years of age, just in the perfection of his young strength and beauty, his real troubles began, for now his owner undertook to break him to ride. He was as tricky and vicious as he was handsome, and the first day's experience was a terrible battle between the horse trainer and the beautiful colt.

But the man was skillful. He knew how to apply his power, and all the wild plunging, bucking, rearing, and rolling of the wild one had no desirable result. With all his strength, the horse was hopelessly helpless in the hand of the skillful horseman; and Coaly-bay was so far mastered at length that a good rider could use him. But each time the saddle went on, he made a new fight. After a few months of this the colt seemed to realize that it was useless to resist, it simply won for him lashings and spurrings, so he pretended to reform. For a week he was ridden each day and not once did he buck, but on the last day he came home lame.

His owner turned him out to pasture. Three days later he seemed all right; he was caught and saddled. He did not buck, but within five minutes he went lame as before. Again he was turned out to pasture, and after a week, saddled, only to go lame again.

His owner did not know what to think, whether the horse really had a lame leg or was only shamming, but he took the first chance to get rid of him, and though Coaly-bay was easily worth fifty dollars, he sold him for twenty-five. The new owner felt he had a bargain, but after being ridden half a mile Coaly-bay went lame. The rider got off to examine the foot, whereupon Coaly-bay broke away and galloped back to his old pasture. Here he was caught, and the new owner, being neither gentle nor sweet, applied spur without mercy, so that the next twenty miles was covered in less than two hours and no sign of lameness appeared.

Now they were at the ranch of this new owner. Coaly-bay was led from the door of the house to the pasture, limping all the way, and then turned out. He limped over to the other horses. On one side of the pasture was the garden of a neighbor. This man was very proud of his fine vegetables and had put a six-foot fence around the place. Yet the very night after Coaly-bay arrived, certain of the horses got into the garden somehow and did a great deal of damage. But they leaped out before daylight and no one saw them.

The gardener was furious, but the ranchman stoutly maintained that it must have been some other horses, since his were behind a six-foot fence.

Next night it happened again. The ranchman went out very early and saw all his horses in the pasture, with Coaly-bay behind them. His lameness seemed worse now instead of better. In a few days, however, his horse was seen walking all right, so the ranchman's son caught him and tried to ride him. But this seemed too good a chance to lose; all his old wickedness returned to the horse; the boy was bucked off at once and hurt. The ranchman himself now leaped into the saddle; Coaly-bay bucked for ten minutes, but finding he could not throw the man, he tried to crush his leg against a post, but the rider guarded himself well. Coaly-bay reared and threw himself backward; the rider slipped off, the horse fell, jarring heavily, and before he could rise the man was in the saddle again. The horse now ran away, plunging and bucking; he stopped short, but the rider did not go over his head, so Coaly-bay turned, seized the man's foot in his teeth, and but for heavy blows on the nose would have torn him dreadfully. It was quite clear now that Coaly-bay was an "outlaw"— that is an incurably vicious horse.

The saddle was jerked off, and he was driven, limping, into the pasture.

The raids on the garden continued, and the two men began to quarrel over it. But to prove that his horses were not guilty the ranchman asked the gardener to sit up with him and watch. That night as the moon was brightly shining they saw, not all the horses, but Coaly-bay, walk straight up to the garden fence—no sign of a limp now—easily leap over it, and proceed to gobble the finest things he could find. After they had made sure of his identity, the men ran forward. Coaly-bay cleared the fence like a deer, lightly raced over the pasture to mix with the horse herd, and when the men came near him he had—oh, such an awful limp.

"That settles it," said the rancher. "He's a fraud, but he's a beauty, and good stuff, too."

"Yes, but it settles who took my garden truck," said the other.

"Wall, I suppose so," was the answer; "but luk-a-here, neighbor, you ain't lost more'n ten dollars in truck. That horse is easily worth —a hundred. Give me twenty-five dollars, take the horse, an' call it square."

"Not much I will," said the gardener. "I'm out twenty-five dollars' worth of truck; the horse ain't worth a cent more. I take him and call it even."

And so the thing was settled. The ranchman said nothing about Coaly-bay being vicious as well as cunning, but the gardener found out, the very first time he tried to ride him, that the horse was as bad as he was beautiful. Next day a sign appeared on the gardener's gate:

FOR SALE
First-class horse, sound
and gentle. $10.00

Now at this time a band of hunters came riding by. There were three mountaineers, two men from the city, and the writer of this story. The city men were going to hunt bear. They had guns and everything needed for bear-hunting, except bait. It is usual to buy some worthless horse or cow, drive it into the mountains where the bears are, and kill it there. So seeing the sign up, the hunters called to the gardener:

"Haven't you got a cheaper horse?"

The gardener replied:

"Look at him there, ain't he a beauty? You won't find a cheaper horse if you travel a thousand miles."

"We are looking for an old bear bait, and five dollars is our limit," replied the hunter.

Horses were cheap and plentiful in that country; buyers were scarce. The gardener feared that Coaly-bay would escape. "Wall, if that's the best you can do, he's yourn."

The hunter handed him five dollars, then said: "Now stranger, bargain's settled. Will you tell me why you sell this fine horse for five dollars?"

"Mighty simple. He can't be rode. He's dead slow when he's going your way and sound as a dollar going his own; no fence in the country can hold him; he's a dangerous outlaw. He's wickeder nor Old Nick."

"Well, he's an almighty handsome bear bait," and the hunters rode on.

Coaly-bay was driven with the pack-horses, and limped dreadfully on the trail. Once or twice he tried to go back, but he was easily turned by the men behind him. His limp grew worse, and toward night it was painful to see him. The leading guide remarked: "That thar limp ain't no fake. He's got some deep-seated trouble."

Day after day the hunters rode farther into the mountains, driving the horses along and hobbling them at night. Coaly-bay went with the rest, limping along, tossing his head and his long splendid mane at every step. One of the hunters tried to ride him and nearly lost his life, for the horse seemed possessed of a demon as soon as the man was on his back.

The road grew harder as it rose. A very bad bog had to be crossed one day. Several horses were mired in it, and as the men rushed to the rescue, Coaly-bay saw his chance of escape. He wheeled in a moment and turned himself from a limping, low-headed, sorry, bad-eyed creature into a high-spirited horse. Head and tail aloft now, shaking their black streamers in the wind, he gave a joyous neigh, and, without a trace of lameness, dashed for his home one hundred miles away, threading each narrow trail with perfect certainty, though he had seen them but once before; and in a few minutes he had steamed away from their sight.

The men were furious, but one of them, saying not a word, leaped on his horse—to do what? Follow that free ranging racer? Sheer folly. Oh, no!—he knew a better plan. He knew the country. Two miles around by the trail, half a mile by the rough cutoff that he took, was Panther Gap. The runaway must pass through that, and

Coaly-bay raced down the trail to find the guide below awaiting him. Tossing his head with anger, he wheeled on up the trail again, and within a few yards recovered his monotonous limp and his evil expression. He was driven into camp, and there he vented his rage by kicking in the ribs of a harmless little packhorse.

HIS DESTINED END

This was bear country, and the hunters resolved to end his dangerous pranks and make him useful for once. They dared not catch him, it was not really safe to go near him, but two of the guides drove him to a distant glade where bears abounded. A thrill of pity came over me as I saw that beautiful untamable creature going away with his imitation limp.

"Ain't you coming along?" called the guide.

"No, I don't want to see him die," was the answer. Then as the tossing head was disappearing I called: "Say, fellows, I wish you would bring me that mane and tail when you come back!"

Fifteen minutes later a distant rifle crack was heard, and in my mind's eye I saw that proud head and those superb limbs, robbed of their sustaining indomitable spirit, falling flat and limp—to suffer the unsightly end of fleshly things. Poor Coaly-bay; he would not bear the yoke. Rebellious to the end, he had fought against the fate of all his kind. It seemed to me the spirit of an eagle or a wolf it was that dwelt behind those full bright eyes—that ordered all his wayward life.

I tried to put the tragic finish out of mind, and had not long to battle with the thought; not even one short hour, for the men came back.

Down the long trail to the west they had driven him; there was no chance for him to turn aside. He must go on, and the men behind felt safe in that.

Farther away from his old home on the Bitterroot River he had gone each time he journeyed. And now he had passed the high divide and was keeping the narrow trail that leads to the valley of bears and on to Salmon River, and still away to the open wild

Columbian Plains, limping sadly as though he knew. His glossy hide flashed back the golden sunlight, still richer than it fell, and the men behind followed like hangmen in the death train of a nobleman condemned—down the narrow trail till it opened into a little beaver meadow, with rank rich grass, a lovely mountain stream and winding bear paths up and down the waterside.

"Guess this'll do," said the older man. "Well, here goes for a sure death or a clean miss," said the other confidently, and, waiting till the limper was out in the middle of the meadow, he gave a short, sharp whistle. Instantly Coaly-bay was alert. He swung and faced his tormentors, his noble head erect, his nostrils flaring; a picture of horse beauty—yes, of horse perfection.

The rifle was leveled, the very brain its mark, just on the crossline of the eyes and ears, that meant sure, sudden, painless death.

The rifle cracked. The great horse wheeled and dashed away. It was sudden death or miss—and the marksman *missed*.

Away went the wild horse at his famous best, not for his eastern home, but down the unknown western trail, away and away; the pine woods hid him from the view, and left behind was the rifleman vainly trying to force the empty cartridge from his gun.

Down that train with an inborn certainty he went, and on through the pines; then leaped a great bog, and splashed an hour later through the limpid Clearwater and on, responsive to some unknown guide that subtly called him from the farther west. And so he went till the dwindling pines gave place to scrubby cedars, and these in turn were mixed with sage, and onward still, till the faraway flat plains of Salmon River were about him, and ever on, tireless as it seemed, he went, and crossed the canyon of the mighty Snake, and up again to the high wild plains where the wire fence still is not, and on, beyond the Buffalo Hump, till moving specks on the far horizon caught his eager eyes, and coming on and near, they moved and rushed aside to wheel and face about. He lifted up his voice and called to them, the long shrill neigh of his kindred when they bugled to each other on the far Chaldean plain; and back their answer came. This way and that they wheeled and sped and caracoled, and Coaly-bay drew nearer, called and gave the countersigns his kindred knew, till this they were assured—he was their kind, he was of the wild free blood that man had never tamed. And when the night came down on the purpling plain, his place was in the herd as one who after many a long hard journey in the dark had found his home.

There you may see him yet, for still his strength endures, and his beauty is not less. The riders tell me they have seen him many times by Cedra. He is swift and strong among the swift ones, but it is that flowing mane and tail that mark him chiefly from afar.

There on the wild free plains of sage he lives: the stormwind smites his glossy coat at night, and the winter snows are driven hard on him at times; the wolves are there to harry all the weak ones of the herd, and in the spring the mighty grizzly, too, may come to claim his toll. There are no luscious pastures made by man, no grain foods; nothing but the wild hard hay, the wind and the open plains; but here at last he found the thing he craved—the one worth all the rest. Long may he roam—this is my wish, and this—that I may see him once again in all the glory of his speed, with his black mane on the wind, the spurgalls gone from his flanks, and in his eye the blazing light that grew in his far-off forebears' eyes as they spurned Arabian plains to leave behind the racing wild beast and the fleet gazelle—yes, too, the driving sandstorm that overwhelmed the rest, but strove in vain on the dusty wake of the Desert's highest born.

GULLIVER THE GREAT

By WALTER A. DYER

I T was a mild evening in early spring, and the magnolias were in
bloom. We motored around the park, turned up a side street,
and finally came to a throbbing standstill before the Churchwarden
Club.

There was nothing about its exterior to indicate that it was a
clubhouse at all, but within there was an indefinable atmosphere of
early Victorian comfort. There was something about it that suggested Mr. Pickwick. Old prints of horses and ships and battles
hung upon the walls, and the oak was dark and old. There seemed
to be no decorative scheme or keynote, and yet the atmosphere was
utterly distinctive. It was my first visit to the Churchwarden Club,
of which my quaint, old-fashioned Uncle Ford had long been a
member, and I was charmed.

We dined in the rathskeller, the walls of which were completely
covered with long churchwarden pipes, arranged in the most intricate and marvelous patterns; and after our mutton chop and ale and
plum pudding, we filled with the choicest of tobaccos the pipes
which the old major-domo brought us.

Then came Jacob R. Enderby to smoke with us.

Tall and spare he was, with long, straight, black hair, large
aquiline nose, and piercing eyes. I disgraced myself by staring at
him. I didn't know that such a man existed in New York, and yet
I couldn't decide whether his habitat should be Arizona or Cape
Cod.

Enderby and Uncle Ford were deep in a discussion of the states-
manship of James G. Blaine, when a waiter summoned my uncle
to the telephone.

I neglected to state that my uncle, in his prosaic hours, is a phy-
sician; and this was a call. I knew it the moment I saw the waiter
approaching. I was disappointed and disgusted.

Uncle Ford saw this and laughed.

"Cheer up!" said he. "You needn't come with me to visit the sick. I'll be back in an hour, and meanwhile Mr. Enderby will take care of you; won't you, Jake?"

For answer Enderby arose, and, refilling his pipe, took me by the arm, while my uncle got into his overcoat. As he passed us on the way out, he whispered in my ear, "Talk about dogs."

I heard and nodded.

Enderby led me to the lounge or loafing room, an oak-paneled apartment in the rear of the floor above, with huge leather chairs and a seat in the bay window. Except for a gray-haired old chap dozing over a copy of *Simplicissimus,* the room was deserted.

But no sooner had Enderby seated himself on the window seat, than there was a rush and a commotion, and a short, glad bark; and Nubbins, the steward's bull terrior, bounded in and landed at Enderby's side with canine expressions of great joy.

I reached forward to pat him, but he paid absolutely no attention to me.

At last his wriggling subsided, and he settled down with his head on Enderby's knee, the picture of content. Then I recalled my uncle's parting injunction. "Friend of yours?" I suggested.

Enderby smiled. "Yes," he said, "we're friends, I guess. And the funny part of it is that he doesn't pay any attention to anyone else except his master. They all act that way with me, dogs do." And he pulled Nubbins's stubby ears.

"Natural attraction, I suppose," said I.

"Yes, it is," he answered, with the modest frankness of a big man. "It's a thing hard to explain, though there's a sort of reason for it in my case."

I pushed toward him a little tobacco-laden teakwood stand hopefully. He refilled and lighted.

"It's an extraordinary thing, even so," he said, puffing. "Every dog nowadays seems to look upon me as his long-lost master, but it wasn't always so. I hated dogs and they hated me."

Not wishing to say "Really!" or "Indeed?" to this big, outdoor man, I simply grunted my surprise.

"Yes, we were born enemies. More than that, I was afraid of dogs

A little fuzzy toy dog, ambling up to me in a room full of company, with his tail wagging, gave me the shudders. I couldn't touch the beast. And as for big dogs out of doors, I feared them like the plague. I would go blocks out of my way to avoid one.

"I don't remember being particularly cowardly about other things, but I just couldn't help this. It was in my blood, for some reason or other. It was the bane of my existence. I couldn't see what the brutes were put into the world for, or how anyone could have anything to do with them.

"And the dogs reciprocated. They disliked and distrusted me. The most docile old Brunos would growl and show their teeth when I came near."

"Did the change come suddenly?" I asked.

"Quite. It was in 1901. I accepted a commission from an importing and trading company to go to the Philippines to do a little quiet exploring, and spent four months in the sickly place. Then I got the fever, and when I recovered I couldn't get out of there too soon.

"I reached Manila just in time to see the mail steamer disappearing around the point, and I was mad. There would be another in six days, but I couldn't wait. I was just crazy to get back home.

"I made inquiries and learned of an old tramp steamer, named the *Old Squaw*, making ready to leave for Honolulu on the following day with a cargo of hemp and stuff, and a bunch of Moros for some show in the States; and I booked passage on that.

"She was the worst old tub you ever saw. I didn't learn much about her, but I verily believe her to have been a condemned excursion boat. She wouldn't have been allowed to run to Coney Island.

"She was battered and unpainted, and she wallowed horribly. I don't believe she could have reached Honolulu much before the next regular boat, but I couldn't wait, and I took her.

"I made myself as comfortable as possible, bribed the cook to insure myself against starvation, and swung a hammock on the forward deck as far as possible from the worst of the vile smells.

"But we hadn't lost sight of Manila Bay when I discovered that there was a dog aboard—and such a dog! I had never seen one that sent me into such a panic as this one, and he had free range of the

ship. A Great Dane he was, named Gulliver, and he was the pride
of the captain's rum-soaked heart.

"With all my fear, I realized he was a magnificent animal, but
I looked on him as a gigantic devil. Without exception, he was the
biggest dog I ever saw, and as muscular as a lion. He lacked some
points that show judges set store by, but he had the size and the
build.

"I have seen Vohl's Vulcan and the Württemberg breed, but they
were fox terriers compared with Gulliver. His tail was as big around
as my arm and the cook lived in terror of his getting into the galley
and wagging it; and he had a mouth that looked to me like the
crater of Mauna Loa, and a voice that shook the planking when
he spoke. I first caught sight of him appearing from behind a huge
coil of cordage in the stern. He stretched and yawned, and I nearly
died of fright.

"I caught up a belaying pin, though little good that would have
done me. I think he saw me do it, and doubtless he set me down for
an enemy then and there.

"We were well out of the harbor, and there was no turning back,
but I would have given my right hand to be off that boat. I fully
expected him to eat me up, and I slept with that belaying pin sticking into my ribs in the hammock, and with my revolver loaded
and handy.

"Fortunately, Gulliver's dislike for me took the form of sublime
contempt. He knew I was afraid of him, and he despised me for it.
He was a great pet with the captain and crew, and even the Moros
treated him with admiring respect when they were allowed on deck.
I couldn't understand it. I would as soon have made a pet of a
hungry boa constrictor.

"On the third day out, the poor old boiler burst and the *Old
Squaw* caught fire. She was dry and rotten inside, and she burned
like tinder. No attempt was made to extinguish the flames, which
got into the hemp in the hold in short order.

"The smoke was stifling, and in a jiffy all hands were struggling
with the boats. The Moros came tumbling up from below and added
to the confusion with their terrified yells.

"The davits were old and rusty, and the men were soon fighting among themselves. One boat dropped stern foremost, filled, and sank immediately, and the *Old Squaw* herself was visibly settling.

"I saw there was no chance of getting away in the boats, and I recalled a life raft on the deck forward near my hammock. It was a sort of catamaran—a double platform on a pair of hollow, watertight, cylindrical buoys. It wasn't twenty feet long and about half as broad, but it would have to do. I fancy it was a forgotten relic of the old excursion-boat days.

"There was no time to lose, for the *Old Squaw* was bound to sink presently. Besides, I was aft with the rest, and the flames were licking up the deck and running gear in the waist of the boat.

"The galley, which was amidships near the engine room, had received the full force of the explosion, and the cook lay moaning in the lee scuppers with a small water cask thumping against his chest. I couldn't stop to help the man, but I did kick the cask away.

"It seemed to be nearly full, and it occurred to me that I should need it. I glanced quickly around, and luckily found a tin of biscuits that had also been blown out of the galley. I picked this up, and rolling the cask of water ahead of me as rapidly as I could, I made my way through the hot, stifling smoke to the bow of the boat.

"I kicked at the life raft; it seemed to be sound, and I lashed the biscuits and water to it. I also threw on a coil of rope and a piece of sailcloth. I saw nothing else about that could possibly be of any value to me. I abandoned my trunk for fear it would only prove troublesome.

"Then I hacked the raft loose with my knife and shoved it over to the bulwark. Apparently no one had seen me, for there was no one else forward of the sheet of flame that now cut the boat in two.

"The raft was a might heavy affair, but I managed to raise one end to the rail. I don't believe I would ever have been able to heave it over under any circumstances, but I didn't have to.

"I felt a great upheaval, and the prow of the *Old Squaw* went up into the air. I grabbed the ropes that I had lashed the food on with and clung to the raft. The deck became almost perpendicular, and it was a miracle that the raft didn't slide down with me into the flames. Somehow it stuck where it was.

"Then the boat sank with a great roar, and for about a thousand years, it seemed to me, I was under water. I didn't do anything. I couldn't think. I was only conscious of a tremendous weight of water and a feeling that I would burst open. Instinct alone made me cling to the raft.

"When it finally brought me to the surface I was as nearly dead as I care to be. I lay there on the thing in a half-conscious condition for an endless time. If my life had depended on my doing something, I would have been lost.

"Then gradually I came to, and began to spit out salt water and gasp for breath. I gathered my wits together and sat up. My hands were absolutely numb, and I had to loosen the grip of my fingers with the help of my toes. Odd sensation.

"Then I looked about me. My biscuits and water and rope were safe, but the sailcloth had vanished. I remember that this annoyed me hugely at the time, though I don't know what earthly good it would have been. The sea was fairly calm, and I could see all about. Not a human being was visible, only a few floating bits of wreckage. Every man on board must have gone down with the ship and drowned, except myself.

"Then I caught sight of something that made my heart stand still. The huge head of Gulliver was coming rapidly toward me through the water! The dog was swimming strongly, and must have leaped from the *Old Squaw* before she sank. My raft was the only thing afloat large enough to hold him, and he knew it.

"I drew my revolver, but it was soaking wet and useless. Then I sat down on the cracker tin and gritted my teeth and waited. I had been alarmed, I must admit, when the boiler blew up and the panic began, but that was nothing to the terror that seized me now.

"Here I was all alone on the top of the Pacific Ocean with a horrible demon making for me as fast as he could swim. My mind was benumbed, and I could think of nothing to do. I trembled and my teeth rattled. I prayed for a shark, but no shark came.

"Soon Gulliver reached the raft and placed one of his forepaws on it and then the other. The top of it stood six or eight inches above the water, and it took a great effort for the dog to raise himself. I wanted to kick him back, but I didn't dare to move.

"Gulliver struggled mightily. Again and again he reared his great shoulders above the sea, only to be cast back, scratching and kicking, at a lurch of the raft.

"Finally a wave favored him, and he caught the edge of the under platform with one of his hind feet. With a stupendous effort he heaved his huge bulk over the edge and lay sprawling at my feet, panting and trembling."

Enderby paused and gazed out of the window with a big sigh, as though the recital of his story had brought back some of the horror of his remarkable experience.

Nubbins looked up inquiringly, and then snuggled closer to his friend, while Enderby smoothed the white head.

"Well," he continued, "there we were. You can't possibly imagine how I felt unless you, too, have been afflicted with dog fear. It was awful. And I hated the brute so. I could have torn him limb from limb if I had had the strength. But he was vastly more powerful than I. I could only fear him.

"By and by he got up and shook himself. I cowered on my cracker tin, but he only looked at me contemptuously, went to the other end of the raft, and lay down to wait patiently for deliverance.

"We remained this way until nightfall. The sea was comparatively calm, and we seemed to be drifting but slowly. We were in the path of ships likely to be passing one way or the other, and I would have been hopeful of the outcome if it had not been for my feared and hated companion.

"I began to feel faint, and opened the cracker tin. The biscuits were wet with salt water, but I ate a couple, and left the cover of the tin open to dry them. Gulliver looked around, and I shut the tin hastily. But the dog never moved. He was not disposed to ask any favors. By kicking the sides of the cask and prying with my knife, I managed to get the bung out and took a drink. Then I settled myself on the raft with my back against the cask, and longed for a smoke.

"The gentle motion of the raft produced a lulling effect on my exhausted nerves, and I began to nod, only to awake with a start, with fear gripping at my heart. I dared not sleep. I don't know what I thought Gulliver would do to me, for I did not understand dogs, but I felt that I must watch him constantly. In the starlight I could see that his eyes were open. Gulliver was watchful too.

All night long I kept up a running fight with drowsiness. I dozed at intervals, but never for long at a time. It was a horrible night, and I cannot tell you how I longed for day and welcomed it when it came.

"I must have slept toward dawn, for I suddenly became conscious of broad daylight. I roused myself, stood up, and swung my arms and legs to stir up circulation, for the night had been chilly. Gulliver arose, too, and stood silently watching me until I ceased for fear. When he had settled down again, I got my breakfast out of the cracker tin. Gulliver was restless, and was evidently interested.

"'He must be hungry,' I thought, and then a new fear caught me. I had only to wait until he became very hungry and then he would surely attack me. I concluded that it would be wiser to feed him, and I tossed him a biscuit.

"I expected to see him grab it ravenously, and wondered as soon as I had thrown it if the taste of food would only serve to make him more ferocious. But at first he would not touch it. He only lay there with his great head on his paws and glowered at me. Distrust was plainly visible in his face. I had never realized before that a dog's face could express the subtler emotions.

"His gaze fascinated me, and I could not take my eyes from his. The bulk of him was tremendous as he lay there, and I noticed the big, swelling muscles of his jaw. At last he arose, sniffed suspiciously at the biscuit, and looked up at me again.

"'It's all right; eat it!' I cried.

"The sound of my own voice frightened me. I had not intended to speak to him. But in spite of my strained tone he seemed somewhat reassured.

"He took a little nibble, and then swallowed the biscuit after one or two crunches, and looked up expectantly. I threw him another and he ate that. 'That's all,' I said. 'We must be sparing of them.'

"I was amazed to discover how perfectly he understood. He lay down again and licked his chops.

"Late in the forenoon I saw a line of smoke on the horizon, and soon a steamer hove into view. I stood up and waved my coat frantically, but to no purpose. Gulliver stood up and looked from me to the steamer, apparently much interested.

"'Too far off,' I said to Gulliver. 'I hope the next one will come nearer.'

"At midday I dined, and fed Gulliver. This time he took the two biscuits quite without reserve and whacked his great tail against the raft. It seemed to me that his attitude was less hostile, and I wondered at it.

"When I took my drink from the cask, Gulliver showed signs of interest.

"'I suppose dogs get thirsty, too.' I said aloud.

"Gulliver rapped with his tail. I looked about for some sort of receptacle, and finally pulled off my shoe, filled it with water, and shoved it toward him with my foot. He drank gratefully.

"During the afternoon I sighted another ship, but it was too distant to notice me. However, the sea remained calm and I did not despair.

"After we had had supper, I settled back against my cask, resolved to keep awake, for still I did not trust Gulliver. The sun set suddenly and the stars came out, and I found myself strangely lonesome. It seemed as though I had been alone out there on the Pacific for weeks. The miles and miles of heaving waters, almost on a level with my eye, were beginning to get on my nerves. I longed for someone to talk to, and wished I had dragged the half-breed cook along with me for company. I sighed loudly, and Gulliver raised his head.

"'Lonesome out here, isn't it?' I said, simply to hear the sound of my own voice.

"Then for the first time Gulliver spoke. He made a deep sound in his throat, but it wasn't a growl, and with all my ignorance of dog language I knew it.

"Then I began to talk. I talked about everything—the people back home and all that—and Gulliver listened. I know more about dogs now, and I know that the best way to make friends with a dog is to talk to him. He can't talk back, but he can understand a heap more than you think he can.

"Finally Gulliver, who had kept his distance all this time, arose and came toward me. My words died in my throat. What was he going to do? To my immense relief he did nothing but sink down at my feet with a grunt and curl his huge body into a semicircle. He had dignity, Gulliver had. He wanted to be friendly, but he would not presume. However, I had lost interest in conversation, and sat watching him and wondering.

"In spite of my firm resolution, I fell asleep at length from sheer exhaustion, and never woke until daybreak. The sky was clouded and our craft was pitching. Gulliver was standing in the middle of the raft, looking at me in evident alarm. I glanced over my shoulder, and the blackness of the horizon told me that a storm was coming, and coming soon.

"I made fast our slender provender, tied the end of a line about my own waist for safety, and waited.

"In a short time the storm struck us in all its tropical fury. The raft pitched and tossed, now high up at one end, and now at the other, and sometimes almost engulfed in the waves.

"Gulliver was having a desperate time to keep aboard. His blunt claws slipped on the wet deck of the raft, and he fell and slid about dangerously. The thought flashed across my mind that the storm might prove to be a blessing in disguise, and that I might soon be rid of the brute.

"As I clung there to the lashings, I saw him slip down to the farther end of the raft, his hind quarters actually over the edge. A wave swept over him, but still he clung, panting madly. Then the raft righted itself for a moment, and as he hung there he gave me a look I shall never forget—a look of fear, of pleading, of reproach, and yet of silent courage. And with all my stupidity, I read that look. Somehow it told me that I was the master, after all, and he the dog. I could not resist it. Cautiously I raised myself and loosened the spare rope I had saved. As the raft tipped the other way Gulliver regained his footing and came sliding toward me.

"Quickly I passed the rope around his body, and as the raft dived again I hung on to the rope with one hand, retaining my own hold with the other. Gulliver's great weight nearly pulled my arm from its socket, but he helped mightily, and during the next moment of equilibrium I took another turn about his body and made the end of the rope fast.

"The storm passed as swiftly as it had come, and though it left us drenched and exhausted, we were both safe.

"That evening Gulliver crept close to me as I talked, and I let him: Loneliness will make a man do strange things.

"On the fifth day when our provisions were nearly gone, and I had begun to feel the sinking dullness of despair, I sighted a steamer apparently coming directly toward us. Instantly I felt new life in my limbs and around my heart, and while the boat was yet miles away I began to shout and to wave my coat.

"'I believe she's coming, old man!' I cried to Gulliver; 'I believe she's coming!'

"I soon wearied of this foolishness and sat down to wait. Gulliver came close and sat beside me, and for the first time I put my hand on him. He looked up at me and rapped furiously with his tail. I patted his head—a little gingerly, I must confess. It was a big, smooth head, and it felt solid and strong. I passed my hand down his neck, his back, his flanks. He seemed to quiver with joy. He leaned his huge body against me. Then he bowed his head and licked my shoe.

"A feeling of intense shame and unworthiness came over me, with the realization of how completely I had misunderstood him. Why should this great, powerful creature lick my shoe? It was incredible.

"Then, somehow, everything changed. Fear and distrust left me, and a feeling of comradeship and understanding took their place. We two had been through so much together. A dog was no longer a frightful beast to me; he was a dog! I cannot think of a nobler word. And Gulliver had licked my shoe! Doubtless it was only the fineness of his perception that had prevented him from licking my hand. I might have resented that. I put my arms suddenly around Gulliver's neck and hugged him. I loved that dog!

"Slowly, slowly, the steamer crawled along, but still she kept to her course. When she was about a mile away, however, I saw that she would not pass as near to us as I had hoped; so I began once more my waving and yelling. She came nearer, nearer, but still showed no sign of observing us.

"She was abreast of us, and passing. I was in a frenzy!

"She was so near that I could make out the figure of the captain on the bridge and other figures on the deck below. It seemed as though they must see us, though I realized how low in the water we stood, and how pitifully weak and hoarse my voice was. I had been a fool to waste it. Then an idea struck me. 'Speak!' I cried to Gulliver, who stood watching beside me. 'Speak, old man!'

"Gulliver needed no second bidding. A roar like that of all the bulls of Bashan rolled out over the blue Pacific. Again and again Gulliver gave voice, deep, full, powerful. His great sides heaved with the mighty effort, his red, cavernous mouth open, and his head raised high. 'Good, old man!' I cried. 'Good!' And again that magnificent voice boomed forth.

"Then something happened on board the steamer. The figures came to the side. I waved my coat and danced. Then they saw us.

"I was pretty well done up when they took us aboard, and I slept for twenty-four hours straight. When I awoke there sat Gulliver by my bunk, and when I turned to look at him he lifted a great paw and put it on my arm."

Enderby ceased, and there was silence in the room save for the light snoring of Nubbins.

"You took him home with you, I suppose?" I asked.

Enderby nodded.

"And you have him still?" I certainly wanted to have a look at that dog.

But he did not answer. I saw an expression of great sadness come into his eyes as he gazed out of the window, and I knew that Jacob Enderby had finished his story.

BROWN WOLF

By JACK LONDON

SHE had delayed because of the dew-wet grass, in order to put on her overshoes, and when she emerged from the house found her waiting husband absorbed in the wonder of a bursting almond bud. She sent a questing glance across the tall grass and in and out among the orchard trees.

"Where's Wolf?" she asked.

"He was here a moment ago." Walt Irvine drew himself away with a jerk from the metaphysics and poetry of the organic miracle of blossom, and surveyed the landscape. "He was running a rabbit the last I saw of him."

"Wolf! Wolf! Here, Wolf!" she called, as they left the clearing and took the trail that led down through the waxen-belled manzanita jungle to the county road.

Irvine thrust between his lips the little finger of each hand and lent to her efforts a shrill whistling.

She covered her ears hastily and made a wry grimace.

"My! for a poet, delicately attuned and all the rest of it, you can make unlovely noises. My eardrums are pierced. You outwhistle——"

"Orpheus."

"I was about to say a street arab," she concluded severely.

"Poesy does not prevent one from being practical—at least it doesn't prevent *me*. Mine is no futility of genius that can't sell gems to the magazines."

He assumed a mock extravagance, and went on:

"I am no attic singer, no ballroom warbler. And why? Because I am practical. Mine is no squalor of song that cannot transmute itself, with proper exchange value, into a flower-crowned cottage, a sweet mountain meadow, a grove of redwoods, an orchard of thirty-seven trees, one long row of blackberries and two short rows of strawberries, to say nothing of a quarter of a mile of gurgling brook."

"Oh, that all your song transmutations were as successful!" she laughed.

"Name one that wasn't."

"Those two beautiful sonnets that you transmuted into the cow that was accounted the worst milker in the township."

"She was beautiful——" he began.

"But she didn't give milk," Madge interrupted.

"But she *was* beautiful now, wasn't she?" he insisted.

"And here's where beauty and utility fall out," was her reply. "And there's the Wolf!"

From the thicket-covered hillside came a crashing of underbrush, and then, forty feet above them, on the edge of a sheer wall of rock, appeared a wolf's head and shoulders. His braced forepaws dislodged a pebble, and with sharp-pricked ears and peering eyes he watched the fall of the pebble until it struck at their feet. Then he transferred his gaze and with open mouth laughed down at them.

"You Wolf, you!" and "You blessed Wolf!" the man and the woman called out to him.

The ears flattened back and down at the sound, and the head seemed to snuggle under the caress of an invisible hand.

They watched him scramble backward into the thicket, then proceeded on their way. Several minutes later, rounding a turn in the trail where the descent was less precipitous, he joined them in the midst of a miniature avalanche of pebbles and loose soil. He was not demonstrative. A pat and a rub around the ears from the man, and a more prolonged caressing from the woman, and he was away down the trail in front of them, gliding effortlessly over the ground in true wolf fashion.

In build and coat and brush he was a huge timber wolf; but the lie was given to his wolfhood by his color and marking. There the dog unmistakably advertised itself. No wolf was ever colored like him. He was brown, deep brown, red-brown, an orgy of browns. Back and shoulders were a warm brown that paled on the sides and underneath to a yellow that was dingy because of the brown that lingered in it. The white of the throat and paws and the spots over the eyes was dirty because of the persistent and ineradicable brown, while the eyes themselves were twin topazes, golden and brown.

The man and woman loved the dog very much; perhaps this was because it had been such a task to win his love. It had been no easy matter when he first drifted in mysteriously out of nowhere to their little mountain cottage. Footsore and famished, he had killed a rabbit under their very noses and under their very windows, and then crawled away and slept by the spring at the foot of the blackberry bushes. When Walt Irvine went down to inspect the intruder, he was snarled at for his pains, and Madge likewise was snarled at when she went down, to present as a peace offering, a large pan of bread and milk.

A most unsociable dog he proved to be, resenting all their advances, refusing to let them lay hands on him, menacing them with bared fangs and bristled hair. Nevertheless he remained, sleeping and resting by the spring, and eating the food they gave him after they set it down at a safe distance and retreated. His wretched physical condition explained why he lingered; and when he had recuperated, after several days' sojourn, he disappeared.

And this would have been the end of him, so far as Irvine and his wife were concerned, had not Irvine at that particular time been called away to the northern part of the state. Riding along on the train, near the line between California and Oregon, he chanced to look out of the window and saw his unsociable guest sliding along the wagon road, brown and wolfish, tired yet tireless, dust-covered and soiled with two hundred miles of travel.

Now Irvine was a man of impulse, a poet. He got off the train at the next station, bought a piece of meat at a butcher shop, and captured the vagrant on the outskirts of the town. The return trip was made in the baggage car, and so Wolf came a second time to the mountain cottage. Here he was tied up for a week and made love to by the man and woman. But it was very circumspect love-making. Remote and alien as a traveler from another planet, he snarled down their soft-spoken love words. He never barked. In all the time they had him he was never known to bark.

To win him became a problem. Irvine liked problems. He had a metal plate made, on which was stamped: "Return to Walt Irvine,

Glen Ellen, Sonoma County, California." This was riveted to a
collar and strapped about the dog's neck. Then he was turned loose,
and promptly he disappeared. A day later came a telegram from
Mendocino County. In twenty hours he had made over a hundred
miles to the north, and was still going when captured.

He came back by Wells Fargo Express, was tied up three days,
and was loosed on the fourth and lost. This time he gained southern
Oregon before he was caught and returned. Always, as soon as he
received his liberty, he fled away, and always he fled north. He was
possessed of an obsession that drove him north. The homing instinct,
Irvine called it, after he had expended the selling price of a sonnet
in getting the animal back from northern Oregon.

Another time the brown wanderer succeeded in traversing half
the length of California, all of Oregon, and most of Washington,
before he was picked up and returned "Collect." A remarkable thing
was the speed with which he traveled. Fed up and rested, as soon as
he was loosed he devoted all his energy to getting over the ground.
On the first day's run he was known to cover as high as a hundred
and fifty miles, and after that he would average a hundred miles a
day until caught. He always arrived back lean and hungry and
savage, and always departed fresh and vigorous, cleaving his way
northward in response to some prompting of his being that no one
could understand.

But at last, after a futile year of flight, he accepted the inevitable
and elected to remain at the cottage where he first had killed the
rabbit and slept by the spring. Even after that, a long time elapsed
before the man and woman succeeded in patting him. It was a great
victory, for they alone were allowed to put hands on him. He was
fastidiously exclusive, and no guest at the cottage ever succeeded in
making up to him. A low growl greeted such approach; if anyone
had the hardihood to come nearer, the lips lifted, the naked fangs
appeared, and the growl became a snarl—a snarl so terrible and
malignant that it awed the stoutest of them, as it likewise awed the
farmers' dogs that knew ordinary dog snarling, but had never seen
wolf snarling before.

He was without antecedents. His history began with Walt and Madge. He had come up from the south, but never a clew did they get of the owner from whom he had evidently fled. Mrs. Johnson, their nearest neighbor and the one who supplied them with milk, proclaimed him a Klondike dog. Her brother was burrowing for frozen pay streaks in that far country, and so she constituted herself an authority on the subject.

But they did not dispute her. There were the tips of Wolf's ears, obviously so severely frozen at some time that they would never quite heal again. Besides, he looked like the photographs of the Alaskan dogs they saw published in magazines and newspapers. They often speculated over his past, and tried to conjure up (from what they had read and heard) what his northland life had been. That the northland still drew him, they knew; for at night they sometimes heard him crying softly; and when the north wind blew and the bite of frost was in the air, a great restlessness would come upon him and he would lift a mournful lament which they knew to be the long wolf howl.

Yet he never barked. No provocation was great enough to draw from him that canine cry.

Long discussion they had, during the time of winning him, as to whose dog he was. Each claimed him, and each proclaimed loudly any expression of affection made by him. But the man had the better of it at first, chiefly because he was a man. It was patent that Wolf had had no experience with women. He did not understand women. Madge's skirts were something he never quite accepted. The swish of them was enough to set him a-bristle with suspicion, and on a windy day she could not approach him at all.

On the other hand, it was Madge who fed him; also it was she who ruled the kitchen, and it was by her favor, and her favor alone, that he was permitted to come within that sacred precinct. It was because of these things that she bade fair to overcome the handicap of her garments. Then it was that Walt put forth special effort, making it a practice to have Wolf lie at his feet while he wrote, and, between petting and talking, losing much time from his work. Walt won in the end, and his victory was most probably due to the fact that he was a man, though Madge averred that they would have had another quarter of a mile of gurgling brook, and at least two west winds sighing through their redwoods, had Walt properly devoted his energies to song transmutation and left Wolf alone to exercise a natural taste and an unbiased judgment.

"It's about time I heard from those triolets," Walt said, after a silence of five minutes, during which they had swung steadily down the trail. "There'll be a check at the post office, I know, and we'll transmute it into beautiful buckwheat flour, a gallon of maple syrup, and a new pair of overshoes for you."

"And into beautiful milk from Mrs. Johnson's beautiful cow," Madge added. "Tomorrow's the first of the month, you know."

Walt scowled unconsciously; then his face brightened, and he clapped his hand to his breast pocket.

"Never mind. I have here a nice, beautiful, new cow, the best milker in California."

"When did you write it?" she demanded eagerly. Then, reproachfully, "And you never showed it to me."

"I saved it to read to you on the way to the post office, in a spot remarkably like this one," he answered, indicating, with a wave of his hand, a dry log on which to sit.

A tiny stream flowed out of a dense fernbrake, slipped down a mossy-lipped stone, and ran across the path at their feet. From the valley arose the mellow song of meadowlarks, while about them, in and out, through sunshine and shadow, fluttered great yellow butterflies.

Up from below came another sound that broke in upon Walt reading softly from his manuscript. It was a crunching of heavy feet, punctuated now and again by the clattering of a displaced stone. As Walt finished, and looked to his wife for approval, a man came into view around the turn of the trail. He was bareheaded and sweaty. With a handkerchief in one hand he mopped his face, while in the other hand he carried a new hat and a wilted starched collar which he had removed from his neck. He was a well-built man, and his muscles seemed on the point of bursting out of the painfully new and ready-made black clothes he wore.

"Warm day," Walt greeted him. Walt believed in country democracy, and never missed an opportunity to practise it.

The man paused and nodded.

"I guess I ain't used much to the warm," he vouchsafed half apologetically. "I'm more accustomed to zero weather."

"You don't find any of that in this country," Walt laughed.

"Should say not," the man answered. "An' I ain't here a-lookin' for it neither. I'm tryin' to find my sister. Mebbe you know where she lives. Her name's Johnson, Mrs. William Johnson."

"You're not her Klondike brother!" Madge cried, here eyes bright with interest, "About whom we've heard so much?"

"Yes'm, that's me," he answered modestly. "My name's Miller, Skiff Miller. I just thought I'd s'prise her."

"You are on the right track then. Only you've come by the footpath." Madge stood up to direct him, pointing up the canyon a quarter of a mile. "You see that blasted redwood? Take the little trail turning off to the right. It's the short cut to her house. You can't miss it."

"Yes'm, thank you, ma'am," he said.

He made tentative efforts to go, but seemed awkwardly rooted to the spot. He was gazing at her with an open admiration of which he was quite unconscious, and which was drowning, along with him, in the rising sea of embarrassment in which he floundered.

"We'd like to hear you tell about the Klondike," Madge said. Mayn't we come over some day while you're at your sister's? Or, better yet, won't you come over and have dinner with us?"

"Yes'm, thank you, ma'am," he mumbled mechanically. Then he caught himself up and added: "I ain't stoppin long. I got to be pullin' north again. I go out on tonight's train. You see, I've got a mail contract with the government."

When Madge had said that it was too bad, he made another futile effort to go. But he could not take his eyes from her face. He forgot his embarrassment in his admiration, and it was her turn to flush and feel uncomfortable.

It was at this juncture, when Walt had just decided it was time for him to be saying something to relieve the strain, that Wolf, who had been away nosing through the brush, trotted wolflike into view.

Skiff Millers' abstraction disappeared. The pretty woman before him passed out of his field of vision. He had eyes only for the dog, and a great wonder came into his face.

"Well, I'll be hanged!" he enunciated slowly and solemnly.

He sat down ponderingly on the log, leaving Madge standing. At the sound of his voice, Wolf's ears flattened down, then his mouth had opened in a laugh. He trotted slowly up to the stranger and first smelled his hands, then licked them with his tongue.

Skiff Miller patted the dog's head, and slowly and solemnly repeated, "Well, I'll be hanged!"

"Excuse me, ma'am," he said the next moment, "I was just s'prised some, that was all."

"We're surprised, too," she answered lightly. "We never saw Wolf make up to a stranger before."

"Is that what you call him—Wolf?" the man asked.

Madge nodded. "But I can't understand his friendliness toward you—unless it's because you're from the Klondike. He's a Klondike dog, you know."

"Yes'm," Miller said absently. He lifted one of Wolf's forelegs and examined the footpads, pressing them and denting them with his thumb. "Kind of soft," he remarked. "He ain't been on trail for a long time."

"I say," Walt broke in, "it is remarkable the way he lets you handle him."

Skiff Miller arose, no longer awkward with admiration of Madge, and in a sharp, businesslike manner asked, "How long have you had him?"

But just then the dog, squirming and rubbing against the newcomer's legs, opened his mouth and barked. It was an explosive bark, brief and joyous, but a bark.

"That's a new one on me," Skiff Miller remarked.

Walt and Madge stared at each other.

The miracle had happened. Wolf had barked.

"It's the first time he ever barked," Madge said.

"First time I ever heard him, too," Miller volunteered.

Madge smiled at him. The man was evidently a humorist.

"Of course," she said, "since you have only seen him for five minutes."

Skiff Miller looked at her sharply, seeking in her face the guile her words had led him to suspect.

"I thought you understood," he said slowly. "I thought you'd tumbled to it from his makin' up to me. He's my dog. His name ain't Wolf. It's Brown."

"Oh, Walt!" was Madge's instinctive cry to her husband.

Walt was on the defensive at once.

"How do you know he's your dog?" he demanded.

"Because he is," was the reply.

"Mere assertion," Walt said sharply.

In his slow and pondering way, Skiff Miller looked at him, then asked, with a nod of his head toward Madge:

"How d'you know she's your wife? You just say, 'Because she is,' and I'll say it's mere assertion. The dog's mine. I bred 'm an' raised 'm, an' I guess I ought to know. Look here. I'll prove it to you."

Skiff Miller turned to the dog. "Brown!" His voice rang out sharply, and at the sound the dog's ears flattened down as to a caress. "Gee!" The dog made a swinging turn to the right. "Now mush on!" And the dog ceased his swing abruptly and started straight ahead, halting obediently at command.

"I can do it with whistles," Skiff Miller said proudly. "He was my lead dog."

"But you are not going to take him away with you?" Madge asked tremulously. The man nodded.

"Back into that awful Klondike world of suffering?"

He nodded and added: "Oh, it ain't so bad as all that. Look at me. Pretty healthy specimen, ain't I?"

"But the dogs! The terrible hardship, the heart-breaking toil, the starvation, the frost! Oh, I've read about it and I know."

"I nearly ate him once, over on Little Fish River," Miller volunteered grimly. "If I hadn't got a moose that day was all that saved 'm."

"I'd have died first!" Madge cried.

"Things is different down here," Miller explained. You don't have to eat dogs. You think different just about the time you're all in. You've never been all in, so you don't know anything about it."

"That's the very point," she argued warmly. "Dogs are not eaten in California. Why not leave him here? He is happy. He'll never want for food—you know that. He'll never suffer from cold and hardship. Here all is softness and gentleness. Neither the human nor nature is savage. He will never know a whiplash again. And as for the weather—why, it never snows here."

"But it's all-fired hot in summer, beggin' your pardon," Skiff Miller laughed.

"But you do not answer," Madge continued passionately. "What have you to offer him in that northland life?"

"Grub, when I've got it, and that's most of the time," came the answer.

"And the rest of the time?"

"No grub."

"And the work?"

"Yes, plenty of work," Miller blurted out impatiently. "Work without end, an' famine, an' frost, an' all the rest of the miseries— that's what he'll get when he comes with me. But he likes it. He is used to it. He knows that life. He was born to it an' brought up to it. An' you don't know anything about it. You don't know what you're talking about. That's where the dog belongs, and that's where he'll be happiest."

"The dog doesn't go," Walt announced in a determined voice. "So there is no need of further discussion."

"What's that?" Skiff Miller demanded, his brows lowering and an obstinate flush of blood reddening his forehead.

"I said the dog doesn't go, and that settles it. I don't believe he's your dog. You may have seen him sometime. You may even some-time have driven him for his owner. But his obeying the ordinary driving commands of the Alaskan trail is no demonstration that he is yours. Any dog in Alaska would obey you as he obeyed. Besides, he is undoubtedly a valuable dog, as dogs go in Alaska, and that is sufficient explanation of your desire to get possession of him. Anyway, you've got to prove property."

Skiff Miller, cool and collected, the obstinate flush a trifle deeper on his forehead, his huge muscles bulging under the black cloth of his coat, carefully looked the poet up and down as though measuring the strength of his slenderness.

The Klondiker's face took on a contemptuous expression as he said finally: "I reckon there's nothin' in sight to prevent me takin' the dog right here an' now."

Walt's face reddened, and the striking-muscles of his arms and shoulders seemed to stiffen and grow tense. His wife fluttered apprehensively into the breach.

"Maybe Mr. Miller is right," she said. "I am afraid that he is. Wolf does seem to know him, and certainly he answers to the name 'Brown.' He made friends with him instantly, and you know that's something he never did with anybody before. Besides, look at the way he barked. He was just bursting with joy. Joy over what? Without doubt at finding Mr. Miller."

Walt's striking muscles relaxed, and his shoulders seemed to droop with hopelessness.

"I guess you're right, Madge," he said. "Wolf isn't Wolf, but Brown, and he must belong to Mr. Miller."

"Perhaps Mr. Miller will sell him," she suggested. "We can buy him."

Skiff Miller shook his head, no longer belligerent, but kindly, quick to be generous in response to generousness.

"I had five dogs," he said, casting about for the easiest way to temper his refusal. "He was the leader. They was the crack team of Alaska. Nothin' could touch 'em. In 1898 I refused five thousand dollars for the bunch. Dogs was high, then, anyway; but that wasn't what made the fancy price. It was the team itself. Brown was the best in the team. That winter I refused twelve hundred for 'm. I didn't sell 'm then, and I ain't a-sellin' 'm now. Besides I think a mighty lot of that dog. I've been lookin' for 'm for three years. It made me fair sick when I found he'd been stole—not the value of him, but the—well, I liked 'm so, that's all. I couldn't believe my eyes when I seen 'm just now. I thought I was dreamin'. It was too good to be true. Why, I was his nurse. I put 'm to bed, snug every night. His mother died, and I brought 'm up on condensed milk at two dollars a can when I could n't afford it in my own coffee. He never knew any mother but me. He used to suck my finger regular, the darn little pup—that finger right there!"

And Skiff Miller, too overwrought for speech, held up a forefinger for them to see.

"That very finger," he managed to articulate, as though it somehow clinched the proof of ownership and the bond of affection.

He was still gazing at his extended finger when Madge began to speak.

"But the dog," she said. "You haven't considered the dog."

Skiff Miller looked puzzled.

"Have you thought about him?" she asked.

"Don't know what you're drivin' at," was the response.

"Maybe the dog has some choice in the matter," Madge went on. "Maybe he has his likes and desires. You have not considered him. You give him no choice. It has never entered your mind that possibly he might prefer California to Alaska. You consider only what you like. You do with him as you would with a sack of potatoes or a bale of hay."

This was a new way of looking at it, and Miller was visibly impressed as he debated it in his mind. Madge took advantage of his indecision.

"If you really love him, what would be happiness to him would be your happiness also," she urged.

Skiff Miller continued to debate with himself, and Madge stole a glance of exultation to her husband, who looked back warm approval.

"What do you think?" the Klondiker suddenly demanded.

It was her turn to be puzzled.

"What do you mean?" she asked.

"D'ye think he'd sooner stay in California?"

She nodded her head with positiveness. "I am sure of it."

Skiff Miller again debated with himself, though this time aloud, at the same time running his gaze in a judicial way over the mooted animal.

"He was a good worker. He's done a heap of work for me. He never loafed on me, an' he was a joe-dandy at hammerin' a raw team into shape. He's got a head on him. He can do everything but talk. He knows what you say to him. Look at 'm now. He knows we're talking about him."

The dog was lying at Skiff Miller's feet, head close down on paws, ears erect and listening, and eyes that were quick and eager to follow the sound of speech as it fell from the lips of first one and then the other.

"An' there's a lot of work in 'm yet. He's good for years to come. An' I do like him." Once or twice after that Skiff Miller opened his mouth and closed it again without speaking. Finally he said:

"I'll tell you what I'll do. Your remarks, ma'am, has some weight in them. The dog's worked hard, and maybe he's earned a soft berth an' has got a right to choose. Anyway, we'll leave it up to him. Whatever he says, goes. You people stay right here settin' down. I'll say good-bye and walk off casual-like. If he wants to stay, he can stay. If he wants to come with me, let 'm come. I won't call 'm to come and don't you call 'm to come back."

He looked with sudden suspicion at Madge, and added, "Only you must play fair. No persuadin' after my back is turned."

"We'll play fair," Madge began, but Skiff Miller broke in on her assurances.

"I know the ways of women," he announced. "Their hearts is soft. When their hearts is touched they're likely to stack the cards, look at the bottom of the deck, an' lie—beggin' your pardon, ma'am. I'm only discoursin' about women in general."

"I don't know how to thank you," Madge quavered.

"I don't see as you've got any call to thank me," he replied. "Brown ain't decided yet. Now you won't mind if I go away slow? It's no more'n fair, seein' I'll be out of sight inside a hundred yards."

Madge agreed, and added, "And I promise you faithfully that we won't do anything to influence him."

"Well, then, I might as well be gettin' along," Skiff Miller said in the ordinary tones of one departing.

At this change in his voice, Wolf lifted his head quickly, and still more quickly got to his feet when the man and woman shook hands. He sprang up on his hind legs, resting his forepaws on her hip and at the same time licking Skiff Miller's hand. When the latter shook hands with Walt, Wolf repeated his act, resting his weight on Walt and licking both men's hands.

"It ain't no picnic, I can tell you that," were the Klondiker's last words, as he turned and went slowly up the trail.

For the distance of twenty feet Wolf watched him go, himself all eagerness and expectancy, as though waiting for the man to turn and retrace his steps. Then, with a quick low whine, Wolf sprang after him, overtook him, caught his hand between his teeth with reluctant tenderness, and strove gently to make him pause.

Failing in this Wolf raced back to where Walt Irvine sat, catching his coat sleeve in his teeth and trying vainly to drag him after the retreating man.

Wolf's perturbation began to wax. He desired ubiquity. He wanted to be in two places at the same time, with the old master and the new, and steadily the distance between them was increasing. He sprang about excitedly, making short nervous leaps and twists, now toward one, now toward the other, in painful indecision, not knowing his own mind, desiring both and unable to choose, uttering quick sharp whines and beginning to pant.

He sat down abruptly on his haunches, thrusting his nose upward, the mouth opening and closing with jerking movements, each time opening wider. These jerking movements were in unison with the recurrent spasms that attacked the throat, each spasm severer and more intense than the preceding one. And in accord with jerks and spasms the larynx began to vibrate, at first silently, accompanied by the rush of air expelled from the lungs, then sounding a low, deep note, the lowest in the register of the human ear. All this was the nervous and muscular preliminary to howling.

But just as the howl was on the verge of bursting from the full throat, the wide-opened mouth was closed, the paroxysms ceased, and he looked long and steadily at the retreating man. Suddenly Wolf turned his head, and over his shoulder just as steadily regarded Walt. The appeal was unanswered. Not a word nor a sign did the dog receive, no suggestion and no clew as to what his conduct should be.

A glance ahead to where the old master was nearing the curve of the trail excited him again. He sprang to his feet with a whine, and then, struck by a new idea, turned his attention to Madge. Hitherto, he had ignored her, but now, both masters failing him, she alone was left. He went over to her and snuggled his head in her lap, nudging her arm with his nose—an old trick of his when begging for favors. He backed away from her and began writhing and twisting playfully, curvetting and prancing, half rearing and striking his forepaws to the earth, struggling with all his body, from the wheedling eyes and flattening ears to the wagging tail, to express the thought that was in him and that was denied him utterance.

This, too, he soon abandoned. He was depressed by the coldness of these humans who had never been cold before. No response could he draw from them, no help could he get. They did not consider him. They were as dead.

He turned and silently gazed after the old master. Skiff Miller was rounding the curve. In a moment he would be gone from view. Yet he never turned his head, plodding straight onward, slowly and methodically, as though possessed of no interest in what was occurring behind his back.

And in this fashion he went out of view. Wolf waited for him to reappear. He waited a long minute, silently, quietly, without movement, as though turned to stone—withal stone quick with eagerness and desire. He barked once, and waited. Then he turned and trotted back to Walt Irvine. He sniffed his hand and dropped down heavily at his feet, watching the trail where it curved emptily from view.

The tiny stream slipping down the mossy-lipped stone seemed suddenly to increase the volume of its gurgling noise. Save for the meadow larks, there was no other sound. The great yellow butterflies drifted silently through the sunshine and lost themselves in the drowsy shadows. Madge gazed triumphantly at her husband.

A few minutes later Wolf got upon his feet. Decision and deliberation marked his movements. He did not glance at the man and woman. His eyes were fixed up the trail. He had made up his mind. They knew it. And they knew, so far as they were concerned, that the ordeal had just begun.

He broke into a trot, and Madge's lips pursed, forming an avenue for the caressing sound that it was the will of her to send forth. But the caressing sound was not made. She was impelled to look at her husband, and she saw the sternness with which he watched her. The pursed lips relaxed, and she sighed inaudibly.

Wolf's trot broke into a run. Wider and wider were the leaps he made. Not once did he turn his head, his wolf's brush standing out straight behind him. He cut sharply across the curve of the trail and was gone.

THE ASSAULT OF WINGS

By CHARLES G. D. ROBERTS

IN his high place in the unclouded blue, a thousand feet above the topmost pinnacle of Bald Face, the great white-headed eagle stared downward toward the far-off reek and roofs of the busy town by the sea. It was not often that his eyes troubled themselves to turn in that direction, for all his concern was with the inland lakes and water courses which linked themselves tranquilly about the spreading bases of Old Bald Face, and he hated the acrid smoke clouds which rose from the chimneys of the town. But this morning his gaze—that miraculous vision which could scrutinize a rabbit or an ailing lamb at a distance when our eyes would hardly discern an elephant—had been caught by an apparition which amazed and disconcerted him.

Flying in wide circles above a green field on the outskirts of the city was a gigantic bird, in form and stature quite unlike any other bird that the great eagle had ever seen. As it passed over a red brick cottage at one corner of the field, quite blotting it from view for an instant, he got an impression of its incredible size, and felt, with a pang of angry dread, that his own stately dimensions would have seemed little better than a sparrow's beside it. Its vast white wings were square at the tip, and of the same width from tip to base—an inexplicable innovation in wings—and he noted with apprehension that they flew without any motion at all.

He himself, soaring in the blue heights as he was, flew *almost* without motion of the wings, riding by subtle poise and balance on the thrust of the light aerial draught. But even now, the breeze failing, he had to recover his impetus by a rushing descent. He tipped his snowy head and shoulders forward, and the air hissed sharply in the tense web of the hinder edges of his wings as he swept down the viewless slopes of air, turning upward again after a swoop of a hundred yards or so, which was as nothing at that height. A slow stroke or two restored him to his former level, with impetus to spare for his splendid effortless soaring. But, meanwhile, he had not taken his eyes for a moment from that portentous shape circling so mysteriously over the green field on the outskirts of the town, and he had not seen it either swoop or mount or once flap its flat-spread wings.

Moved from his accustomed arrogant indifference, the eagle flew over toward the town to get a better look at this disquieting phenomenon. On nearer approach he made out that the monstrous square-winged bird was ridden by one of those man-creatures whom he so hated and despised—ridden as he had seen, with wonder and scorn, that horses permitted themselves to be. The man sat in a hollow in the strange bird's back, between its wings, and seemed to master and guide it even as he would master and guide a horse.

The eagle hated man, because man was the only creature that had ever given him, hitherto, the loathed sensation of fear. He despised man because he saw the proud and cunning creature chained to earth, compelled to crawl upon earth's surface even as a sheep or a woodchuck. But now, if man were able to ride the dwellers of the air, there would be no escaping his tyranny.

The eagle had been conscious for some moments of a curious humming roar in his ears, the source of which was not at once obvious to him. Suddenly he realized that it was the noise of the blunt-winged monster's flight. The realization daunted him. How was it possible that such an awful sound should come from those unmoving wings? He was inclined to turn and fly back to the shelter of Old Bald Face, but, after a moment's irresolution, his stout heart arose to the magnitude of the peril. He flew onward, till soon he was directly over the field, but so high that to the spectators around the edges of the field he was a scarcely visible speck against the blue.

At this moment the aeroplane began to mount skyward. It scaled the air swiftly in a steep spiral. The eagle was almost panic-stricken to observe that even now, when mounting so directly, it did not flap its wings, although there was no wind on which to rise. At the curious blunt beak of the monster he discerned a sort of circle of faint haze, a bluish blur, but this was something which did not seem to concern him, and he made no effort to understand it. What did concern him was that the monster, with its human rider, was apparently coming after him. His courage and his curiosity gave way together, and he fled in a panic to his ledge in the recesses of Old Bald Face.

The extreme summit of Bald Face was a level plateau of granite some dozens of acres in extent, with a needlelike pinnacle of splintered granite at its eastern or seaward end. The broad southeastern face of the summit was of naked granite, whitened by the storm and frost of ages, whence the name of Old Bald Face. But between this bleak, wind-harried front and the rich plain country by the sea were many lesser pinnacles and ridges, with deep ravines between, all clothed with dark spruce woods and tangled undergrowth. Around to full south and west and north lay an infertile region, thin-soiled and rocky, producing little timber but hemlock and stunted paper birch, and therefore not worth the attention of either the lumberman or the squatter. The whole of this district was interlaced with watercourses and sown with lakes having their ultimate outlet in the tidal estuary which washed the wharves of the town.

If the land in this region skirting Old Bald Face was barren, its waters were not. They swarmed with fish—lake trout, white fish, and huge suckers, as well as the ordinary brook trout. They supplied hunting ground, therefore, for not only a number of fish hawks, but also for no less than three pairs of the fish hawks' dreaded tyrants, the white-headed eagles. These three pairs of eagles had their nests in the uppermost and most inaccessible ledges of Bald Face; and the wild country below was divided among them into six ranges, each great bird having his or her own hunting ground, upon which not even their own mates could poach with impunity.

The nests of the three royal pairs were all within a distance of perhaps half a mile of each other, but each was austerely secluded and jealously hidden from its neighbors. Each pair regarded its neighbors with a coldly tolerant aversion, and kept an aloof but vigilant watch upon them as possible poachers.

When the first eagle, smitten with fear by the vision of the swiftly mounting aeroplane, fled back to his eyrie to warn his fierce-eyed mate of this portentous monster of the air, his perturbation was detected by the female of the next pair, who chanced to be homing at that moment with a fish for her hungry nestlings. Fear seems to travel by some uncomprehended but very efficient wireless, and fear in the lords of the air was a thing too unusual to be ignored. Hastily depositing her burden, the newcomer flapped upward and around to the east, till she, too, caught sight of the mounting monoplane. It was far off, indeed, but already so high above earth that to her eyes it stood out dark and sinister against the pale expanse of sea beyond the town. She flapped over for a nearer view, flew close enough to hear the mysterious roar of the motor and to detect the man-creature riding the monster's neck, and fled back to her nestlings with rage and terror at her heart. No longer could she feel secure on the dizziest and remotest ledges of the peaks, no longer were even the soundless deeps of sky inaccessible to man! Within an hour every eagle of Bald Face knew of this dreadful invasion of their hitherto impregnable domain. It was the time of the year when their nestlings were most helpless, and that is the time of the year when the white-headed eagles will face all odds with an incomparable ferocity of valor at the hint of menace to their skyey homes.

. . . . .

The airman at the town of X—— was one Rob MacCreedy, who had recently been making a name for himself at the aviation grounds some hundred miles down the coast. He had come up to X—— primarily to turn a needed penny by exhibition flights and passenger-carrying over the spacious and level fields behind the town. But his secondary object was to experiment with the dangerous eddies and windholes that were likely to be met with above the profound ravines of Bald Face and its buttressing hills. His purpose was to go to Europe and win fame by some sensational flights over the Alps or the Pyrenees; and having a very practical Canadian ambition to survive, for the enjoyment of the fame he planned to win, he was determined to prepare himself effectively for the perils that would confront him.

But MacCreedy had another object in view, which he did not talk about lest matter-of-fact folks should call him childish. He wanted to see what there was on top of Old Bald Face. That gaunt gray summit was regarded as practically unscalable. It had indeed been scaled, men said, some thirty or forty years ago, after desperate effort and altogether hair-raising adventure, by a greatly daring trapper, who had barely survived to tell of his exploit. Since then, the men of X—— not being wholehearted or skilled mountain climbers, all such attempts had ended in failure. Among the legends which had gathered about the austere summit, there was none to suggest that gold might be found thereon, else the cloudy sanctuary had doubtless been violated without unnecessary delay. . . . They told of a remarkable level plateau, like a table for the gods, with a little lake of black crystal set in the center of it, ice cold and of unfathomable depth. It was, according to tradition, bottomless.

To MacCreedy's eager and boyish imagination this lofty plateau and this mysterious uninvestigated lake were irresistible. He was determined to know more about them both; and as the top of Bald Face, for all its inaccessibility, was less than five thousand feet above sea-level, his monoplane seemed to offer him an easy way to it.

The third day after MacCreedy's arrival at X—— was windless and without a cloud in the blue. The air almost sparkled with its clarity, and there was an un-springlike tang in it which made Mac-Creedy's nerves tingle for adventure. After he had given the crowd their money's worth in swift mountings and breath-taking *vols-planés,* he started off, at a height of some two thousand feet, toward the mountain standing pallid and grim against the intense blue. He mounted swiftly as he went, and the spectators stared after him doubtfully, till they grasped his purpose.

"He's going to visit the top of Old Bald Face!" went the murmur round the crowded edges of the field. And a feeling that he might bring back some interesting information made them content to wait without grumbling for his return.

Since their first sight of the giant-winged monster soaring and humming over X——, the eagles of Bald Face had not dared to venture far from home in their foragings. Their nerves were raw with angry anxiety for their nests. MacCreedy, as he came within a mile or two of the mountain, took note of an eagle not far ahead, circling at a higher level than himself.

"The old bird thinks he can fly some," mused MacCreedy, "but I bet I'm going to give him the surprise of his life!"

A few moments more and he was himself surprised, as the solitary sentinel was joined by another, and another, and another, till presently there were six of the great birds flapping and whirling between him and Bald Face, about at the level of the edge of the plateau.

"Seem to be as interested in aeroplanes as any of us humans," thought MacCreedy, and gave his plane a lift that should carry him over the plateau at a height of not much over a hundred feet. He would make a hasty observation first, then circle around and effect a landing, if the surface looked smooth enough for him to attempt it without too much risk.

He was surprised somewhat by the attitude of the eagles, who were now circling nearer, and seemed to be more angry than curious or terrified at his approach. Then his attention was abruptly withdrawn from their threatening evolutions. It was all required, and urgently, by the aeroplane.

Having arrived over the deeply cleft and ridged outworks of Bald Face, the aeroplane had plunged into a viewless turmoil of air-currents and vortices. It dropped with startling suddenness into a "pocket," and fell as if a vacuum had opened beneath it. MacCreedy saw a vicious granite ridge, whiskered with fir trees, lurch up at him insanely from a thousand feet below. He was almost upon it before his plane bit upon solid air again and glided off from the peril, slanting upward rockingly over a gaping abyss. Yelping with triumph, the eagles had swooped down after him; but he could not hear their cries, of course, through the roar of the Gnome; and of eagles, at that moment, he was thinking not at all.

Realizing the imminence of his danger from these vortices, MacCreedy changed his course and swept back again as fast as he could toward the open, his machine careening wickedly in the eddies and upthrusts of air. He decided that he must get far above this area of disturbance, and then spiral down directly over the plateau, where, as he calculated, the currents would be less tumultuous.

The eagles, imagining that the loud monster had been put to flight by their threats, came following in its wake, determined to see it safely off their premises and give it no time to recover from what they conceived to be its panic. But they were far too sagacious to attack, and force a more than doubtful conflict. They were filled with awe of this gigantic being which flew with rigid wings and such appalling roar, yet allowed itself to be ridden by the man between its shoulders. They were perplexed, too, by the fierce wind which streamed out behind its level wings. Their amazement was heightened by the fact that their own long and powerful wings, which were able to overtake so easily the flight of the agile fish hawk, were forced to beat furiously in order to keep up with this incomprehensible stranger, who was apparently making no effort at all.

A swift motorcar, which had followed MacCreedy's flight at top speed across the plain, had halted at the point where the highway passed nearest to the broken and impassable region surrounding the mountain. Its occupants, watching MacCreedy's movements through their field glasses, and noting the great birds crowding behind him, thought at first that the eagles had put him to flight and forced him to give up his venture. They were undeceived, however. Then they saw him turn—at such a height that, even to their powerful glasses, the pursuing eagles were no more than specks—and soar back till he was directly over the summit.

At the height which he had now gained, the air was icy cold but still as a dream. The world below looked like a vast, shallow bowl, the sides concaving upward around him to the horizon. Two-thirds of this horizon rim were of dark green woods, threaded with the gleaming silver of watercourses. The remaining third was of sea, which looked as if it overhung the town of X——, and was withheld only by a miracle from flowing in and filling the bowl. Directly beneath him, two to three thousand feet down, the mighty summit of Old Bald Face looked insignificant. It lay outspread quite flat and shelterless in the sun, its secrets clean revealed, and there, sure enough, at its center, was the pool of tradition, gleaming upward, glassy still. At the same time he saw, though without much interest, the eagles. They were very far below him now, hardly above the level of the plateau, flying in occasionally in over its edges, but for the most part circling out above the surrounding gulfs. In a casual way MacCreedy inferred that they must have nests in the ledges of the precipices.

In a somewhat narrow spiral he now began his descent, gradually and under power, that he might be in full readiness to grapple with the treacherous gusts which came leaping up at him from under the brink of the plateau. He was surprised to see that, as he descended, the eagles rose hurriedly to meet him; but at first he paid no attention to them, being intent upon the search for a good landing place, and upon the mystery of the sky-inhabiting pool. A minute or two more, however, and it was no longer possible for him to ignore the approaching birds, who were rising at him with unmistakable manifestations of rage. For the first time it occurred to him that they might be thinking he had come to rob their nests. "Plucky beggars!" he said to himself admiringly, "To think of showing fight to a grown-up aeroplane!"

The next moment, as he noted the spread of those flapping wings, the shining, snowy, out-stretched heads and necks, the firm and formidable half-opened beaks, a sweat of apprehension broke out all over him. What if one of the misguided birds should foul his propeller or come blundering aboard and snap a stay or control wire? The idea of being dashed to pieces in that skyey solitude was somehow more daunting to his spirit than the prospect which he faced indifferently every day—that of being hurled down upon familiar earth.

For a few seconds MacCreedy was tempted to drive his plane heavenward again and withdraw from the situation, to return another day with a passenger and a shotgun for his defense. Then he grew angry and obstinate. He had come to explore the summit of Bald Face, and he was not going to be balked by a flock of birds. He was low enough now to satisfy himself that the plateau afforded a good landing, so he dipped his descent to a steeper angle, making haste to get through the suspense.

Immediately the eagles were all about him. To his relief, they seemed afraid to fly directly in front of him, as if apprehending that this monstrous bird of his might carry some terrible weapon in its blunt-faced beak. Mounting swiftly, they passed the descending aeroplane on either side, and then gathered in above it, swooping and yelping. Through the roar of his motor MacCreedy caught the strident shrillness of their cries. He felt that at any moment one might pluck up courage to pounce upon the plane or upon his head. He wondered if his leather cap would be stout enough to resist the clutch of those edged talons which he saw opening and shutting viciously above him. He wished himself safely landed.

He was low enough now to choose his landing place. He was just about to shut off the engine for the final glide, when one of the female eagles, growing desperate, swooped and struck the right wing of the plane not far from its tip. The extended talons went right through the cloth, tearing a long gash, and, before the bird could recover herself, she was caught by one of the strong wires that braced the wing. The aeroplane rocked under her struggles, but in the next moment she was thrown clear, so badly crumpled that she fell topsy-turvy through the air for some little distance before she could pull her wits together and right herself. Then, disheveled and cowed, she flew off to one side, with no more stomach left for another assault.

MacCreedy had brought his plane to a level keel, the better to withstand the attack. Now he laughed grimly and resumed his descent. Almost at the same instant he realized that an immense eagle was swooping straight at his head. He ducked—the only way to save his face. The grasping claws sunk deep into his shoulders. With a yell he straightened himself backward violently. His assailant, unable for a moment to free his claws from the tough tweed or the jacket, and swept backward by the plane, plunged down among the supporting stays, where he struggled and flapped wildly to extricate himself.

Smarting with pain and wrath, and with his heart in his mouth lest the stays should snap and the plane collapse, MacCreedy cut off the power and slid sharply downward. The eagle behind him got free, and flapped off, much daunted by the encounter. The remaining four birds hung immediately over the swiftly dropping plane, but hesitated to attack after the rough experience of their fellows.

MacCreedy touched ground at somewhat higher speed than he had calculated upon, and found the level stone, swept by the storm of ages, so smooth that his wheels ran along it much too easily. Thus he found himself confronted by a new peril, Could he check himself before reaching the brink? He steered a long curve around the edge of the shining pool, gathered his legs under him so that he might jump clear, if necessary, and came to a stop with his vacillating propeller almost peering over the abyss. Just before him was a drop of a cool thousand feet. He sprang out, hauled the machine back a dozen yards or so, and drew the longest breath of relief that had been forced from his lungs since his first ventures in aeroplaning.

Then he snatched the heaviest wrench from his tool kit and turned in a rage to settle accounts with his tormentors. But the eagles were now in a less militant frame of mind. Two of their number had had more than enough, and were already flapping back dejectedly toward their nests. The others seemed to realize that the monster, now that its rider had dismounted, was merely another of the man-creature's tools, such as a boat or canoe, inanimate and harmless except when its dreaded master chose to animate it. Moreover, now that MacCreedy was out of the machine, erect upon his feet, glaring up at them with masterful eyes, and shouting at them in those human tones which all the wild kindreds find so disconcerting, they were much more afraid of him than before. Their anger began to die away into a mere nervous dread and aversion. It seemed to occur to them that perhaps, after all, the man did not want their nests. He was nowhere near them. They yelped indignantly at him, and flew off to perch on their eyries and brood over the problem.

MacCreedy watched them go and dropped his weapon back into the kit. Then he went over his precious machine minutely, to assure himself that it had sustained no damage except that slit in one wing, which was not enough to give serious trouble. Then, with a rush of exultation, he ran over to examine the mysterious pool. He found it beautiful enough, in its crystal-clear austerity; but, alas, its utter clearness was all that was needed to shatter its chief mystery. It was deep, indeed, but it was certainly not bottomless, for he could discern its bottom, from one shore or the other, in every part. He contented himself, however, with the thought that there was mystery enough for the most exacting in the mere existence of this deep and brimming tarn on the crest of a granite peak. As far as he could judge from his reading, which was extensive, this smooth flat granite top of Bald Face, with its little pinnacle at one end and its deep transparent tarn in the center, was unlike any other known summit in the world. He was contented with his explorations, and ready now to return and tell about them.

But if content with his explorations, he was far from content on the score of his adventure with the eagles. He felt that it had been rather more of a close call than it appeared; and there was nothing he desired less than an immediate repetition of it. What he dreaded was that the starting of the motor might revive the fears of the great birds in regard to their nests, and bring them once more swooping upon him. He traversed the circuit of the plateau, peering downward anxiously, and at last managed roughly to locate the three nests. They were all on the south and southeast faces of the summit. He decided that he would get off as directly and swiftly as possible, and by way of the northwest front; and by this self-effacing attitude he trusted to convince the birds that he had no wish to trespass on their domesticity.

He allowed himself all too brief a run, and the plane got into the air but a few feet before reaching the brink. So narrow a margin was it, indeed, that he caught his breath with a gasp before she lifted. It looked as if he were going to dive into space. But he rose instead, and as he sailed out triumphantly across the abyss, the eagles came flapping up over the rim of the plateau behind. They saw that he was departing, so they sank again to their eyries, and congratulated themselves on having driven him away. A few minutes later, at an unprovocative height, he swept around and headed for home. As he came into view once more to the anxious watchers in the automobile, who had been worried over his long disappearance, the car turned and raced back over the plain to X——, ambitious to arrive before him and herald his triumph. But the fact that that triumph was not altogether an unqualified one remained a secret between MacCreedy and the eagles.

SEA OTTER

By SAMUEL SCOVILLE, JR.

Illustration by Frank Shields

THE short Arctic summer had flung its flower fields among the glaciers of the Siberian coast, like many-colored jewels set in crystal. Flocks of skuas, jaegers, and little auks circled and screamed above the smoky green waters of the Straits; and far out from shore a bed of kelp writhed and tossed like a mass of golden-brown sea snakes.

There, cradled on the swaying stems, a water baby was born. He had a funny little nose, with a padded cushion on top which made it look like the ace of spades, and his round, blunt head was of a dingy white color, while the rest of his fifteen inches was covered with a loose, kinky, gray-brown coat. Its harsh outer surface, sprinkled with long white hairs, covered a velvet-like inner fur that gave promise of the glory that was yet to be.

In spite of his insignificant appearance, the little cub was of blood royal, of the lineage of the sea otter, that king of fur bearers, who wears a fortune on his back and is dogged by death every moment of his life. Vitus Behring and his shipwrecked crew discovered them in 1741, in the surf and shallows around a barren island, in the sea which now bears his name. When they won their way back to Asia, sly, wise Chinese merchants paid their weight in silver for the new furs, so lustrous, silky and durable, which the sailors had been using for coats and blankets. In Russia they came to be worth their weight in gold, outranking even the royal sables, which none but the Tzar and his nobles might wear. Today the pelt of a sea otter is worth its weight in platinum or palladium.

This last-born princeling soon learned how to float on his back, with his round little head just showing above the kelp. For the most part, however, he lived clasped in his mother's arms and wrapped in the silky folds of her fur, while he nuzzled and fed against her warm breast, making happy little chirps and grunts of satisfaction, quite like a human baby.

Today, as they rocked back and forth in the swinging water, the kelp carpet in front of them parted, and a great, blunt, misshapen head thrust itself into the air a few yards away. It had little eyes set high in the skull, while the ears showed below the grinning mouth filled full of blunt teeth like white water-worn pebbles—the hallmark of a sea otter.

The newcomer was none other than Father Otter, come to look over his son and heir. He did not come very close to his family, for mother otters do not permit even their mates to approach too near a new-born cub. As the old dog otter stretched himself out on the kelp raft, his cylindrical body, all gleaming ebony and silver in the sunlight, showed nearly as long as that of a man, and weighed perhaps a hundred and twenty-five pounds. It was the great otter's pelt, however, that stamped him as the sea king that he was. Lustrous as light on the water, the inner fur had a close pile like velvet and, frosted with long white hairs, showed a tinge of silver-purple gleaming through its long loose folds.

For some time the old dog otter gravely surveyed his mate and his new cub approvingly. Then he scanned sea and sky and kelp, listening the while with a pair of the sharpest ears that ever guarded the life of one of the wild folk, at the same time winnowing the air through a pair of nostrils that could smell smoke—that danger signal to all wild people—a mile away. There was no sign of danger anywhere, and a moment later he disappeared under the water, after the food which his vibrant body unceasingly required.

For long after his disappearance the mother otter anxiously studied the horizon for the tiniest danger signal. Convinced at last that all was well, she stretched herself out on the slow-swinging kelp, for one of those periods of quiet happiness which come even into the lives of the hunted. While her cub snuggled against her soft fur, she tossed a kelp bulb high into the air, catching it like a ball, first in one bare little palm, then in the other, while she sang the cradle-song which all little sea otters know. High and shrill she chirped and twittered like a bird, in the midst of that lonely sea, clasping her sleepy baby closer as she sang.

There seemed no living thing near, yet death is never far from the sea otter. From mid-sky what seemed a dark wisp of cloud drifted toward the sea. Driven down by hunger from the North, an eagle owl, all buff and gray and brown, was crossing from Asia to America; for, unlike most of his fierce clan, he hunted by day. Larger than that death-in-the-dark, the great-horned owl, or that fierce white ghost of the North, the snowy owl, he skimmed down toward the kelp bed, his round, fixed eyes gleaming red and horrible in the sunlight. Muffled by the softest of down, his great wings, although they had a spread of nearly five feet, were absolutely noiseless.

Not until the shadow of the bird, like the shadow of death itself, fell upon her cub, did the otter have the slightest warning of any danger. By that time it would have been too late for any other creature to escape. No animal, however, on land or sea can dive with the sea otter. Just as the crooked talons were closing, she slipped through the kelp into the water, without a splash, like something fluid, her cub clasped close, while overhead the baffled owl snapped its beak like a pistol shot, and flew on toward the Alaskan coast.

Down through the swaying tangles she twisted her way like an eel, until she passed clear through the floating bed of this strange growth of the sea, which grows with its roots in the air. There the water darkened, and as she neared the bottom a shape flashed ahead of her, lighted with that phosphorescence which all dwellers in the northern seas seem to acquire. The otter recognized the glowing figure as that of a sea bass, a bronze-green fish hardly to be distinguished from the small-mouthed black bass of fresh water. The bass was no mean swimmer, but the long oarlike, webbed hind legs of the sea otter twisted over and over each other like the screw of a propeller, and drove her through the water with such tremendous speed that, in spite of the handicap of the cub, she soon swam down the fish, following its every twist and turn, and in less than a minute had caught it in her blunt teeth. Then, with the plump fish in her jaws, she swam up again through the kelp, and fed full, never for a moment, however, loosening her grip of her cub—for the babies of the sea folk who wander only a few feet from their mothers may never return.

The meal finished the great otter climbed out on a pinnacle of rock just showing above the kelp. Immediately, from a miracle of lithe, swift grace, she changed into one of the slowest and most awkward of animals. The webbed flipper-like hind feet, which drove her with such speed through the water, were of very little use on land, and her tiny forepaws were so short that they seemed to have no wrists at all. Slowly and painfully she waddled up on the rock, and there preened and cleaned and combed and licked every inch of her fur just as a cat would do, until it shone in the sunlight like a black opal.

As the weeks went by, the cub was trained in the lessons of the sea. He learned to enjoy salads of kelp sprouts, and to dive with his mother to the bottom of the shallows, and watch her grind her way through the great clams of the northwest, whose bivalves are a foot in width, or crunch with her pebble-like teeth into the white meat of the vast armored crabs of those seas. Another one of her favorite foods was the sea urchin—that chestnut burr of the sea. Protected by a bristling hedge of steel-sharp spines, it would seem safe from any attack. Yet, just as the squirrel on land opens without injury the real chestnut burr, so the sea otter had learned the combination which unlocked this little spiked safe of the sea, and devoured with much relish every one she could find.

As the weeks went by, the larder of the kelp bed began to empty. The clam beds had been stripped, the sea urchins were gone, and the fish had learned to keep away. Little by little, the mother otter hunted farther and farther from the safety of the kelp; until there came a day, when driven by hunger, she followed a fleeing pollock out into the open sea. The big gleaming fish, with the black line along its silver sides, swam far and fast. Yet, if the otter had not been hampered by her clinging cub, the chase would have been a short one. As it was, she did not overtake the fugitive until it was fully a quarter of a mile away from the kelp. In desperation it swam down into the lower depth, until the dull green of the water changed to black; but always the weasel of the sea was hard on its track, following the phosphorescent trail which the fleeing fish left behind.

Suddenly, as the pollock dived to even lower depths, in the hope that the water pressure might drive back its pursuer, a grotesquely horrible head thrust itself up from the darkness right in its path. Dark, and shining like wet rubber, the shape resembled nothing so much as that of a great double-headed sledge hammer. From either of the living hammer heads gleamed a greenish, malignant eye. Before the pollock could dart aside, the great hammer-head shark turned partly over, there was a flash of sharp teeth, and the fugitive fish disappeared.

A second later the ridged, gray, fifteen-foot body shot toward the otter with such speed that the water fairly hissed from the scimitar-shaped side fins. The sea otter is among the swiftest swimmers of the mammals, but no air-breathing creature can compete in speed with a shark. Almost instantly the hammer head was upon her. The jaws of all the sharks are so undershot that, in order to grip their prey, they must perforce turn over on their sides. This peculiarity of their kind was all that saved the otter. For a second the grim head overshadowed her. Then, with a twist of its long tail, shaped like the fluke of an anchor, the shark turned over and the vast mouth swung open, armed with six rows of inch-long, steel-sharp, triangular teeth, whose edges were serrated like a saw. Each separate tooth was curved back toward the gullet, so that for any living thing caught in their dreadful grip there was no more chance of escape than there would be from the interlocking cog-wheels of a stone crusher.

As the jaws of death gaped for the sea otter, with a writhe of her swift body she flashed to one side, while the little cub whimpered in her arms and the fatal teeth of the shark just grazed her trailing, flipper-like hind legs, so close they snapped behind her. Swerving beneath the great bulk, the otter began a desperate flight for life. Every foot of the shark's gaunt, stripped body was built for speed. There was not a bone anywhere under his drab and livid skin—only rings and strips and columns of tough, springy cartilage, which enabled him to cut through the water like a blade of tempered gray steel. With the rush of a torpedo the grim figure shot after the fleeing otter, who had but one advantage and that was in length. It takes a six-foot body less time to turn than one that measures fifteen feet. In a straightaway race, the fish would have overtaken the mammal in a few seconds; but when it came to twisting, turning, and doubling, the sea otter had an advantage, albeit of the slightest. Again and again the desperate sea mother avoided death by an inch. More than once the ringing jaws of the great fish snapped together just behind her, and only the tiny tick of time which it took to turn over saved her. Desperately she sought to win the refuge of the kelp bed; but always the gray shape thrust itself between her and safety.

At last an ally of the sea folk joined in the hunt. Water was claiming her toll of oxygen from the alien within her depths. A sea otter can stay under for half an hour at a pinch—but not when swimming at full speed, with the laboring heart pumping blood at capacity; and this one realized despairingly that soon she must breathe or die. Little by little she shaped her course toward the surface, dreadfully fearing lest the second she must spend in drawing one deep breath would be her last. She flashed upward through a whole gamut of greens—chrome, cedar, jasper, myrtle, malachite, emerald, ending with the pulsing, golden sap green of the surface. Swim as she would, however, the monstrous head was always just at her flank, and the slightest pause would give those fatal teeth their grip. Once again she avoided by a hair's breadth a snap of the deadly jaws, and struggled despairingly toward the upper air.

As the great fish turned to follow, out from the sunlight, through the gleaming water, shot a long dark body. Away from the safety of the kelp to the head of horror with its implacable eyes came the old dog otter, for the creed of the sea otter is unchanging—one mate for life and death. With his round misshapen head bristling and his snaky black eyes gleaming like fire, this one crossed the vast back of the shark like a shadow. As the great fish turned to follow the fleeing mother, the blunt pebble teeth of the dog otter, which can grind the flintiest shells to powder, fastened themselves with a bulldog grip just behind the last fin of the shark, where its long, sinuous tail joined the body. With all the force of his tremendous jaws, the great sea otter clamped his teeth through the masses of muscles, deep into the cartilage column, crushing one of its ball-and-socket joints.

Like a steel spring, the shark bent almost double on itself. Just as the gaping jaws were about to close, with a quick flirt of his body the otter swung across to the other side, without relaxing for an instant the grip of those punishing teeth. The undershot jaws of the great fish could not reach the head of its tormentor, fixed as it was in the central ridge of the shark's back. Again and again the hammer head bent from side to side; but each time the old dog otter evaded the clashing teeth and ground to bits joint after joint of the shark's spine, while the lashing tail strokes became feebler and feebler. Not until the mother otter and her cub were safe on their way to the kelp bed, breathing great life-saving draughts of fresh air at the surface, did the grim jaws of the old otter relax. Then, with an arrowy dive and double, he shot under and over the disabled fish, and sped away to join his mate in the hidden thickets of the kelp.

The swift Arctic summer soon passed, to be followed by the freezing gales of an Arctic winter. With the storms would come an enemy from the land, fiercer and more fatal than any foe that menaced the sea otter family by sea or sky; for these sea otters were among the last of their race, and there was a price upon their pelts beyond the dreams of avarice of a thousand murky Aleuts and oily Kolash and Kadiakers, to say nothing of a horde of white adventurers from all the five continents of earth. Only in storms, when the kelp beds are broken and the otter are forced to seek the shelter of beaches and sea caves, do hunters still have a chance to secure these rarest of all the fur bearers.

At last came the first of the great winter gales. Day after day the wind howled up from the southeast, the storm quarter of that coast, and the air throbbed with the boom of breakers, while all the way down the Straits the white caps foamed and roared among a tangle of crosscurrents.

Out at sea, the great kelp raft on which the otter family had lived since spring was at last broken and scattered under the pounding of the gale. Otter need sleep as much as humans, and like them, too, must sleep where they can breathe. Battered and blinded by the gale, the little family started to hunt for some refuge where they might slumber out the storm. Along all the miles of coast, and among the myriads of barren islands, there seemed to be no place where they could find a yard of safety. At the first sign of bad weather every strip of beach was patrolled and every islet guarded.

To lonely little Saanak the dog otter first led them, hoping to find some tiny stretch of safe beach among the water-worn boulders piled high along the shore. A mile to windward he stopped, thrust his blunt muzzle high up into the gale, and winnowed the salt-laden air through the meshes of his wonderful nostrils. Then he turned away at right angles, toward another island. A band of Indian hunters, starved with cold, had built far back among the rocks a tiny fire.

Smoke smells death to a sea otter. Beyond Saanak the wary veteran visited other beaches, only to detect the death scent of human footprints, although they had been washed by waves and covered by tides. In faraway Oonalaska, he sought the entrance of a sea cave in whose winding depths, many years before, he had found refuge. As he thrust his head into the hidden opening, his sturdy breast struck the strands of a net made of sea-lion sinews, so soaked and bleached by salt water that it bore even to his matchless nostrils no smell of danger. With a warning chirp, he halted his mate following close behind, and backed out carefully, without entangling himself among the wide meshes.

Agonizing for sleep, the little band turned back and journeyed wearily to the far away islet of Attoo, the westernmost point of land in North America. In its lee was a sheltered kelp raft never broken by the waves, although too near shore to be a safe refuge except in a storm. There, in the very center of the heaving bed, with the waves booming outside, the otter family slept the sleep of utter exhaustion, their heads buried under the kelp stems and their shimmering bodies showing on the surface.

At the foot of a high bluff on Kadiak Island crouched Dick Barrington, on his first otter-hunt. Dick was the son of a factor of the Hudson's Bay Company, which, in spite of kings and parliaments, still rules Arctic America. With him as a guide was Oonga, the chief of a tribe of Aleutian hunters.

"Stick to old Oonga," the factor had advised. "He knows more about sea otter than any man in his tribe. At that there's only one chance in a thousand that you'll get one."

The old chief had allowed the rest of the band to slip away one by one, each choosing the islet or bit of shore where he hoped to draw the winning number in this lottery of the sea. Hour after hour went by, and still the old man sat huddled under the lee of the cliff. At last, he suddenly stood up. Although the gale seemed still at its height, his practiced eye saw signs that it was about to break, and in a moment, with Dick's help, he had launched the triple-pointed, high-sterned *bidarka,* a little craft made of oiled sea-lion skins, and as unsinkable as any boat could be.

A few quick strokes of the paddle, and they were beyond the breakers. Then, straight across the bay, through the rush and smother of the storm, they shot toward Attoo. Steering by unknown ranges and glimpses of dim islands, old Oonga held his course unfalteringly, until, just as the gale began to slacken, they reached the kelp bed in the lee of the little island. Across the hollow tendrils the old chief guided the bidarka silently, in a zigzag course. Suddenly he stretched out his paddle, and, touching Dick on the shoulder, pointed to a dark spot showing against the kelp a hundred yards away.

With infinite care the two edged the canoe along until there before them lay asleep the mother otter, her cub clasped tight in her arms. Even as they watched, the little otter nuzzled its small white nose against its mother's warm breast. As she felt its touch, without opening her eyes she clasped the cub tighter in her arms, with a curiously human gesture, and wrapped it close in her long silky fur, which had a changing shimmer and ripple through it like watered silk—a pelt with which a man might ransom his life.

As Dick gripped the short heavy club which the old chief had placed at his feet at the beginning of the voyage, and looked down upon the pair, it seemed to him as if the great sea had taken him into her confidence and entrusted the sleeping mother and child to him. Suddenly, in the silence, with sea and sky watching, he knew that he could no more strike down that mother sleeping before him with her dear-loved cub in her arms, than he could have killed a human child entrusted to his care. With a quick motion, he splashed the water over the sleeping otter with the end of his club. So swiftly that the eye could scarcely follow her motion, the great otter flashed out of sight under the kelp, with her cub still held close. Once again, mother love had been too strong for death.

Illustration by Frank Shields

LASSIE COME-HOME

By ERIC KNIGHT

Illustration by Tom Hall

THE dog had met the boy by the school gate for five years. Now she couldn't understand that times were changed and she wasn't supposed to be there any more. But the boy knew.

So when he opened the door of the cottage, he spoke before he entered.

"Mother," he said, "Lassie's come home again."

He waited a moment, as if in hope of something. But the man and woman inside the cottage did not speak.

"Come in, Lassie," the boy said.

He held open the door, the tricolor collie walked in obediently. Going head down, as a collie when it knows something is wrong, it went to the rug and lay down before the hearth, a black-white-and-gold aristocrat. The man, sitting on a low stool by the fireside, kept his eyes turned away. The woman went to the sink and busied herself there.

"She was waiting at school for me, just like always," the boy went on. He spoke fast, as if racing against time. "She must ha' got away again. I thought, happen this time, we might just—"

"No!" the woman exploded.

The boy's carelessness dropped. His voice rose in pleading.

"But this time, mother! Just this time. We could hide her. They wouldn't ever know."

"Dogs, dogs, dogs!" the woman cried. The words poured from her as if the boy's pleading had been a signal gun for her own anger. "I'm sick o' hearing about tykes around this house. Well, she's sold and gone and done with, so the quicker she's taken back the better. Now get her back quick, or the first thing ye know we'll have Hynes round here again. Mr. Hynes!"

Her voice sharpened in imitation of the Cockney accent of the

343

south: "Hi know you Yorkshiremen and yer come-'ome dogs. Training yer dogs to come 'ome so's yer can sell 'em hover and hover again.

"Well, she's sold, so ye can take her out o' my house and home to them as bought her!"

The boy's bottom lip crept out stubbornly, and there was silence in the cottage. Then the dog lifted its head and nudged the man's hand, as a dog will when asking for a patting. But the man drew away and stared, silently, into the fire.

The boy tried again, with the ceaseless guile of a child, his voice coaxing.

"Look, feyther, she wants thee to bid her welcome. Aye, she's that glad to be home. Happen they don't tak' good care on her up there? A bit o' linseed strained through her drinking water—that's what I'd gi' her."

Still looking in the fire, the man nodded. But the woman, as if perceiving the boy's new attack, sniffed.

"Aye, tha wouldn't be a Carraclough if tha didn't know more about tykes nor breaking eggs wi' a stick. Nor a Yorkshireman. My goodness, it seems to me sometimes that chaps in this village thinks more on their tykes nor they do o' their own flesh and blood. They'll sit by their firesides and let their own bairns starve so long as t' dog gets fed."

The man stirred, suddenly, but the boy cut in quickly.

"But she does look thin. Look, truly—they're not feeding her right. Just look!"

"Aye," the woman chattered. "I wouldn't put it past Hynes to steal t' best part o' t' dog meat for himself. And Lassie always was a strong eater."

"She's fair thin now," the boy said.

Almost unwillingly the man and woman looked at the dog for the first time.

"My gum, she is off a bit," the woman said. Then she caught herself. "Ma goodness, I suppose I'll have to fix her a bit o' summat. She can do wi' it. But soon as she's fed, back she goes. And never another dog I'll have in my house. Never another. Cooking and nursing for 'em, and as much trouble to bring up as a bairn!"

So, grumbling and chatting as a village woman will, she moved about, warming a pan of food for the dog. The man and boy watched the collie eat. When it was done, the boy took from the mantelpiece a folded cloth and a brush, and began prettying the collie's coat. The man watched for several minutes, and then could stand it no longer.

"Here," he said.

He took the cloth and brush from the boy and began working expertly on the dog, rubbing the rich, deep coat, then brushing the snowy whiteness of the full ruff and the apron, bringing out the heavy leggings on the forelegs. He lost himself in his work, and the boy sat on the rug, watching contentedly. The woman stood it as long as she could.

"Now will ye please tak' that tyke out o' here?"

The man flared in anger.

"Well, ye wouldn't have me tak' her back looking like a mucky Monday wash, wouldta?"

He bent again, and began fluffing out the collie's petticoats.

"Joe!" the woman pleaded. "Will ye tak' her out o' here? Hynes'll be nosing round afore ye know it. And I won't have that man in my house. Wearing his hat inside, and going on like he's the duke himself—him and his leggings!"

"All right, lass."

"And this time, Joe, tak' young Joe wi' ye."

"What for?"

"Well, let's get the business done and over with. It's him that Lassie runs away for. She comes for young Joe. So if he went wi' thee, and told her to stay, happen she'd be content and not run away no more, and then we'd have a little peace and quiet in the home—though heaven knows there's not much hope o' that these days, things being like they are." The woman's voice trailed away, as if she would soon cry in weariness.

The man rose. "Come, Joe," he said. "Get thy cap."

The Duke of Rudling walked along the gravel paths of his place with his granddaughter, Philippa. Philippa was a bright and knowing young woman, allegedly the only member of the duke's family he could address in unspotted language. For it was also alleged that the duke was the most irascible, vile-tempered old man in the three Ridings of Yorkshire.

"Country going to pot!" the duke roared, stabbing at the walk with his great blackthorn stick. "When I was a young man! Hah! Women today not as pretty. Horses today not as fast. As for dogs—ye don't see dogs today like—"

Just then the duke and Philippa came round a clump of rhododendrons and saw a man, a boy and a dog.

"Ah," said the duke, in admiration. Then his brow knotted. "Damme, Carraclough! What're ye doing with my dog?"

He shouted it quite as if the others were in the next county, for it was also the opinion of the Duke of Rudling that people were not nearly so keen of hearing as they used to be when he was a young man.

"It's Lassie," Carraclough said. "She's runned away again and I brought her back."

Carraclough lifted his cap, and poked the boy to do the same, not in any servile gesture, but to show that they were as well brought up as the next.

"Damme, ran away again!" the duke roared. "And I told that utter nincompoop Hynes to—where is he? Hynes! Hynes! Damme, Hynes, what're ye hiding for?"

"Coming, your lordship!" sounded a voice, far away behind the shrubberies. And soon Hynes appeared, a sharp-faced man in check coat, riding breeches, and the cloth leggins that grooms wear.

"Take this dog," roared the duke, "and pen her up! And damme, if she breaks out again, I'll—I'll—"

The duke waved his great stick threateningly, and then, without so much as a thank you or kiss the back of my hand to Joe Carraclough, he went stamping and muttering away.

"I'll pen 'er up," Hynes muttered, when the duke was gone. "And if she ever gets awye agyne, I'll—"

Tom Hall

"*Mother! Oh, mother! Lassie's come home!*"

[See page 351]

He made as if to grab the dog, but Joe Carraclough's hob-nailed boot trod heavily on Hynes' foot.

"I brought my lad wi' me to bid her stay, so we'll pen her up this time—Eigh—sorry! I didn't see I were on thy foot. Come, Joe, lad."

They walked down the crunching gravel path, along by the neat kennel buildings. When Lassie was behind the closed door, she raced into the high wire run where she could see them as they went. She pressed close against the wire, waiting.

The boy stood close, too, his fingers through the meshes touching the dog's nose.

"Go on, lad," his father ordered. "Bid her stay!"

The boy looked around, as if for help that he did not find. He swallowed, and then spoke, low and quickly.

"Stay here, Lassie, and don't come home no more," he said. "And don't come to school for me no more. Because I don't want to see ye no more. 'Cause tha's a bad dog, and we don't love thee no more, and we don't want thee. So stay here forever and leave us be, and don't never come home no more."

Then he turned, and because it was hard to see the path plainly, he stumbled. But his father, who was holding his head very high as they walked away from Hynes, shook him savagely, and snapped roughly: "Look where tha's going!"

Then the boy trotted beside his father. He was thinking that he'd never be able to understand why grownups sometimes were so bad-tempered with you, just when you needed them most.

After that, there were days and days that passed, and the dog did not come to the school gate any more. So then it was not like old times. There were so many things that were not like old times.

The boy was thinking that as he came wearily up the path and opened the cottage door and heard his father's voice, tense with anger: ". . . walk my feet off. If tha thinks I like—"

Then they heard his opening of the door and the voice stopped and the cottage was silent.

That's how it was now, the boy thought. They stopped talking in front of you. And this, somehow, was too much for him to bear.

He closed the door, ran out into the night, and onto the moor, that great expanse of land where all the people of that village walked in lonesomeness when life and its troubles seemed past bearing.

A long while later, his father's voice cut through the darkness.

"What's tha doing out there, Joe lad?"

"Walking."

"Aye."

They went on together, aimlessly, each following his own thoughts. And they both thought about the dog that had been sold.

"Tha maun't think we're hard on thee, Joe," the man said at last. "It's just that a chap's got to be honest. There's that to it. Sometimes, when a chap doesn't have much, he clings right hard to what he's got. And honest is honest, and there's no two ways about it.

"Why, look, Joe. Seventeen year I worked in that Clarabelle Pit till she shut down, and a good collier, too. Seventeen year! And butties I've had by the dozen, and never a man of 'em can ever say that Joe Carraclough kept what wasn't his, nor spoke what wasn't true. Not a man in this riding can ever call a Carraclough dishonest.

"And when ye've sold a man summat, and ye've taken his brass, and ye've spent it—well, then done's done. That's all. And ye've got to stand by that."

"But Lassie was—"

"Now, Joe! Ye can't alter it, ever. It's done—and happen it's for i' best. No two ways, Joe, she were getting hard to feed. Why, ye wouldn't want Lassie to be going around getting peaked and pined, like some chaps round here keep their tykes. And if ye're fond of her, then just think on it that now she's got lots to eat, and a private kennel, and a good run to herself, and living like a varritable princess, she is. Ain't that best for her?"

"We wouldn't pine her. We've always got lots to eat."

The man blew out his breath angrily. "Eigh, Joe, nowt pleases thee. Well, then, tha might as well have it. Tha'll never see Lassie no more. She run home once too often, so the duke's taken her wi' him up to his place in Scotland, and there she'll stay. So it's good-by and good luck to her, and she'll never come home no more, she won't. Now, I weren't off to tell thee, but there it is, so put it in thy pipe and smoke it, and let's never say a word about it no more— especially in front of thy mother."

The boy stumbled on in the darkness. Then the man halted.

"We ought to be getting back, lad. We left thy mother alone."

He turned the boy about, and then went on, but as if he were talking to himself.

"Tha sees, Joe, women's not like men. They have to stay at home and manage best they can, and just spend the time in wishing. And when things don't go right, well, they have to take it out in talk and give a man hades. But it don't mean nowt, really, so tha shouldn't mind when thy mother talks hard.

"Ye just got to learn to be patient and let 'em talk, and just let it go up t' chimney wi' th' smoke."

Then they were quiet, until, over the rise, they saw the lights of the village. Then the boy spoke: "How far away is Scotland, feyther?"

"Nay, lad, it's a long, long road."

"But how far, feyther?"

"I don't know—but it's a longer road than thee or me'll ever walk. Now, lad. Don't thee fret no more, and try to be a man— and don't plague thy mother no more, wilta?"

Joe Carraclough was right. It is a long road, as they say in the North, from Yorkshire to Scotland. Much too far for a man to walk—or a boy. And though the boy often thought of it, he remembered his father's words on the moor, and he put the thought behind him.

But there is another way of looking at it; and that's the distance from Scotland to Yorkshire. And that is just as far as from Yorkshire to Scotland. A matter of about four hundred miles, it would be, from the Duke of Rudling's place far up in the Highlands, to the village of Holdersby. That would be for a man, who could go fairly straight.

To an animal, how much farther would it be? For a dog can

study no maps, read no signposts, ask no directions. It could only go blindly, by instinct, knowing that it must keep on to the south, to the south. It would wander and err, quest and quarter, run into firths and lochs that would send it side-tracking and back-tracking before it could go on its way—south.

A thousand miles, it would be going that way—a thousand miles over strange terrain.

There would be moors to cross, and burns to swim. And then those great, long lochs that stretch from one side of that dour land to another would bar the way and send a dog questing a hundred miles before it could find a crossing that would allow it to go south.

And, too, there would be rivers to cross, wide rivers like the Forth and the Clyde, the Tweed and the Tyne, where one must go miles to find bridges. And the bridges would be in towns. And in the towns there would be officials—like the one in Lanarkshire. In all his life he had never let a captured dog get away—except one. That one was a gaunt, snarling collie that whirled on him right in the pound itself, and fought and twisted loose to race away down the city street—going south.

But there are kind people, too; ones knowing and understanding in the ways of dogs. There was an old couple in Durham who found a dog lying exhausted in a ditch one night—lying there with its head to the south. They took that dog into their cottage and warmed it and fed it and nursed it. And because it seemed an understanding, wise dog, they kept it in their home, hoping it would learn to be content. But, as it grew stronger, every afternoon toward four o'clock it would go to the door and whine, and then begin pacing back and forth between the door and the window, back and forth as the animals do in their cages at the zoo.

They tried every wile and every kindness to make it bide with them, but finally, when the dog began to refuse food, the old people knew what they must do. Because they understood dogs, they opened the door one afternoon and they watched the collie go, not down the road to the right, or to the left, but straight across a field toward the south; going steadily at a trot, as if it knew it still had a long, long road to travel.

Ah, a thousand miles of tor and brae, of shire and moor, of path and road and plowland, of river and stream and burn and brook and beck, of snow and rain and fog and sun, is a long way, even for a human being. But it would seem too far—much, much too far—for any dog to travel blindly and win through.

And yet—and yet—who shall say why, when so many weeks had passed that hope against hope was dying, a boy coming out of school, out of the cloakroom that always smelled of damp wool drying, across the concrete play yard with the black, waxed slides, should turn his eyes to a spot by the school gate from force of five years of habit, and see there a dog? Not a dog, this one, that lifted glad eyes above a proud, slim head with its black-and-gold mask; but a dog that lay weakly, trying to lift a head that would no longer lift, trying to wag a tail that was torn and blotched and matted with dirt and burs, and managing to do nothing much except to whine in a weak, happy, crying way as a boy on his knees threw arms about it, and hands touched it that had not touched it for many a day.

Then who shall picture the urgency of a boy, running awkwardly, with a great dog in his arms, running through the village, past the empty mill, past the Labor Exchange, where the men looked up from their deep ponderings on life and the dole? Or who shall describe the high tones of a voice—a boy's voice, calling as he runs up a path: "Mother! Oh, mother! Lassie's come home! Lassie's come home!"

Nor does anyone who ever owned a dog need to be told the sound a man makes as he bends over a dog that has been his for years; nor how a woman moves quickly, preparing food—which might be the family's condensed milk stirred into warm water; nor how the jowl of a dog is lifted so that raw egg and brandy, bought with precious pence, should be spooned in; nor how bleeding pads are bandaged, tenderly.

That was one day. There was another day when the woman in the cottage sighed with pleasure, for a dog lifted to its feet for the first time to stand over a bowl of oatmeal, putting its head down and lapping again and again while its pinched flanks quivered.

And there was another day when the boy realized that, even now, the dog was not to be his again. So the cottage rang again with protests and cries, and a woman shrilling: "Is there never to be no more peace in my house and home?" Long after he was in bed that night the boy heard the rise and fall of the woman's voice, and the steady, reiterative tone of the man's. It went on long after he was asleep.

In the morning the man spoke, not looking at the boy, saying the words as if he had long rehearsed them.

"Thy mother and me have decided upon it that Lassie shall stay here till she's better. Anyhow, nobody could nurse her better than us. But the day that t' duke comes back, then báck she goes, too. For she belongs to him, and that's honest, too. Now tha has her for a while, so be content."

In childhood, "for a while" is such a great stretch of days when seen from one end. It is a terribly short time seen from the other.

The boy knew how short it was that morning as he went to school and saw a motorcar driven by a young woman. And in the car was a gray-thatched, terrible old man, who waved a cane and shouted: "Hi! Hi, there! Damme, lad! You there! Hi!"

Then it was no use running, for the car could go faster than you, and soon it was beside you and the man was saying: "Damme, Philippa, will you make this smelly thing stand still a moment? Hi, lad!"

"Yes, sir."

"You're What's-'is-Name's lad, aren't you?"

"Ma feyther's Joe Carraclough."

"I know. I know. Is he home now?"

"No, sir. He's away to Allerby. A mate spoke for him at the pit and he's gone to see if there's a chance."

"When'll he be back?"

"I don't know. I think about tea."

"Eh, yes. Well, yes. I'll drop round about fivish to see that father of yours. Something important."

It was hard to pretend to listen to lessons. There was only waiting for noon. Then the boy ran home.

"Mother! T' duke is back and he's coming to take Lassie away."

"Eigh, drat my buttons. Never no peace in this house. Is tha sure?"

"Aye. He stopped me. He said tell feyther he'll be round at five. Can't we hide her? Oh, mother!"

"Nay, thy feyther—"

"Won't you beg him? Please, please. Beg feyther to—"

"Young Joe, now it's no use. So stop thy teasing! Thy feyther'll not lie. That much I'll give him. Come good, come bad, he'll not lie."

"But just this once, mother. Please beg him, just this once. Just one lie wouldn't hurt him. I'll make it up to him. I will. When I'm growed up, I'll get a job. I'll make money. I'll buy him things—and you, too. I'll buy you both anything you want if you'll only—"

For the first time in his trouble the boy became a child, and the mother, looking over, saw the tears that ran openly down his contorted face. She turned her face to the fire, and there was a pause. Then she spoke.

"Joe, tha mustn't," she said softly. "Tha must learn never to want nothing in life like that. It don't do, lad. Tha mustn't want things bad, like tha wants Lassie."

The boy shook his clenched fists in impatience.

"It ain't that, mother. Ye don't understand. Don't ye see—it ain't me that wants her. It's her that wants us! Tha's wha made her come all them miles. It's her that wants us, so terrible bad!"

The woman turned and stared. It was as if, in that moment, she were seeing this child, this boy, this son of her own, for the first time in many years. She turned her head down toward the table. It was surrender.

"Come and eat, then," she said. "I'll talk to him. I will that, all right. I feel sure he won't lie. But I'll talk to him, all right. I'll talk to Mr. Joe Carraclough. I will indeed."

At five that afternoon, the Duke of Rudling, fuming and muttering, got out of a car at a cottage gate to find a boy barring his way.

This was a boy who stood, stubbornly, saying fiercely: "Away wi' thee! Thy tyke's net here!"

"Damme, Philippa, th' lad's touched," the duke said. "He is. He's touched."

Scowling and thumping his stick, the old duke advanced until the boy gave way, backing down the path out of the reach of the waving blackthorn stick.

"Thy tyke's net here," the boy protested.

"What's he saying?" the girl asked.

"Says my dog isn't here. Damme, you going deaf? I'm supposed to be deaf, and I hear him plainly enough. Now, ma lad, what tyke o' mine's net here?"

As he turned to the boy, the duke spoke in broadest Yorkshire, as he did always to the people of the cottages—a habit which the Duchess of Rudling, and many more members of the duke's family, deplored.

"Coom, coom, ma lad. Whet tyke's net here?"

"No tyke o' thine. Us hasn't got it." The words began running faster and faster as the boy backed away from the fearful old man who advanced. "No tyke could have done it. No tyke can come all them miles. It isn't Lassie. It's another one that looks like her. It isn't Lassie!"

"Why, bless ma heart and sowl," the duke puffed. "Where's thy father, ma lad?"

The door behind the boy opened, and a woman's voice spoke.

"If it's Joe Carraclough ye want, he's out in the shed—and been there shut up half the afternoon."

"What's this lad talking about—a dog of mine being here?"

"Nay," the woman snapped quickly. "He didn't say a tyke o' thine was here. He said it wasn't here."

"Well, what dog o' mine isn't here, then?"

The woman swallowed, and looked about as if for help. The duke stood, peering from under his jutting eyebrows. Her answer, truth or lie, was not spoken, for then they heard the rattle of a door opening, and a man making a pursing sound with his lips, as he will when he wants a dog to follow, and then Joe Carraclough's voice said: "This is t' only tyke us has here. Does it look like any dog that belongs to thee?"

With his mouth opening to cry one last protest, the boy turned. And his mouth stayed open. For there he saw his father, Joe Carraclough, the collie fancier, standing with a dog at his heels—a dog that sat at his left heel patiently, as any well-trained dog should do— as Lassie used to do. But this dog was not Lassie. In fact, it was ridiculous to think of it at the same moment as you thought of Lassie.

For where Lassie's skull was aristocratic and slim, this dog's head was clumsy and rough. Where Lassie's ears stood in twin-lapped symmetry, this dog had one ear draggling and the other standing up Alsatian fashion in a way to give any collie breeder the cold shivers. Where Lassie's coat was rich tawny gold, this dog's coat had ugly patches of black; and where Lassie's apron was a billowing stretch of snow-white, this dog had puddles of off-color blue-merle mixture. Besides, Lassie had four white paws, and this one had one paw white, two dirty-brown, and one almost black.

That is the dog they all looked at as Joe Carraclough stood there, having told no lie, having only asked a question. They all stood, waiting the duke's verdict.

But the duke said nothing. He only walked forward, slowly, as if he were seeing a dream. He bent beside the collie, looking with eyes that were as knowing about dogs as any Yorkshireman alive. And those eyes did not waste themselves upon twisted ears, or blotched marking, or rough head. Instead they were looking at a paw, that the duke lifted, looking at the underside of the paw, staring intently at five black pads, crossed and recrossed with the scars where thorns had lacerated, and stones had torn.

For a long time the duke stared, and when he got up he did not speak in Yorkshire accents any more. He spoke as a gentleman should, and he said: "Joe Carraclough, I never owned this dog. 'Pon my soul, she never belonged to me. Never!"

Then he turned and went stumping down the path, thumping his cane and saying, "Bless my soul. Four hundred miles! Damme, wouldn't ha' believed it. Damme—five hundred miles!"

He was at the gate when his granddaughter whispered to him fiercely.

"Of course," he cried. "Mind your own business. Exactly what I came for. Talking about dogs made me forget. Carraclough! Carraclough! What're ye hiding for?"

"I'm still here, sir."

"Ah, there you are. You working?"

"Eigh, now. Working," Joe said. That's the best he could manage.

"Yes, working, working!" The duke fumed.

"Well, now—" Joe began.

Then Mrs. Carraclough came to his rescue, as a good housewife in Yorkshire will.

"Why, Joe's got three or four things that he's been considering," she said, with proper display of pride. "But he hasn't quite said yes or no to any of them yet."

"Then say no, quick," the old man puffed. "Had to sack Hynes. Didn't know a dog from a drunken filly. Should ha' known all along no Londoner could handle dogs fit for Yorkshire taste. How much, Carraclough?"

"Well, now," Joe began.

"Seven pounds a week, and worth every penny," Mrs. Carraclough chipped in. "One o' them offers may come up to eight," she lied, expertly. For there's always a certain amount of lying to be done in life, and when a woman's married to a man who has made a lifelong cult of being honest, then she's got to learn to do the lying for two.

"Five," roared the duke—who, after all, was a Yorkshireman, and couldn't help being a bit sharp about things that pertained to money.

"Six," said Mrs. Carraclough.

"Five pound ten," bargained the duke, cannily.

"Done," said Mrs. Carraclough, who would have been willing to settle for three pounds in the first place. "But, o' course, us gets the cottage, too."

"All right," puffed the duke. "Five pounds ten and the cottage. Begin Monday. But—on one condition. Carraclough, you can live on my land, but I won't have that thick-skulled, screw-lugged, gay-

tailed eyesore of a misshapen mongrel on my property. Now never
let me see her again. You'll get rid of her?"

He waited, and Joe fumbled for words. But it was the boy who
answered, happily, gaily: "Oh, no, sir. She'll be waiting at school for
me most o' the time. And, anyway, in a day or so we'll have her
fixed up and coped up so's ye'd never, never recognize her."

"I don't doubt that," puffed the duke, as he went to the car. "I
don't doubt ye could do just exactly that."

It was a long time afterward, in the car, that the girl said: "Don't
sit there like a lion on the Nelson column. And I thought you were
supposed to be a hard man."

"Fiddlesticks, m'dear. I'm a ruthless realist. For five years I've
sworn I'd have that dog by hook or crook, and now, egad, at last
I've got her."

"Pooh! You had to buy the man before you could get his dog."

"Well, perhaps that's not the worst part of the bargain."

JODY FINDS THE FAWN

By *MARJORIE KINNAN RAWLINGS*

Illustration by Tom Hall

A CART had turned around in the sand to the right of the pen. The wheel tracks led down a dim scrub road toward Forresters' Island. Penny said, "All right, boy. Here's our way."

The sun was near the horizon. The cumulus clouds were white puff-balls, stained with the red and yellow wash of the sunset. The south was filled with darkness, like the smoke of gunpowder. A chill air moved across the scrub and was gone, as though a vast being had blown a cold breath and then passed by. Jody shivered and was grateful for the hot air that fell in behind it. A wild grape-vine trailed across the thin-rutted road. Penny leaned to pull it aside.

He said, "When there's trouble waitin' for you, you jest as good go to meet it."

The rattler struck him from under the grape-vine without warning. Jody saw the flash, blurred as a shadow, swifter than a martin, surer than the slashing claws of a bear. He saw his father stagger backward under the force of the blow. He heard him give a cry. He wanted to step back, too. He wanted to cry out with all his voice. He stood rooted to the sand and could not make a sound. It was lightning that had struck, and not a rattler. It was a branch that broke, it was a bird that flew, it was a rabbit running——

Penny shouted, "Git back! Hold the dogs!"

The voice released him. He dropped back and clutched the dogs by the scruff of their necks. He saw the mottled shadow lift its flat head, knee-high. The head swung from side to side, following his father's slow motions. He heard the rattles hum. The dogs heard. They winded. The fur stood stiff on their bodies. Old Julia whined and twisted out of his hand. She turned and slunk down the trail. Her long tail clung to her hindquarters. Rip reared on his hind feet, barking.

As slowly as a man in a dream, Penny backed away. The rattles sung. They were not rattles—Surely it was a locust humming. Surely it was a tree-frog singing—Penny lifted his gun to his shoulder and fired. Jody quivered. The rattler coiled and writhed in its spasms. The head was buried in the sand. The contortions moved down the length of the thick body, the rattles whirred feebly and were still. The coiling flattened into slow convolutions, like a low tide ebbing. Penny turned and stared at his son.

He said, "He got me."

He lifted his right arm and gaped at it. His lips lifted dry over his teeth. His throat worked. He looked dully at two punctures in the flesh. A drop of blood oozed from each.

He said, "He was a big un."

Jody let go his hold on Rip. The dog ran to the dead snake and barked fiercely. He made sorties and at last poked the coils with one paw. He quieted and snuffed about in the sand. Penny lifted his head from his staring. His face was like hickory ashes.

He said, "Ol' Death goin' to git me yit."

He licked his lips. He turned abruptly and began to push through the scrub in the direction of the clearing. The road would be shorter going, for it was open, but he headed blindly for home in a direct line. He plowed through the low scrub oaks, the gallberries, the scrub palmettos. Jody panted behind him. His heart pounded so hard that he could not see where he was going. He followed the sound of his father's crashing across the undergrowth. Suddenly the denseness ended. A patch of higher oaks made a shaded clearing. It was strange to walk in silence.

Penny stopped short. There was a stirring ahead. A doe-deer leaped to her feet. Penny drew a deep breath, as though breathing were for some reason easier. He lifted his shotgun and leveled it at the head. It flashed over Jody's mind that his father had gone mad. This was no moment to stop for game. Penny fired. The doe turned a somersault and dropped to the sand and kicked a little and lay still. Penny ran to the body and drew his knife from its scabbard. Now Jody knew his father was insane. Penny did not cut the throat, but slashed into the belly. He laid the carcass wide open. The pulse still throbbed in the heart. Penny slashed out the liver. Kneeling, he changed his knife to his left hand. He turned his right arm and stared again at the twin punctures. They were now closed. The forearm was thick-swollen and blackening. The sweat stood out on his forehead. He cut quickly across the wound. A dark blood gushed and he pressed the warm liver against the incision.

He said in a hushed voice, "I kin feel it draw——"

He pressed harder. He took the meat away and looked at it. It was venomous green. He turned it and applied the fresh side.

He said, "Cut me out a piece o' the heart."

Jody jumped from his paralysis. He fumbled with the knife. He hacked away a portion.

Penny said, "Another."

He changed the application again and again.

He said, "Hand me the knife."

He cut a higher gash in his arm where the dark swelling rose the thickest. Jody cried out.

"Pa! You'll bleed to death!"

"I'd ruther bleed to death than swell. I seed a man die——"

The sweat poured down his cheeks.

"Do it hurt bad, Pa?"

"Like a hot knife was buried to the shoulder."

The meat no longer showed green when he withdrew it. The warm vitality of the doe's flesh was solidifying in death. He stood up.

He said quietly, "I cain't do it no more good. I'm going on home. You go to the Forresters and git 'em to ride to the Branch for Doc Wilson."

"Reckon they'll go?"

"We got to chance it. Call out to 'em quick, sayin', afore they chunk somethin' at you or mebbe shoot."

He turned back to pick up the beaten trail. Jody followed. Over his shoulder he heard a light rustling. He looked back. A spotted fawn stood peering from the edge of the clearing, wavering on uncertain legs. Its dark eyes were wide and wondering.

He called out, "Pa! The doe's got a fawn."

"Sorry, boy. I cain't help it. Come on."

An agony for the fawn came over him. He hesitated. It tossed its small head, bewildered. It wobbled to the carcass of the doe and leaned to smell it. It bleated.

Penny called, "Git a move on, young un."

Jody ran to catch up with him. Penny stopped an instant at the dim road.

"Tell somebody to take this road in to our place and pick me up in case I cain't make it in. Hurry."

The horror of his father's body, swollen in the road, washed over him. He began to run. His father was plodding with a slow desperation in the direction of Baxter's Island.

Jody moved through a tortuous dream. With his father beside him, he fought a nest of rattlesnakes. They crawled across his feet, trailing their rattles, clacking lightly. The nest resolved itself into one snake, gigantic, moving toward him on a level with his face. It struck and he tried to scream but could not. He looked for his father. He lay under the rattler, with his eyes open to a dark sky. His body was swollen to the size of a bear. He was dead. Jody began to move backward away from the rattler, one agonized step at a time. His feet were glued to the ground. The snake suddenly vanished and he stood alone in a vast windy place, holding the fawn in his arms. Penny was gone. A sense of sorrow filled him so that he thought his heart would break. He awakened, sobbing.

He sat up on the hard floor. Day was breaking over the clearing. A pale light lay in streaks beyond the pine trees. The room was filled with grayness. For an instant he was still conscious of the fawn against him. Then he remembered. He scrambled to his feet and looked at his father.

Penny was breathing with a greater ease. He was still swollen and fevered, but he looked no worse than when the wild honey bees had stung him. Ma Baxter was asleep in her rocker with her head thrown far back. Old Doc lay across the foot of the bed.

Jody whispered, "Doc."

Doc grunted and lifted his head.

"What is it—what is it—what is it?"

"Doc! Look at Pa!"

Doc shifted his body and eased himself on one elbow. He blinked and rubbed his eyes. He sat up. He leaned over Penny.

"Lord o' the jay-birds, he's made it."

Ma Baxter said, "Eh?"

She sat upright. "He dead?"

"Not by a long sight."

She burst out crying.

Doc said, "You sound like you're sorry."

She said, "You jest don't know what 'twould mean, him leavin' us here." Jody had never heard her speak so gently.

Doc said, "Why, you got you another man here. Look at Jody, now. Big enough to plow and reap and do the huntin'."

She said, "Jody's a'right, but he ain't a thing but boy. Got his mind on nothin' but prowlin' and playin'."

He hung his head. It was true.

She said, "His Pa encourages him."

Doc said, "Well, boy, be glad you got encouragement. Most of us live our lives without it. Now, Ma'am, let's get some more milk down this feller, time he wakes."

Jody said eagerly, "I'll go milk, Ma."

She said with satisfaction, "About time."

He passed through the front room. Buck was sitting up on the floor, rubbing his head sleepily. Mill-wheel was still asleep.

Jody said, "Doc says Pa's done made it."

"I be dogged. I woked up, fixin' to go he'p bury him."

"Go tell the men-folks to wash theirselves and come to table."

He called them. The three men went outside to the watershelf and slapped water over their faces, dabbled their hands. He brought them a clean towel.

Jody was proud of the table. There were not as many different dishes as the Forresters served, but there was enough of everything. The men ate greedily. At last they pushed away their plates and lit their pipes.

Mill-wheel said, "Seems like Sunday, don't it?"

Ma Baxter said, "Sickness allus do seem like Sunday, someway. Folks settin' around, and the men not goin' to the field."

Jody had never seen her so amiable. She had waited to eat until the men were done, for fear of their not having plenty. She sat now eating with relish. The men chatted idly. Jody allowed his thoughts to drift back to the fawn. He could not keep it out of his mind. It stood in the back of it as close as he had held it, in his dreaming, in his arms. He slipped from the table and went to his father's bedside. Penny lay at rest. His eyes were open and clear, but the pupils were still dark and dilated.

Jody said, "How you comin', Pa?"

"Jest fine, son. Ol' Death gone thievin' elsewhere. But wa'n't it a close squeak!"

"I mean."

Penny said, "I'm proud of you, boy, the way you kept your head and done what was needed."

"Pa——"

"Yes, son."

"Pa, you recollect the doe and the fawn?"

"I cain't never forget 'em. The pore doe saved me, and that's certain."

"Pa, the fawn may be out there yit. Hit's hongry, and likely mighty skeert."

"I reckon so."

"Pa, I'm about growed and don't need no milk. How about me goin' out and seein' kin I find the fawn?"

"And tote it here?"

"And raise it."

Penny lay quiet, staring at the ceiling.

"Boy, you got me hemmed in."

"Hit won't take much to raise it, Pa. Hit'll soon git to where it kin make out on leaves and acorns."

"Dogged if you don't figger the farrest of ary young un I've ever knowed."

"We takened its mammy, and it wa'n't no-ways to blame."

"Shore don't seem grateful to leave it starve, do it? Son, I ain't got it in my heart to say 'No' to you. I never figgered I'd see daylight, come dawn today."

"Kin I ride back with Mill-wheel and see kin I find it?"

"Tell your Ma I said you're to go."

He sidled back to the table and sat down. His mother was pouring coffee for everyone.

He said, "Ma, Pa says I kin go bring back the fawn."

She held the coffee-pot in mid-air. "What fawn?"

"The fawn belonged to the doe we kilt, to use the liver to draw out the pizen and save Pa."

She gasped. "Well, for pity sake——"

"Pa says hit'd not be grateful, to leave it starve."

Doc Wilson said, "That's right, Ma'am. Nothing in the world don't ever come quite free. The boy's right and his daddy's right."

Mill-wheel said, "He kin ride back with me. I'll help him find it."

She set down the pot helplessly.

"Well, if you'll give it your milk— We got nothin' else to feed it."

"That's what I aim to do. Hit'll be no time, and it not needin' nothin'."

The men rose from the table.

Doc said, "I don't look for nothing but progress, Ma'am, but if he takes a turn for the worse, you know where to find me."

She said, "Well. What do we owe you, Doc? We cain't pay right now, but time the crops is made——"

"Pay for what? I've done nothing. He was safe before I got here. I've had a night's lodging and a good breakfast. Send me some syrup when your cane's ground."

"You're mighty good, Doc. We been scramblin' so, I didn't know folks could be so good."

"Hush, woman. You got a good man there. Why wouldn't folks be good to him?"

Buck said, "You reckon that ol' horse o' Penny's kin keep ahead o' me at the plow? I'm like to run him down."

Doc said, "Get as much milk down Penny as he'll take. Then give him greens and fresh meat, if you can get it."

Buck aid, "Me and Jody'll tend to that."

Mill-wheel said, "Come on, boy. We got to git ridin'.' "

Ma Baxter asked anxiously, "You'll not be gone long?"

Jody said, "I'll be back shore, before dinner."

"Reckon you'd not git home a-tall," she said, "if 'twasn't for din-ner-time."

Doc said, "That's man-nature, Ma'am. Three things bring a man home again—his bed, his woman, and his dinner."

Buck and Mill-wheel guffawed. Doc's eye caught Jody's cream-col-ored 'coonskin knapsack.

"Now ain't that a pretty something? Wouldn't I like such as that to tote my medicines?"

Jody had never before possessed a thing that was worth giving away. He took it from its nail, and put it in Doc's hands.

"Hit's mine," he said. "Take it."

"Why, I'd not rob you, boy."

"I got no use for it," he said loftily. "I kin git me another."

"Now thank you. Every trip I make, I'll think, 'Thank you, Jody Baxter.' "

He was proud with old Doc's pleasure. They went outside to water the horses and feed them from the scanty stock of hay in the Baxter barn.

Buck said to Jody, "You Baxters is making' out and that's about all, ain't it?"

Doc said, "Baxter's had to carry the work alone. Time the boy here gets some size to him, they'll prosper."

Buck said, "Size don't seem to mean much to a Baxter."

Mill-wheel mounted his horse and pulled Jody up behind him. Doc mounted and turned away in the opposite direction. Jody waved after him. His heart was light.

He said, "Cut to the north, Mill-wheel. Hit were up here Pa got snake-bit and kilt the doe and I seed the fawn."

"What was you and your daddy doin' up this road?"

Jody hesitated. "We was huntin' our hogs."

"Oh— Huntin' your hogs, eh? Well, don't fret about them hogs. I jest got a idee they'll be home by sundown."

"Ma and Pa'll shore be proud to see 'em come in."

"I had no idee, you-all was runnin' so tight."

"We ain't running tight. We're all right."

"You Baxters has got guts, I'll say that."

"You reckon Pa'll not die?"

"Not him. His chitlin's is made o' iron. . . . Now whereabouts you want to go, huntin' that fawn? Hit's gettin' right thick up this trail."

Suddenly, Jody was unwilling to have Mill-wheel with him. If the fawn was dead, or could not be found, he could not have his disappointment seen. And if the fawn was there, the meeting would be so lovely, and so secret that he could not endure to share it.

He said, "Hit's not fur now, but hit's powerful thick for a horse. I kin make it a-foot."

"But I'm daresome to leave you, boy. Suppose you was to git lost, or snake-bit, too?"

"I'll take keer. Hit'll take me likely a long time to find the fawn, if he's wandered. Leave me off right here."

"All right, but you go mighty easy now, pokin' in them palmeeters. This is rattlesnake Heaven in these parts. You know north here, and east?"

"There, and there. That fur tall pine makes a bearin'."

"That's right. Now do things go wrong again, you or Buck, one, ride back for me. So long."

"So long, Mill-wheel. I'm shore obliged."

He waved after him. He waited for the sound of the hooves to end, then cut to the right. The scrub was still. Only his own crackling of twigs sounded across the silence. He was eager almost past caution, but he broke a bough and pushed it ahead of him where the growth was thick and the ground invisible. Rattlers got out of the way when they had a chance. Penny had gone farther into the oak thicket than he remembered. He wondered for an instant if he had mistaken his direction. Then a buzzard rose in front of him and flapped into the air. He came into the clearing under the oaks. Buzzards sat in a circle around the carcass of the doe. They turned their heads on their long scrawny necks and hissed at him. He threw his bough at them and they flew into an adjacent tree. Their wings creaked and whistled like rusty pump-handles. The sand showed

Tom Hall

He whispered, "It's me!"

large cat-prints, he could not tell whether of wild-cat or of panther. But the big cats killed fresh, and they had left the doe to the carrion birds. He asked himself whether the sweeter meat of the fawn had scented the air for the curled nostrils.

He skirted the carcass and parted the grass at the place where he had seen the fawn. It did not seem possible that it was only yesterday. The fawn was not there. He circled the clearing. There was no sound, no sign. The buzzards clacked their wings, impatient to return to their business. He returned to the spot where the fawn had emerged and dropped to all fours, studying the sand for the small hoof-prints. The night's rain had washed away all tracks except those of cat and buzzards. But the cat-sign had not been made in this direction. Under a scrub palmetto he was able to make out a track, pointed and dainty as the mark of a ground-dove. He crawled past the palmetto.

Movement directly in front of him startled him so that he tumbled backward. The fawn lifted its face to his. It turned its head with a wide, wondering motion and shook him through with the stare of its liquid eyes. It was quivering. It made no effort to rise or run. Jody could not trust himself to move.

He whispered, "It's me."

The fawn lifted its nose, scenting him. He reached out one hand and laid it on the soft neck. The touch made him delirious. He moved forward on all fours until he was close beside it. He put his arms around its body. A light convulsion passed over it but it did not stir. He stroked its sides as gently as though the fawn were a china deer and he might break it. Its skin was softer than the white 'coonskin knapsack. It was sleek and clean and had a sweet scent of grass. He rose slowly and lifted the fawn from the ground. It was no heavier than old Julia. Its legs hung limply. They were surprisingly long and he had to hoist the fawn as high as possible under his arm.

He was afraid that it might kick and bleat at sight and smell of its mother. He skirted the clearing and pushed his way into the thicket. It was difficult to fight through with his burden. The fawn's legs caught in the bushes and he could not lift his own with freedom. He tried to shield its face from prickling vines. Its head bobbed with his stride. His heart thumped with the marvel of its acceptance of him. He reached the trail and walked as fast as he could until he came to the intersection with the road home. He stopped to rest and set the fawn down on its dangling legs. It wavered on them. It looked at him and bleated.

He said, enchanted, "I'll tote you time I git my breath."

He remembered his father's saying that a fawn would follow that had been first carried. He started away slowly. The fawn stared after him. He came back to it and stroked it and walked away again. It took a few wobbling steps toward him and cried piteously. It was willing to follow him. It belonged to him. It was his own. He was light-headed with his joy. He wanted to fondle it, to run and romp with it, to call to it to come to him. He dared not alarm it. He picked it up and carried it in front of him over his two arms. It seemed to him that he walked without effort. He had the strength of a Forrester.

His arms began to ache and he was forced to stop again. When he walked on, the fawn followed him at once. He allowed it to walk a little distance, then picked it up again. The distance home was nothing. He could have walked all day and into the night, carrying it and watching it follow. He was wet with sweat but a light breeze blew through the June morning, cooling him. The sky was as clear as spring water in a blue china cup. He came to the clearing. It was fresh and green after the night's rain. He could see Buck Forrester following old Cæsar at the plow in the cornfield. He fumbled with the gate latch and was finally obliged to set down the fawn to manage it. It came to him that he would walk into the house, into Penny's bedroom, with the fawn walking behind him. But at the steps, the fawn balked and refused to climb them. He picked it up and went to his father. Penny lay with closed eyes.

Jody called, "Pa! Lookit!"

Penny turned his head. Jody stood beside him, the fawn clutched hard against him. It seemed to Penny that the boy's eyes were as bright as the fawn's. His face lightened, seeing them together.

He said, "I'm proud you found him."

MOTI GUJ—MUTINEER

By RUDYARD KIPLING

ONCE upon a time there was a coffee planter in India who wished to clear some forest land for coffee-planting. When he had cut down all the trees and burned the underwood, the stumps still remained. Dynamite is expensive and slow fire slow. The happy medium for stump clearing is the lord of all beasts, who is the elephant. He will either push the stump out of the ground with his tusks, if he has any, or drag it out with ropes. The planter, therefore, hired elephants by twos and threes, and fell to work. The very best of all the elephants belonged to the very worst of all the drivers, or mahouts; and this superior beast's name was Moti Guj. He was the absolute property of his mahout, which would never have been the case under native rule; for Moti Guj was a creature to be desired by kings, and his name, being translated, meant the Pearl Elephant. Because the British government was in the land, Deesa, the mahout, enjoyed his property undisturbed. He was dissipated. When he made much money through the strength of his elephant, he would get extremely drunk and give Moti Guj a beating with a tent peg over the tender nails of the forefeet. Moti Guj never trampled the life out of Deesa on these occasions, for he knew that after the beating was over, Deesa would embrace his trunk and weep and call him his love and his life and the liver of his soul, and give him some liquor. Moti Guj was very fond of liquor—arrack for choice, though he would drink palm tree toddy if nothing better offered. Then Deesa would go to sleep between Moti Guj's forefeet, and as Deesa generally chose the middle of the public road, and as Moti Guj mounted guard over him, and would not permit horse, foot, or cart to pass by, traffic was congested till Deesa saw fit to wake up.

There was no sleeping in the daytime on the planter's clearing: the wages were too high to risk. Deesa sat on Moti Guj's neck and gave him orders, while Moti Guj rooted up the stumps—for he owned a magnificent pair of tusks; or pulled at the end of a rope—

for he had a magnificent pair of shoulders—while Deesa kicked him behind the ears and said he was the king of elephants. At evening time Moti Guj would wash down his three hundred pounds' weight of green food with a quart of arrack, and Deesa would take a share, and sing songs between Moti Guj's legs till it was time to go to bed. Once a week Deesa led Moti Guj down to the river, and Moti Guj lay on his side luxuriously in the shallows, while Deesa went over him with a coir swab and a brick. Moti Guj never mistook the pounding blow of the latter for the smack of the former that warned him to get up and turn over on the other side. Then Deesa would look at his feet and examine his eyes, and turn up the fringes of his mighty ears in case of sores or budding ophthalmia. After inspection the two would "come up with a song from the sea," Moti Guj, all black and shining, waving a torn tree branch twelve feet long in his trunk, and Deesa knotting up his own long wet hair.

It was a peaceful, well-paid life until Deesa felt the return of the desire to drink deep. He wished for an orgy. The little draughts that led nowhere were taking the manhood out of him.

He went to the planter, and "My mother's dead," said he, weeping.

"She died on the last plantation, two months ago, and she died once before that when you were working for me last year," said the planter, who knew something of the ways of nativedom.

"Then it's my aunt, and she was just the same as a mother to me," said Deesa, weeping more than ever. "She has left eighteen small children, entirely without bread, and it is I who must fill their little stomachs," said Deesa, beating his head on the floor.

"Who brought you the news?" said the planter.

"The post," said Deesa.

"There hasn't been a post here for the past week. Get back to your lines!"

"A devastating sickness has fallen on my village, and all my wives are dying," yelled Deesa, really in tears this time.

"Call Chihun, who comes from Deesa's village," said the planter. "Chihun, has this man got a wife?"

"He?" said Chihun. "No. Not a woman of our village would look at him. They'd sooner marry the elephant."

Chihun snorted. Deesa wept and bellowed.

"You will get into a difficulty in a minute," said the planter. "Go back to your work!"

"Now I will speak Heaven's truth," gulped Deesa, with an inspiration. "I haven't been drunk for two months. I desire to depart in order to get properly drunk afar off and distant from this heavenly plantation. Thus I shall cause no trouble."

A flickering smile crossed the planter's face. "Deesa," said he, "you have spoken the truth, and I'd give you leave on the spot if anything could be done with Moti Guj while you're away. You know that he will only obey your orders."

"May the light of the heavens live forty thousand years. I shall be absent but ten little days. After that, upon my faith and honor and soul, I return. As to the inconsiderable interval, have I the gracious permission of the heaven-born to call up Moti Guj?"

Permission was granted, and in answer to Deesa's shrill yell, the mighty tusker swung out of the shade of a clump of trees where he had been squirting dust over himself till his master should return.

"Light of my heart, protector of the drunken, mountain of might, give ear!" said Deesa, standing in front of him.

Moti Guj gave ear and saluted with his trunk. "I am going away," said Deesa.

Moti Guj's eyes twinkled. He liked jaunts as well as his master. One could snatch all manner of nice things from the roadside then.

"But you, you fussy old pig, must stay behind and work."

The twinkle died out as Moti Guj tried to look delighted. He hated stump hauling on the plantation. It hurt his teeth.

"I shall be gone for ten days, O delectable one! Hold up your near forefeet and I'll impress the fact upon it, warty toad of a dried mud puddle." Deesa took a tent peg and banged Moti Guj ten times on the nails. Moti Guj grunted and shuffled from foot to foot.

"Ten days," said Deesa, "you will work and haul and root the trees as Chihun here shall order you. Take up Chihun and set him on your neck!" Moti Guj curled the tip of his trunk, Chihun put his foot there, and was swung on to the neck. Deesa handed Chihun the heavy *ankus*—the iron elephant goad.

Chihun thumped Moti Guj's bald head as a paver thumps a curb-stone.

Moti Guj trumpeted.

"Be still, hog of the backwoods! Chihun's your mahout for ten days. And now bid me good-bye, beast after mine own heart. Oh, my lord, my king! Jewel of all created elephants, lily of the herd, preserve your honored health; be virtuous. Adieu!"

Moti Guj lapped his trunk around Deesa and swung him into the air twice. That was his way of bidding him good-bye.

"He'll work now," said Deesa to the planter. "Have I leave to go?"

The planter nodded, and Deesa dived into the woods. Moti Guj went back to haul stumps.

Chihun was very kind to him, but he felt unhappy and forlorn for all that. Chihun gave him a ball of spices, and tickled him under the chin, and Chihun's little baby cooed to him after the work was over, and Chihun's wife called him a darling; but Moti Guj was a bache-lor by instinct, as Deesa was. He did not understand the domestic emotions. He wanted the light of his universe back again—the drink and the drunken slumber, the savage beatings and the savage caresses.

None the less he worked well, and the planter wondered. Deesa had wandered along the roads until he met a marriage procession of his own caste, and, drinking, dancing, and tippling, had drifted past all knowledge of the lapse of time.

The morning of the eleventh day dawned, and there returned no Deesa. Moti Guj was loosened from his rope for the daily stint. He swung clear, looked round, shrugged his shoulders, and began to walk away, as one having business elsewhere.

"Hi! ho! Come back you!" shouted Chihun. "Come back and put me on your neck, misborn mountain! Return, splendor of the hillsides! Adornment of all India, heave to, or I'll bang every toe off your fat forefoot!"

Moti Guj gurgled gently, but did not obey. Chihun ran after him with a rope and caught him up. Moti Guj put his ears forward, and Chihun knew what that meant, though he tried to carry it off with high words.

"None of your nonsense with me," said he. "To your pickets, devil son!"

"Hrrump!" said Moti Guj, and that was all—that and the fore-bent ears.

Moti Guj put his hands in his pockets, chewed a branch for a toothpick, and strolled about the clearing, making fun of the other elephants who had just set to work.

Chihun reported the state of affairs to the planter, who came out with a dog whip and cracked it furiously. Moti Guj paid the white man the compliment of charging him nearly a quarter of a mile across the clearing and "Hrrumphing" him into his veranda. Then he stood outside the house, chuckling to himself, and shaking all over with the fun of it, as an elephant will.

"We'll thrash him," said the planter. "He shall have the finest thrashing ever elephant received. Give Kala Nag and Nazim twelve foot of chain apiece, and tell them to lay on twenty."

Kala Nag—which means Black Snake—and Nazim were two of the biggest elephants in the lines, and one of their duties was to administer the graver punishment, since no man can beat an elephant properly.

They took the whipping chains and rattled them in their trunks as they sidled up to Moti Guj, meaning to hustle him between them. Moti Guj had never, in all his life of thirty-nine years, been whipped, and he did not intend to begin a new experience. So he waited, waving his head from right to left and measuring the precise spot in Kala Nag's fat side where a blunt tusk could sink deepest. Kala Nag had no tusks, the chain was the badge of his authority; but for all that, he swung wide of Moti Guj at the last minute, and tried to appear as if he had brought the chain out for amusement. Nazim turned round and went home early. He did not feel fighting fit that morning, and so Moti Guj was left standing alone with his ears cocked.

That decided the planter to argue no more, and Moti Guj rolled back to his amateur inspection of the clearing. An elephant who will not work and is not tied up is about as manageable as an eighty-one-ton gun loose in a heavy seaway. He slapped old friends on the back and asked them if the stumps were coming away easily; he talked nonsense concerning labor and the inalienable rights of elephants to a long "nooning"; and, wandering to and fro, he thoroughly demoralized the garden till sundown, when he returned to his picket for food.

"If you won't work, you shan't eat," said Chihun, angrily. "You're a wild elephant, and no educated animal at all. Go back to your jungle."

Chihun's little brown baby was rolling on the floor of the hut, and stretching out its fat arms to the huge shadow in the doorway. Moti Guj knew well that it was the dearest thing on earth to Chihun. He swung out his trunk with a fascinating crook at the end, and the brown baby threw itself, shouting, upon it. Moti Guj made fast and pulled up till the brown baby was crowing in the air twelve feet above his father's head.

"Great Lord!" said Chihun. "Flour cakes of the best, twelve in number, two feet across and soaked in rum, shall be yours, on the instant, and two hundred pounds weight of fresh-cut, young sugar cane therewith. Deign only to put down safely that insignificant brat who is my heart and my life to me!"

Moti Guj tucked the brown baby comfortably between his forefeet, that could have knocked into toothpicks all Chihun's hut, and waited for his food. He ate it, and the brown baby crawled away. Moti Guj dozed and thought of Deesa. One of many mysteries connected with the elephant is that his huge body needs sleep less than anything else that lives. Four or five hours in the night suffice —two just before midnight, lying down on one side; two just after one o'clock, lying down on the other. The rest of the silent hours are filled with eating and fidgeting, and long grumbling soliloquies.

At midnight, therefore, Moti Guj strode out of his pickets, for a thought had come to him that Deesa might be laying drunk somewhere in the dark forest with none to look after him. So all that night he chased through the undergrowth, blowing and trumpeting, and shaking his ears. He went down to the river and blared across the shallows where Deesa used to wash him, but there was no answer. He could not find Deesa, but he disturbed all the other elephants in the lines, and nearly frightened to death some gypsies in the woods.

At dawn Deesa returned to the plantation. He had been very drunk indeed, and he expected to get into trouble for outstaying his leave. He drew a long breath when he saw that the bungalow and the plantation were still uninjured, for he knew something of Moti Guj's temper, and reported himself with many lies and salaams. Moti Guj had gone to his pickets for breakfast. The night exercise had made him hungry.

"Call up your beast," said the planter; and Deesa shouted in the mysterious elephant language that some mahouts believe came from China at the birth of the world, when elephants and not men were masters. Moti Guj heard and came. Elephants do not gallop. They move from places at various rates of speed. If an elephant wished to catch an express train he could not gallop, but he could catch the train. So Moti Guj was at the planter's door almost before Chihun noticed that he had left his pickets. He fell into Deesa's arms trumpeting with joy, and man and beast wept and slobbered over each other, and handled each other from head to heel to see that no harm had befallen.

"Now we will get to work," said Deesa. "Lift me up, my son and my joy!"

Moti Guj swung him up, and the two went to the coffee clearing to look for difficult stumps.

The planter was too astonished to be very angry.

SOURCES OF STORIES IN VOLUME VII

Buster: Zinnia and Her Babies: Jim Crow, from More about Animals, by Margery Williams Bianco. The Macmillan Company.

Jimmie, the Black Bear Cub, from Jimmie, the Story of a Black Bear Cub, by Harold Baynes. The Macmillan Company.

My Friend Toto, by Cherry Kearton. Dodd, Mead & Company, Inc.

The Wild Bull, from Herdboy of Hungary, by Alexander Finta, with Jeanette Eaton. Harper & Brothers.

A Cowboy and His Pony, from Lone Cowboy, by Will James. Charles Scribner's Sons.

Buddy, Seeing Eye Pioneer, from Dogs Against Darkness (chapter 11), by Dickson Hartwell. Dodd Mead and Company.

Shipping Wild Animals, from Trapping Animals in Malay Jungle, by Charles Mayer. Duffield & Company.

King Cobra Takes the Stage, from Thrills of a Naturalist's Quest, by Raymond L. Ditmars. The Macmillan Company.

Leopards and Rhinos, from In Brightest Africa, by Carl E. Akeley. Doubleday, Doran & Company, Inc.

My Fight with a Catamount, by Allen French. *The Youth's Companion.* Perry Mason Company.

Stickeen, by John Muir. Houghton Mifflin Company.

The Cat and the Captain, by Elizabeth Coatsworth. The Macmillan Company.

The Monkey That Would Not Kill, by Henry Drummond. Dodd, Mead & Company, Inc.

Black Beauty, by Anna Sewell. Dodd, Mead & Company, Inc.

"One Minute Longer," from Buff, a Collie, by Albert Payson Terhune. Doubleday, Doran & Company, Inc.

Bringing Up Kari, from Kari the Elephant, by Dhan Gopal Mukerji. E. P. Dutton & Company, Inc.

Coaly-Bay, the Outlaw Horse, from Wild Animal Ways, by Ernest Thompson Seton. Doubleday, Doran & Company, Inc.

Gulliver the Great, from Gulliver the Great and Other Dog Stories, by Walter A. Dyer. D. Appleton-Century Company.

Brown Wolf, from Brown Wolf, and Other Jack London Stories, chosen by Franklin K. Matthews. The Macmillan Company.

The Assault of Wings, from Hoof and Claw, by Charles G. D. Roberts. The Macmillan Company.

Sea Otter, from Wild Folk, by Samuel Scoville, Jr. Little, Brown & Company.

Lassie Come-Home, by Eric Knight. First published in *Saturday Evening Post,* Dec. 17, 1938. An expanded and novel-length form published by John C. Winston Co.

Jody Finds the Fawn, chapters from The Yearling, by Marjorie Kinnan Rawlings. Charles Scribner's Sons.

Moti Guj—Mutineer, from Mine Own People, by Rudyard Kipling. Doubleday, Doran & Company, Inc.